An Introduction to

An Introduction to Soil Mechanics

To Tricia,

Wishing you every success in your career

Peter Berry

Peter L. Berry

and

David Reid

Department of Civil Engineering
University of Salford

McGRAW-HILL BOOK COMPANY

London · New York · St Louis · San Francisco · Auckland
Bogotá · Guatemala · Hamburg · Lisbon · Madrid
Mexico · Montreal · New Delhi · Panama · Paris · San Juan
São Paulo · Singapore · Sydney · Tokyo · Toronto

Published by
McGRAW-HILL Book Company (UK) Limited
MAIDENHEAD · BERKSHIRE · ENGLAND

British Library Cataloguing in Publication Data

Berry, Peter L.
  An introduction to soil mechanics.
  1. Soil Mechanics
  I. Title   II. Reid, David 624.1′5136   TA710

  ISBN 0-07-084164-0

Library of Congress Cataloging-in-Publication Data

Berry, Peter L.
  An introduction to soil mechanics.

  Bibliography: p.
  Includes index.
  1. Soil mechanics. I. Reid, David. II. Title.
TA710.B454 1987   624.1′5136   87–4198
ISBN 0-07-084164-0

1234   BP   8987

Typeset by Eta Services (Typesetters) Ltd, Beccles, Suffolk
Printed and bound in Great Britain at The Bath Press, Avon

CONTENTS

PREFACE

This introductory text on soil mechanics is written primarily for undergraduate students taking a first degree course in civil engineering and related disciplines. It has evolved over the past 17 years from a series of lectures given by the authors at the University of Salford and offers a new perspective on the subject which reflects the extensive teaching experience gained over this period and the many helpful comments and suggestions received from successive generations of students. These factors have combined to shape the philosophy of approach adopted in the presentation of each topic, which is

(a) to *identify* engineering problems particular to the topic and establish clearly the need for an appropriate theory.
(b) to *develop* the relevant theory, and
(c) to *illustrate* the application through worked examples typical of problems encountered in engineering practice.

We attach great importance to the last point, for it is only through a consideration of worked examples that a student is fully able to assimilate the theory and learn how to apply it to the practice of ground engineering. For this reason we have included over 40 worked examples, covering a wide range of field problems, which will enable the student to gain a thorough understanding of the principles of soil mechanics and their practical application.

The choice of subject material is to a certain extent a personal one, but the contents should cover the requirements of most undergraduate courses. In this respect the book includes a number of important topics sometimes omitted in other texts, such as the design of well systems for pressure relief and de-watering purposes, and the design of vertical sand drains to accelerate the consolidation of soft clay deposits. The book also contains new ideas and material not previously published relating to the determination of earth pressures on rigid walls, the stability of slopes and the bearing capacity of shallow foundations. These are all variations of a common problem and, as such, allow a common method of analysis to be applied. This approach simplifies the presentation of a substantial part of the subject and engenders a greater awareness and more informed insight into the factors influencing the stability of soil masses.

Although written primarily as an undergraduate text, some topics are taken to an advanced level and should therefore be of value to postgraduate students, while the large number of worked examples of typical field problems should make the book a suitable desk-top copy for the professional engineer. The book builds on the conventional and well-established approach first put forward in 1925 and later in 1943 by Karl Terzaghi, the founder of this still relatively new engineering discipline. SI units are used throughout and, where appropriate, reference is made to both British and US Standards.

The authors are indebted to Dr I. A. B. Moffat of the Department of Geotechnical Engineering, University of Newcastle-upon-Tyne, for reading the manuscript and for his many helpful comments, and to Mr A. Holmes, former Senior Editor, McGraw-Hill Book Co. (UK) Limited, for his valuable advice, encouragement and unswerving faith in this project. The authors are also indebted to Mrs C. E. Czirok of the Department of Civil Engineering, University of Salford, who prepared the line drawings.

The authors gratefully acknowledge permissions to reproduce material published by the American Society of Civil Engineers and the Institution of Civil Engineers, London. Extracts from BS 5930: 1981 are reproduced by permission of the British Standards Institution, from whom complete copies can be obtained. Figures 2.18, 2.20, 6.28, 7.16, 8.8 and Tables 1.4 and 5.1 are based on source material which is copyright of John Wiley and Sons Inc., reprinted with their kind permission.

Peter L. Berry
David Reid

A; A_b; A_s	Area; base area; shaft area
A	Activity of clay
A, $\bar{A}$; A_f	Pore pressure parameters; value of A at failure
A_r	Air voids content
a_v	Coefficient of compressibility
B	Width, diameter
B, $\bar{B}$	Pore pressure parameters
b	Width
C_c	Compression index
C_U	Coefficient of uniformity
C_Z	Coefficient of curvature
C_α	Coefficient of secondary compression
c_v, c_h	Coefficients of vertical and horizontal consolidation
c; c_u; c_{cu}	Cohesion; undrained cohesion; consolidated–undrained cohesion (total stress shear strength parameters)
c_w	Adhesion between soil and wall (or pile) in terms of total stress
c'; c_d	Effective cohesion; drained cohesion (effective stress shear strength parameters)
c'_w	Effective wall adhesion
D	Particle diameter, depth of soil, depth of foundation, embedded length of pile
D; D_f	Deviator stress; deviator stress at failure
D_r	Relative density
D_c	Critical depth
E	Modulus of elasticity, lateral earth force, efficiency of pile group
e; e_o; e_f	Void ratio; initial void ratio; final void ratio
F; F_u; F_d	Factor of safety; undrained factor of safety; drained factor of safety
F_{bu}; F_{bd}	Undrained and drained factor of safety against bearing failure
F_{su}; F_{sd}	Undrained and drained factor of safety against shear failure
G_s	Particle specific gravity
g	Gravitational acceleration (9.81 m/s^2)
H	Height, maximum drainage path length
h; h_w; h_e	Total head; total head in soil at well; total head in soil at radius of influence
h_{el}	Elevation head
h_p; h_h; h_e	Pressure head; hydrostatic pressure head; excess pressure head
h_v	Velocity head

I	Influence value
I_D	Density index
I_L	Liquidity index
I_P	Plasticity index
I_σ; I_s	Influence factor of stress; influence factor of settlement
i; i_c; i_e	Hydraulic gradient; critical hydraulic gradient; exit hydraulic gradient
i	Angle of inclination of soil surface
K'	Coefficient of effective earth pressure
K'_o	Coefficient of earth pressure at rest
K'_a	Coefficient of active earth pressure
K'_p	Coefficient of passive earth pressure
k	Coefficient of permeability
L	Length
$\ln$	Natural logarithm
M; M_s; M_w	Total mass; mass of solids; mass of water
M_a	Overturning moment due to active thrust
m_v	Coefficient of volume compressibility
N	Normal total force, standard penetration value
N'	Normal effective force
N_c, N_q, N_γ	Bearing capacity factors
N_d; N_f	Number of equipotential drops; number of flow channels
N_p	Number of piles
n	Porosity, ratio r_e/r_w
P_h, P'_h	Horizontal component of total and effective force
P_{ha}, P'_{ha}	Horizontal component of total and effective active force
P_{hp}, P'_{hp}	Horizontal component of total and effective passive force
P_{hw}	Horizontal water force
p	Distance of well to line source
Q	Steady state flow
Q; Q_{ult}	Applied load; ultimate load
q; q_{ult}	Applied pressure; ultimate pressure
q_a	Allowable pressure
q_s	Surcharge pressure
$q_{n(ult)}$	Nett ultimate bearing pressure
$q_{n(all)}$	Nett allowable bearing pressure
$q_{n(app)}$	Nett applied bearing pressure
q_c	Cone penetration value
R	Radius
r	Radial distance, radial direction
r_w; r_e	Radius of well (or sand drain); radius of influence
r_j	Distance from point to centre line of well j ($j = 1, 2, 3, \ldots$)
r_{ij}	Distance from point to centre line of mirror image of well j
S; S_i; S_{con}	Total settlement; immediate settlement; consolidation settlement
S; S_f	Shear force; shear force at failure
S, S'	Total stress and effective stress stability numbers

S_r	Degree of saturation
s	Centre-to-centre spacing of piles
T	Tensile force in reinforcing strip or tie rod
T_v, T_r	Vertical and radial dimensionless time factors
t	Real time
U	Water force
U_v	Degree of vertical consolidation
$\bar{U}_v, \bar{U}_r$	Average degree of vertical and radial consolidation
$\bar{U}_{vr}$	Average degree of consolidation due to combined vertical and radial flow
$u; u_h; u_e$	Porewater pressure; hydrostatic porewater pressure; excess porewater pressure
$V; V_s; V_v$	Total volume; volume of solids; volume of voids
$V_a; V_w$	Volume of air; volume of water
v	Discharge velocity
$W; W_s; W_w$	Total weight; weight of solids; weight of water
W'_s	Effective weight of solids
$w; w_{opt}$	Water content; optimum water content
$w_L; w_P; w_S$	Liquid limit; plastic limit; shrinkage limit
X	Shear force
X_a, X_p	Shear component of active and passive force
x, y, z	Reference directions
α	Angle of inclination, shaft adhesion factor
$\gamma; \gamma_d$	Bulk unit weight; dry unit weight
$\gamma_s; \gamma'$	Saturated unit weight; effective (buoyant, submerged) unit weight
Δ	Change in ..., increment of ...
$\Delta\phi; \Delta\psi$	Interval of potential; interval of stream function
ΔQ	Quantity of seepage through one flow channel
δ_u	Angle of friction between soil and wall in terms of total stress
δ'	Effective angle of friction between soil and wall (or pile)
ε	Strain
θ	Angle, inclination of soil/wall interface, reference direction
θ'	Angle
μ	Skempton–Bjerrum correction factor
ν	Poisson's ratio
ρ	Flexibility number for sheet pile wall
$\rho; \rho_d$	Bulk density; dry density
$\rho_s; \rho'$	Saturated density; effective density
$\rho_c; \rho_p; \rho_w$	Density of concrete; density of pile; density of water
$\sigma; \sigma'$	Normal total stress; normal effective stress
$\sigma_1, \sigma_2, \sigma_3$	Major, intermediate and minor principal total stress
$\sigma'_1, \sigma'_2, \sigma'_3$	Major, intermediate and minor principal effective stress
$\sigma_{ha}, \sigma'_{ha}$	Total and effective horizontal active earth pressure
$\sigma_{hp}, \sigma'_{hp}$	Total and effective horizontal passive earth pressure

τ	Shear stress
τ_f	Shear stress at failure, maximum resistance to shear
τ_w	Shear stress on soil/wall interface
ϕ	Potential function
ϕ; ϕ_u; ϕ_{cu}	Angle of friction; undrained angle of friction; consolidated–undrained angle of friction (total stress shear strength parameters)
ϕ'; ϕ_d	Effective angle of friction; drained angle of friction (effective stress shear strength parameters)
ψ	Stream function

Subscripts

a	active	h	horizontal	p	passive
all	allowable	L	left	r	residual
app	applied	R	right	u	undrained
cu	consolidated–undrained	m	mobilized	ult	ultimate
		max	maximum	v	vertical
d	drained	min	minimum	x, y, z	directional
f	final or failure	o	initial		

PHYSICAL AND CHEMICAL PROPERTIES OF ENGINEERING SOILS

1.1 GEOLOGICAL FORMATION AND NATURE OF SOILS

Introduction

The earth's crust is composed primarily of rock, the geological formation of which has been taking place for many millions of years. However, over the same period of time the surface of the rock mass has suffered continually from disintegration and decomposition by processes referred to as *weathering*. With repeated exposure to atmospheric influences such as floods, glacial activity and wind storms, much of the fragmented rock debris produced by weathering has been carried away, further broken up and abraded, and eventually deposited, for example, along river courses, in lakes and oceans, and along the path of ice flows. With changes in climate and fluctuations in mean sea and land levels, this cycle of erosion, transportation and deposition of weathered material has been interrupted, renewed and repeated countless times over tens of thousands of years.

The result of this is that over much of the present-day surface of the earth the firm, relatively unweathered *bedrock* is now covered by accumulations of uncemented or weakly cemented particulate material, often of a highly variable character and thickness; this is the material that the engineer refers to as *soil*.

In some places the surface layer of soil has become very highly weathered, rich in humus, and capable of supporting the growth of vegetation. This layer is called *topsoil* and is often not more than 0.5 m thick. It is usually stripped off the surface of a site prior to any construction work and replaced during landscaping of the site on completion of the work. The characteristics of topsoil are therefore of importance principally to the agriculturalist. It is the underlying *engineering soil* that engineers use to support structures and in some cases to build structures, and it is this material whose properties and engineering behaviour engineers must understand.

Weathering Processes

The gradual breakdown of the solid rock mass over long periods of time is attributable to two main processes: *physical weathering* and *chemical weathering*.

Physical weathering This takes the form of a physical break-up or disintegration of the rock mass.

Initial fracture of the rock may have resulted from stresses induced by such factors as initial shrinkage on cooling, stress relief following the removal of overlying material, or folding and faulting.

Once the rock mass has fractured it becomes increasingly vulnerable to other forms of physical weathering and to chemical weathering. Water entering the cracks may undergo cycles of freezing and thawing which gradually open up the cracks and eventually cause fragments of rock to break off. The movement of glaciers over exposed rock surfaces, rainstorms and the resulting torrents of flood water carrying vast quantities of rock debris, the action of the sea repeatedly pounding the coast-line—all these contribute in time to the physical break-up of the rock mass and extensive erosion and abrasion of the land surface.

Chemical weathering This takes the form of a chemical decomposition of some or all of the mineral constituents of the rock mass.

For example, carbon dioxide dissolved in rainwater forms a weak solution of carbonic acid which will attack many of the common rock-forming minerals, or oxygen in the atmosphere and in rainwater will cause oxidation, particularly of those rocks containing iron. Rainwater percolating through topsoil may become enriched with carbonic acid and oxygen from decayed vegetable matter or humus.

It is estimated that a mere eight elements account for more than 98 per cent by weight of the earth's crust (Blyth and De Freitas, 1984):

oxygen —46.6%	silicon —27.7%	aluminium—8.1%	iron —5.0%
calcium— 3.6%	sodium— 2.8%	potassium —2.6%	magnesium—2.1%

Therefore most of the rock-forming minerals are compounds of these elements as metallic silicates and oxides. The common rock-forming minerals, their chemical composition, their susceptibility to chemical weathering and the principal soil product are summarized in Table 1.1.

A detailed treatment of the geological processes of weathering and their influence on the formation of engineering soils is given by Blyth and De Freitas (1984), and Flint and Skinner (1977).

Table 1.1 Chemical weathering of the common rock-forming minerals

Rock-forming mineral	Chemical composition	Susceptibility to chemical weathering	Principal soil product
Quartz	Silicon dioxide	Highly resistant	Gravel, sand, silt particles
Orthoclase	Aluminium silicates of potassium	Moderately susceptible	Clay mineral particles of the kaolinite and illite groups
Plagioclase	Aluminium silicates of sodium and calcium		Clay mineral particles of the montmorillonite and illite groups
Mica	Aluminium silicates of potassium, magnesium and iron		
Hornblende	Silicates, principally of magnesium and iron	Highly susceptible	
Augite			
Olivine			

Definition of Particle Size and Shape

The processes of weathering and the actions of transportation and deposition produce individual particles of soil which vary widely in size and shape.

The size of the particles in a soil deposit has a fundamental influence on the properties and engineering behaviour of the deposit, and therefore particles of soil are described according to their size using terms such as *gravel, sand, silt* or *clay* sized. However, there is no universally agreed standard for the use of these terms in the definition of particle size. Britain uses a British Standard classification (BS 5930: 1981), but in the United States various agencies have standards which are in common use. Fortunately, the differences are small. The British system and three of those used by US agencies are shown in Table 1.2.

The sand, gravel and larger-sized particles are generally the products of physical weathering and usually exhibit the same mineralogical composition as the parent rock. Alternatively, they are simply grains of quartz which have remained unaltered during chemical weathering of the parent rock (Table 1.1). These particles tend to be formed with a three-dimensional solid shape which is subsequently modified to a greater or lesser extent by the amount of abrasion which has occurred during transportation. Particles which have experienced little or no abrasion are likely to possess sharp edges and relatively flat faces, and are described as *angular*. Particles which have suffered severe abrasion, however, tend to be *well rounded* in shape. Particles which have been partly shaped by moderate abrasion will exhibit only rounded edges and are described by terms such as *subangular* or *partly rounded*.

The processes of abrasion associated with physical weathering are what produces most of the silt-sized particles.

The majority of clay-sized particles, however, consist of clay minerals which have been formed by chemical weathering (Table 1.1) and which do not exhibit the same mineralogical composition as the parent rock. Nor do clay mineral particles exhibit the three-dimensional solid shape common with sand or gravel particles; electron-microscope studies have shown them generally to have a flat plate-like shape with a diameter/thickness ratio usually in excess of 10 and sometimes as high as 400.

The Nature of Soil Deposits

Table 1.2 demonstrates the use of terms such as gravel, sand, silt and clay to describe individual soil particles of a particular size. However, these same terms are further used by engineers in the description of soil deposits, and in this context the terms frequently have a slightly different interpretation.

Table 1.2 Definitions of particle size

Particle description	Particle size (mm)			
	British Standard†	AASHTO‡	ASTM§	Unified¶
Gravel	60–2	75–2	>2	75–4.75
Sand	2–0.06	2–0.05	2–0.075	4.75–0.075
Silt	0.06–0.002	0.05–0.002	0.075–0.005	<0.075 fines
Clay	<0.002	<0.002	<0.005	

† BS 5930: 1981.
‡ American Association of State Highway and Transportation Officials.
§ American Society for Testing and Materials.
¶ Unified Classification System.

The engineering behaviour of a soil deposit is fundamentally dependent upon the forces that act at the areas of contact between individual particles. These are mainly *gravitational forces*, related to the mass and therefore approximately to the volume of the particles, and *surface forces* derived from electro-chemical activity on the surface of the particles.

Clay mineral particles are not only very small but, because of their plate-like shape, have a large surface-area to volume ratio, and consequently they experience surface forces which predominate over the mass-derived gravitational forces. The dominant influence of these surface forces results in a cohesion or what we shall call '*stiction*'† between individual clay particles, and gives wet clay its characteristic putty-like *plasticity*. If the clay is dried out, the stiction between the particles produces a solid material resistant to plastic deformation. However, to describe a soil deposit as a *clay* does not infer that all the particles are clay-sized, but merely that sufficient clay mineral particles are present to give the soil deposit distinct stiction and plasticity characteristics. Indeed, the proportion by weight of particles in the silt and clay sizes may be as little as 35 per cent of the total.

With the same proportion of fine particles but made up of rather more silt sizes and fewer clay mineral particles, the soil deposit is likely to exhibit less pronounced stiction and plasticity characteristics, and might be described primarily as a silt.

Depending upon the distribution of particle size in the remainder of the deposit, these descriptions may be qualified by the use of such terms as *sandy clay* or *gravelly silt*, etc.

Soil deposits which exhibit the characteristics of stiction and plasticity associated with the presence of a significant quantity of clay mineral particles are often described by the general term *cohesive soils*.

In contrast to clay mineral particles, the much larger sand and gravel-sized particles tend to occur as more or less equidimensional 'bulky' grains and thus have a small surface-area to volume ratio. Consequently the forces derived from surface activity are negligible in comparison with the mass-derived gravitational forces. Therefore, in the absence of any clay mineral particles these materials will exhibit no stiction between individual grains. Sands and gravels are therefore often referred to by the general term *cohesionless soils* or *granular soils*.

Granular soils tend to be described in terms of the predominant particle size present. Thus to describe a soil deposit as a *sand* does not necessarily infer that all the particles are of sand size, but merely that more particles are in the sand size range than any other. Where a smaller but still significant proportion by weight of another particle size is present, the description may be qualified by the use of such terms as *silty sand* or *gravelly sand*.

The division between sand and silt sizes coincides approximately with the limit of visibly distinguishable particles and the limit of mechanical separation by grain size. Thus the term *coarse (grained) soil* is often used to refer to materials which are primarily sand or gravels, and the term *fine (grained) soil* to refer to materials which are primarily silt or clay soils.

Thus, in a typical engineering soil the individual particles, which may vary considerably in size and shape, form a framework of solid material, and between the individual particles is a system of interconnected spaces. The framework of solid particles is referred to as the *soil skeleton* or *soil structure*, and the spaces between the particles as *voids* or *pores*.

With the presence of voids a soil deposit may act as a reservoir for natural groundwater, the upper surface of this reservoir being referred to as the *water table* or *groundwater level*. The pressure in the water at the level of the water table is atmospheric. Rising from sea-level the water table runs approximately parallel to the ground surface and in temperate climates is typically within a few metres of the surface. In arid climates it is likely to lie at a much greater depth.

---

† The term 'cohesion' is used in Soil Mechanics to define one of the shear strength parameters of the soil. To avoid any confusion we will reserve it for that purpose alone, and the word 'stiction' will be used to refer to that characteristic property of clay mineral particles whereby they tend to stick together.

Below the water table the voids in a soil deposit will generally be completely filled with water, while above the water table the voids may contain air only, or more probably air and water. Water in the voids above groundwater level may simply be due to infiltration and percolation of rainwater from the ground surface, or may be the result of capillary rise in the voids, a phenomenon particularly evident in fine-grained soils. When the voids are completely filled with water the soil is said to be *saturated*, and when the voids contain air and water the soil is *partly saturated*.

Since the voids in a soil are interconnected, water is able to flow through the pore spaces. Therefore strictly speaking, all soils are not only porous but permeable. Indeed, it is this characteristic of *permeability* which fundamentally influences the engineering behaviour of a soil deposit in many practical situations. However, the rate at which water can flow through the pore space is influenced by the absolute size of the pores, flow occurring quite freely in the case of sands and gravels which have relatively large pores, but very slowly in the case of clay soils which have very small pores. The term 'permeable' is therefore applied to soils in a relative sense, sands and gravels being described as *permeable* or *free-draining* and clay soils as *impermeable* or *slow-draining*.

We see then that soil is a three-phase material consisting of a skeleton of solid particles encompassing voids filled with water or air or a combination of water and air.

1.2 ORIGIN AND TYPES OF SOIL DEPOSIT

Naturally occurring soil deposits are classed broadly as either residual soils or transported soils.

Residual soils have been formed entirely by *in situ* weathering and have remained at their original location. They occur mainly in tropical regions and other areas not subjected to glaciation. A common example are the *laterites*, materials found to be rich in the oxides of iron and aluminium, which occur in South America, parts of Africa, India, Sri Lanka and Australia.

Transported soils, however, as the term suggests, have been moved from their original location and deposited elsewhere, the principal agents of transportation being water, ice and wind. The size and shape of the particles in a transported soil deposit are strongly influenced by the agent of transportation and the mode of deposition.

Water-deposited Soils

RIVERS are extremely vigorous agents of erosion, transportation and deposition, particularly in times of flood. The material deposited along the course of a river is referred to as *alluvium*, although often this term is particularly applied to the finer material such as fine sand, silt and clay as distinct from the coarse sand, gravel and larger particles.

In its fast-flowing upper reaches the river will carry along all but the largest fragments of rock, quickly eroding the valley floor and abrading the particles to a partly rounded shape. Deposition begins in the middle reaches as the velocity of flow decreases and the carrying capacity of the river diminishes. First to form are deposits of *river gravel*, to be followed further downstream by *river sands*, and then in the slow-moving lower reaches by deposition of *fine alluvial sands* and *alluvial silt*.

In times of flood, when the river overtops its banks, flood water may inundate large areas of relatively flat land in the lower reaches. The flow velocity in all but the central river channel is abruptly reduced and large quantities of material are deposited—the coarser particles first, followed by progressively finer material. Repeated flooding together with meanderings of the river course in its lower reaches can produce extensive alluvial flood plains with successions of *alluvial silt and clay* often interspersed with layers of sand and possibly gravel.

When the river eventually discharges into a body of relatively still water, the velocity of flow is checked and the fine material still in suspension gradually settles out. The soils so formed tend to be named according to the environment of deposition: those formed in fresh water lakes are referred to as *lacustrine* deposits, those in tidal estuaries as *estuarine* deposits, and those that occur as a delta at the river mouth as *deltaic* deposits.

The SEA is also an important agent in the erosion, transportation and deposition cycle. Waves incessantly pounding the coast-line erode the land area by virtue of their own impact and also by that of the debris that they carry. Rock fragments which have been broken down and rounded in shape thus accumulate to form the familiar pebbly and sandy *beach deposits*. The fine material produced by this continual abrasion, together with fines washed into the sea by rivers, may remain in suspension and under current and tidal action be carried out to sea to settle out eventually over large areas of the sea-bed as *marine* deposits.

Thus, transportation and deposition by water produces soil particles having a rounded shape and soil deposits which may be *well-sorted*, i.e., having all particles of approximately the same size, or *stratified* (i.e., layered) with an orderly vertical gradation of particle size.

A more detailed review of the formation and nature of water-deposited soils is given by Blyth and De Freitas (1984), and Flint and Skinner (1977).

Glacial Deposits

At the present time, glaciers exist mainly in Greenland, Antarctica, parts of northern Canada and Alaska, the European Alps, and the Himalayas. However, in the geological past glaciation has affected much of the northern United States and Canada, most of the British Isles and northern Europe, and parts of Asia, with thicknesses of ice ranging from some 300 m to about 3000 m. The most recent periods of glaciation occurred during the Great Ice Age of the Pleistocene Era which began about 1.75 million years ago and ended some 10 000 years ago. Much of the present-day topography in these parts of the world is principally the result of glacial erosion, transportation and deposition processes of this Era.

As the glaciers formed they became embedded with significant quantities of weathered material falling onto the ice or being washed onto the ice by streams. As the thickness of ice increased, a combination of sliding on the land surface and shear along planes within the ice caused a slow creep of the glaciers over large distances, much in the manner of a highly viscous fluid. Extensive erosion and abrasion of the land surface occurred and resulted in vast quantities of debris becoming lodged within and upon the ice. The eventual retreat of the ice left a wide variety of deposits which are included under the general term *glacial drift*.

Material deposited directly by the ice is referred to as *till*, or sometimes as *boulder clay*. Generally glacial tills exist as unsorted mixtures of many particle sizes, but otherwise their characteristics vary widely, depending upon the mode of formation and deposition. For example, *lodgement till* is the material deposited directly underneath the glacier and tends to be stiff, relatively dense and incompressible, often with a significant proportion of fine material including *rock flour*, a term given to silt and clay-sized particles formed by the severe abrasion and grinding of the land surface and the embedded rock debris at the base of the ice. The larger rock fragments in a lodgement till are likely to be partly rounded and striated as a result of this abrasion. On the other hand *ablation till* and *meltout till* are materials which gradually accumulated by being gently lowered to the ground as the ice melted, and therefore may be weaker, less dense and more compressible deposits, generally with fewer fine particles. By being embedded in the ice and so protected from abrasion, the larger particles may be quite angular in shape.

The often ridge-like deposits of material mainly formed around the edges of the glacier are referred to as moraines—a *terminal moraine* being formed at the front edge of the glacier and *lateral moraines* along the sides. The constituent material of a moraine is usually till but may be any type of glacial drift. The term 'moraine' has in the past been used to refer to the constituent material of the deposit but recent practice has been to restrict its use to a description of the topographic feature (Derbyshire, 1975).

Glacial drift may also occur in the form of *fluvio-glacial* deposits of sand and gravel derived by deposition from melt-water streams. These deposits are likely to exhibit the partly rounded particle shape and the sorting or gradation by particle size associated with stream deposition.

In many cases these streams terminated in melt-water lakes impounded around the edge of the ice. The fine particles washed into these lakes eventually settled out, forming deposits of (*glaci*) *lacustrine* silts and clays.

The nature of glacial drift deposits has been further influenced by the fact that the Ice Age was not one continuous period of glaciation, but included a number of ice advance/retreat cycles. Thus, deposits laid down during one cycle may have been reworked and redistributed during subsequent cycles. Furthermore, the drift material may vary greatly in thickness, often displaying a relatively flat surface which conceals hollows or even deep valleys in the underlying bedrock. These wide variations in character and thickness mean that some glacial deposits will be ideal foundation strata while others will prove to be very weak and compressible. Thus, sites which are known to have experienced glaciation require detailed and careful investigation prior to the construction of engineering works.

A more extensive review of glaciation processes and the nature of glacial deposits is given by Fookes *et al.* (1975), Legget (1976), and McGown and Derbyshire (1977).

However, geological activity associated with periods of glaciation has influenced present-day engineering soils in other ways. The great thickness of ice generated very high stresses, typically about 900 kN/m^2 for every 100 m of ice, which forced the individual particles in the soil skeleton to adopt a denser packing arrangement while the volume of void space was reduced. Melting of the ice subsequently removed these stresses, and thus it is now possible to encounter soil deposits which have for some time in the past been acted upon by much higher stresses than those currently acting. Such deposits are described as *overconsolidated* or *preconsolidated*. It will be explained later how this condition of overconsolidation has a marked influence on the engineering behaviour of these deposits.

The eventual melting of the glaciers released vast quantities of water into the oceans and produced a rise in sea-level of probably about 100 m. As a result, many previously land areas became submerged and subjected to long periods of marine deposition, forming what are described as *post-glacial* soil deposits.

However, this rise in sea-level was followed by a gradual local uplift of the earth's crust as a result of stress relief on removal of the ice. For example, around the shores of Finland, Scandinavia and parts of North America there is evidence of an uplift of some 300 m having occurred. Thus some post-glacial deposits have been raised above present-day sea-level, where they may have been subject to further erosion, transportation and deposition.

Wind-blown Soil Deposits

Wind-blown deposits of sand occur widely in desert climates as *dunes* formed by the action of the wind blowing the sand particles along or just above the ground. Because of the limited carrying power of the wind, the dunes tend to consist of particles which are essentially of the same size, and as a result of the severe abrasion to which they have been subjected the grains tend to be well rounded in shape. Sand dunes can be found in the desert areas of North Africa, Asia, the Middle East and the United States.

Wind-blown deposits also occur widely in the form of *loess*, a material formed by the deposition of mainly silt-sized particles picked up by the wind in desert regions and blown over often large distances. For example, the 'black earth' deposits of the Russian steppes are loess which is thought to have been carried from the deserts of North Africa. Although deposited in a loose state at low density, loess is normally a reasonably stable material and will stand as near vertical cliffs, the uniformly sized silt particles being held together principally by clay mineral particles which act as a cement. However, if loess becomes saturated or submerged in water, the cementing action is destroyed and the deposit is liable to collapse. In addition to Russia, loess occurs extensively in the central United States, China and parts of Europe.

Organic Soils

Deposits of clay and silt derived from sediment laid down in lakes, estuaries or river flood plains may contain significant quantities of organic material in the form of decayed animal or vegetable matter. This organic material may have been carried in the river or blown into these areas by the wind. Alternatively, it may have been derived from vegetation growing in these areas during periodic cycles of non-deposition. Where the organic content is significant, these deposits would be described as *organic clays and silts*. The presence of organic matter is usually indicated by a dark grey to black colour and a distinctive odour associated with decaying vegetation.

If the organic matter is extensive with a much reduced mineral content, the material is described as *peat* or *muskeg*. Such deposits frequently overlie organic silts and clays and often develop from the gradual infilling of a lake. The stratigraphy varies with depth, reflecting the different plant communities that were dominant at different stages in the development of the mire. The basal deposits of reed and sedge peat are referred to collectively as *fen* peat, and there is a general trend for the mineral content to decrease with increasing accumulation of peat. With changing environmental conditions the fen peat gives way through a gradual transition zone, to be eventually covered by acid sphagnum peat forming a raised *bog*. Bog peats tend to be brown in colour, fibrous and only lightly decomposed. In contrast, fen peats are usually darker in colour, less fibrous and more highly decomposed, often resembling a black spongy gelatinous mass.

Extensive deposits of peat occur in most countries throughout the world (there being 500 000 sq. miles in Canada alone) and using special construction techniques, known as preloading, large areas have been reclaimed for supporting housing developments, industrial estates and embankments for motorways (Lea and Brawner, 1963; Jonas, 1964; Johnson, 1970; Berry, 1983).

Fill Materials

Material which is placed by man in connection with engineering works is referred to as *fill* or *made ground*. Fill materials generally consist of excavated soil or rock, but may include quarry and colliery waste, building rubble, ashes, and for general infilling purposes even domestic refuse. Examples of the use of fill include: the construction of embankments for roads, railways, dams and breakwaters; land reclamation around coasts and in estuaries and marshlands; and the infilling of old quarries and mine workings.

Fill dumped in a random manner is likely to produce a loose, unstable and highly compressible material of variable and unpredictable character which will require careful investigation if construction on the material is proposed. However, if fill is placed under controlled conditions and adequately compacted, a stable and reasonably predictable engineering material can be produced.

The controlled placement and compaction of fill materials is considered more fully in Sec. 9.2.

In many parts of the world these various environments of soil deposition have been superimposed one upon the other throughout successive geological eras. Thus, the present-day sequence of strata with depth, known as the *soil profile*, reveals the changing environment of each era. Soil profiles typical of what might be encountered are shown in Fig. 1.1.

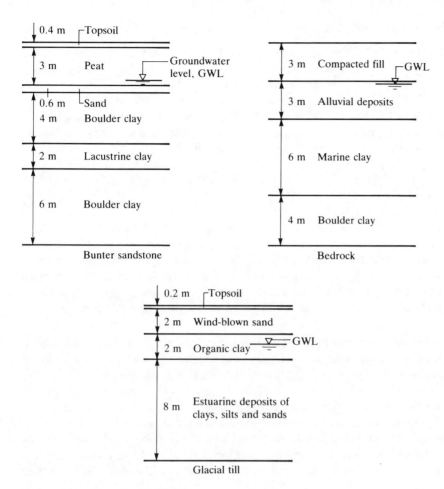

Figure 1.1 Examples of soil profiles.

The structure and engineering properties of the granular soils tend to be relatively uncomplicated and predictable, being influenced mainly by the mass-derived gravitational forces which act within the soil skeleton and the actual distribution of the various particle sizes in the soil deposit. In contrast, the structure and engineering properties of cohesive soils are much more complex. This is due mainly to the dominating influence of the surface forces derived from electro-chemical activity on the surface of the clay mineral particles. Therefore, in the following section we review more fully the electro-chemical properties of clays, and then in Sec. 1.4 we consider the structure of clay deposits.

1.3 ELECTRO-CHEMICAL PROPERTIES OF CLAY MINERALS

Introduction

Soil particles of clay size which exhibit the characteristic properties of stiction and plasticity are referred to as *clay minerals*. Those which do not are mostly rock flour, very finely ground particles of quartz, which is cohesionless and non-plastic. The study of clay minerals has applications not only in Soil Mechanics but also in the ceramics industry and in oil and gas exploration, and has been treated extensively by Grim (1962, 1968).

The Clay Minerals

Clay minerals are the products of chemical weathering (Table 1.1) and are mostly hydrated aluminium silicates. The particles are very small and their behaviour is dominated by electro-chemical activity. In particular, they have a nett negative charge and exhibit an affinity for water.

Clay minerals are generally of a crystalline form constructed from two fundamental building units: the *tetrahedral unit* in which four oxygens enclose one silicon atom as in Fig. 1.2a, and the *octahedral unit* in which one aluminium or magnesium atom is enclosed by six hydroxyl groups as in Fig. 1.2b. According to the arrangement of these building units in the crystal lattice, the clay minerals are divided into three main groups: the *kaolinites*, the *illites* and the *montmorillonites*. The structure of the crystal lattice also influences the magnitude of the nett negative charge and the extent of the affinity for water.

Kaolinite group This group of minerals has a structural block about 7 Å thick consisting of a sheet of tetrahedral units and a sheet of octahedral units. Large numbers of these blocks stack together to form particles 500–1000 Å thick, as in Fig. 1.2c, with a typical diameter/thickness ratio of 10–20. Hydrogen bonding between the blocks creates a relatively stable lattice structure not readily penetrated by water. Thus kaolinites exhibit relatively low water absorption and have relatively low susceptibility to shrinkage and swelling under variations in water content.

Illite group This group has a structural block about 10 Å thick, consisting of a sheet of octahedral units sandwiched between two oppositely oriented sheets of tetrahedral units. However, some of the silicon (Si^{4+}) positions in the tetrahedral units are filled with aluminium (Al^{3+}). This involves an ion of lower valency replacing one of higher valency, and so potassium (K^+) ions attach themselves between the blocks in an attempt to compensate for the charge deficiency. The interlayer bonding of potassium ions allows the blocks to stack together as in Fig. 1.2d, but is less stable than the hydrogen bonding in kaolinite so particles of illite achieve thicknesses only of about 200–300 Å and typical diameter/thickness ratios in the order of 20–50. Illites also exhibit a greater tendency for water absorption than kaolinites, and greater shrinkage and swelling characteristics.

Montmorillonite group This group has a structural block similar to that of the illite group, but in addition to the substitution of aluminium (Al^{3+}) for silicon (Si^{4+}) in the tetrahedral units, some of the aluminium (Al^{3+}) ions in the octahedral units are replaced by magnesium (Mg^{2+}) and iron (Fe^{2+}). These changes result in a large nett negative charge which attracts water molecules and any available cations into the lattice as in Fig. 1.2e. This interlayer water bond is very weak and unstable compared with the potassium ion bonding of the illites, and montmorillonites therefore readily break down into very small particles, possibly 10–30 Å thick with a typical diameter/thickness ratio in the order of 200–400. In addition, montmorillonites exhibit very high water absorption and very high shrinkage and swelling characteristics.

Adsorbed Water

As a result of the nett negative charge on clay mineral particles, some of the water in the voids is attracted to and held strongly against the particle surface. Water molecules are dipolar in character and some may be attracted directly to the particle surface, the positive pole being oriented towards the negatively charged surface. Others may be held directly on the particle surface by hydrogen bonding, or attached to hydrated cations which are themselves attracted to the negative surface. Water which is attracted to and held around clay mineral particles in this manner is referred to as *adsorbed water*.

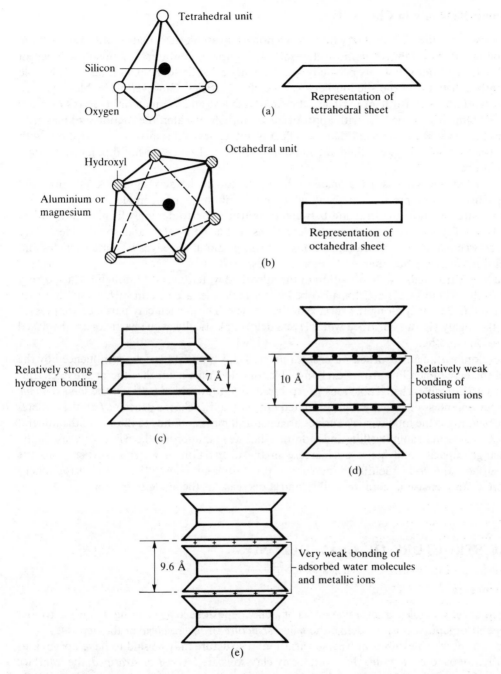

Figure 1.2 Clay mineral building units (a) tetrahedral, (b) octahedral. Structural arrangement of (c) kaolinite, (d) illite, (e) montmorillonite.

The exact nature of adsorbed water is not fully understood, but it is generally accepted that over a thickness of several molecules, at least, the water is held firmly to the clay particle and exhibits low mobility and an extremely high viscosity, maybe 100 times that of ordinary water. Thereafter the attraction decreases with increasing distance from the particle surface and the water gradually reverts to its normal 'free' state.

Stiction and Plasticity in Clay Soils

The property of *plasticity* is the ability to undergo non-recoverable deformation without cracking or crumbling, and is exhibited by most clay soils at intermediate water contents. If a block of plastic clay is dried out it loses its plasticity and becomes a brittle solid, exhibiting considerable dry strength as a result of the stiction between the clay particles. However, if the block is then broken down into its constituent particles, the stiction is lost and the material behaves as a dry powder. On remixing the powder with appropriate quantities of water, the stiction and plasticity properties reappear. It is significant that this effect is not achieved if remixing is carried out with carbon tetrachloride as the pore fluid, a compound whose molecules are not dipolar and which does not ionize.

Thus water in the pores is a major contributory factor in the development of stiction and plasticity. However, the precise manner in which it contributes is not completely understood.

Stiction is attributed to an attraction between the particles derived mainly from Van der Waal forces,† an affinity for certain exchangeable cations in the porewater, and some edge-to-face bonding between minor concentrations of positive charge along the edges of some particles and the general negative surface charge of other particles.

Plasticity is attributed to a deformation of the adsorbed water layers. Although attracted very strongly to the clay mineral particles, adsorbed water molecules are held in such a way that they can move relatively easily along the surface of the particle. Thus, when clay particles are pressed together the highly viscous adsorbed water layers deform plastically as the particles are displaced relative to one another.

The development of an adsorbed water layer around clay mineral particles is influenced by the ability of the clay mineral to attract exchangeable ions and thus neutralize the negative charge. The ability to absorb exchangeable ions is expressed quantitatively in terms of the *ion exchange capacity* per unit mass of dry clay. This is related not only to the charge deficiency on the mineral particles, but also to the total particle surface area per unit mass and thus to the size of the mineral particles. Considering kaolinite, illite and montmorillonite in that order, there is an increase in the ion exchange capacity and hence an increase in the proportion of water adsorbed onto the particle surface, and consequently an increase in plasticity and *activity* (Sec. 1.6). At the macro scale there is an increase in compressibility and a decrease in the angle of friction.

1.4 THE STRUCTURE OF CLAY DEPOSITS

Macrostructure

The larger, usually visible, structural features of a clay deposit such as layering, fissuring, rootlet channels and organic inclusions define the *macrostructure* or *macrofabric* of the deposit.

A clay deposit which exhibits no visible variation in structure may be said to have no obvious macrostructure or to be *uniform*. However, many clay soils are *layered* or *stratified*, the interface between each layer being defined by a bedding plane. Where the individual layers are relatively thin, not more than about 25 mm thick, and parallel with one another, the clay is said to be *laminated*.

Many clay deposits formed in glacial melt-water lakes have been found to exhibit a unique type of laminated structure. These are the so-called *varved* clays. Because of seasonal variations in the flow of melt-water from the glaciers, the deposit consists of alternating layers, or varves, of silt or

---

† These are short-range forces of attraction between adjacent molecules, and are due to the interaction of electric fields generated around the molecules by the electrons orbiting the atomic nuclei.

fine sand deposited rapidly during the summer period of high flow and clay, usually dark in colour deposited slowly over the remaining seasonal period. The silt or fine sand layers act as partings and enable specimens of the soil, when dry, to be split apart into thin laminae.

Many stiff clays exist in their natural state with a network of hair cracks, joints or fissures; such clay deposits are described as *fissured*. The occurrence of fissuring is attributed to a previous presence of high stress levels in the clay, past earth movements and general instability, or to volume changes due to desiccation. In the latter case, sufficiently wide fissures may have formed to permit infilling with silt particles during a subsequent inundation and deposition cycle. A clay deposit which exhibits no evidence of fissuring is described as *intact*.

The presence of a well-defined macrostructure may have a very significant influence on the engineering behaviour of a clay deposit. For example, fissures present in a mass of clay will constitute planes of weakness, with the result that the fissured clay will almost certainly have a lower strength than that of a similar clay in an intact state. Alternatively, layers of silt or sand in a clay deposit, and silt-filled fissures if present, will act as preferential drainage paths. Thus, the mass permeability of a laminated clay will be greater than that of a corresponding uniform clay, and in particular the permeability in a horizontal direction, where flow can occur relatively freely along the laminations of silt and sand, will be many times greater than that in a vertical direction where flow has to occur across the aggregate thickness of all the clay layers.

Microstructure

The structural arrangement of individual particles or groups of particles at a microscopic scale in a clay deposit defines the *microstructure* or *microfabric* of the deposit.

When in suspension in water, clay mineral particles may experience mutual attraction resulting, it is thought, from Van der Waal forces and an affinity for certain exchangeable cations in the suspension, or they may experience mutual repulsion because of the like charges on the particles and the presence of adsorbed water. An alkaline suspension suppresses the effects of repulsion and, if the particles collide or come into close proximity, they are attracted together and form groups or flocs and settle out relatively rapidly. On the other hand, if the suspension is neutralized by the addition of an acidic solution the forces of repulsion dominate and the particles remain dispersed in the suspension for a much longer time.

Thus, it was long believed that the environment of deposition had a major influence on the microstructure of clay deposits. It was thought that deposition through salt water would produce marine clays with a distinctly *flocculated* structure, as in Fig. 1.3a, while deposition through fresh water would produce lacustrine clays or alluvial clays with a less flocculated structure or possibly a *dispersed* structure, as in Fig. 1.3b. Not all researchers were in common agreement on the influence of the environment of deposition and many variations of these structures were proposed.

More recent studies of natural clays using the scanning electron microscope have shown that the microstructure is much more complex and much less predictable than previously suggested (Collins and McGown, 1974; Yong and Warkentin, 1975). The highly parallel, single-plate, dispersed structure has not been observed, whereas groups of clay plates have frequently been identified, often showing evidence of face–face parallel arrangements within the group. Aggregations of these groups were found to be common, sometimes existing as connector assemblages between silt or sand particles. Soils from different depositional environments were found to exhibit similar arrangements of clay groups and silt or sand particles, and there is little support for the belief that a unique relationship exists between the microstructure of a clay deposit and its environment of deposition.

The complex and very varied arrangements of the clay microfabric are difficult to represent visually, but a simple representation of what can commonly occur is shown in Fig. 1.3c.

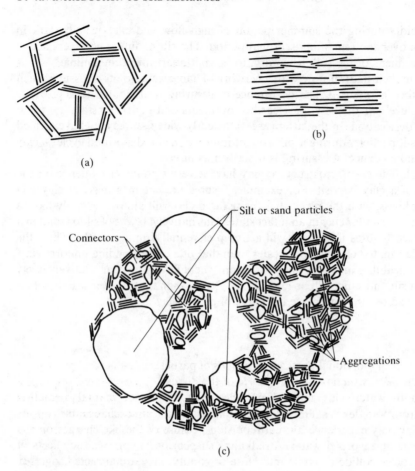

Figure 1.3 (a) Salt-flocculated structure, (b) dispersed structure, (c) representation of natural clay structure.

Sensitivity of Clays

If a mass of clay has been severely disturbed to such an extent that the original structure is destroyed, then the clay is said to have been *remoulded*. Processes which produce remoulding are numerous and varied, ranging from a simple kneading or working of a clay specimen in the hand to massive earthworks involving excavation and replacement of soil under controlled conditions of compaction.

In general, it is found that the strength of remoulded clay is less than the strength of the corresponding undisturbed clay. The loss of strength is attributed to rupture of the electro-chemical bonding between particles and a redistribution of some of the adsorbed water into free water.

The loss of strength on remoulding is described in terms of the *sensitivity* of the clay which is defined as

$$\text{Sensitivity} = \frac{\text{Undisturbed strength}}{\text{Remoulded strength}} \tag{1.1}$$

Some post-glacial marine clays which were uplifted above sea-level by the gradual rise of the earth's crust following the end of the Ice Age suffered infiltration and percolation of fresh groundwater which led to a gradual washing out of the salt content, referred to as *leaching*. This was accompanied by a weakening of the interparticle bonding within the clay structure and a decrease in the proportion of adsorbed water, while the structural arrangement of the particles remained essentially unaltered.

These leached sediments exist today as highly unstable and extremely sensitive deposits which on remoulding or disturbance by shock or vibration are liable to collapse and be transformed into the consistency of a liquid. Such materials are described as *quick* clays, and are known to occur notably in Scandanavia and parts of Canada.

Most normal clays have a sensitivity in the range 1—4, while quick clays may have sensitivity values as high as 100. A scale of sensitivity values based upon the proposals of Skempton and Northey (1952) and Bjerrum (1954) is as follows:

Sensitivity	*Description*
<2	Insensitive
2–4	Medium sensitive
4–8	Sensitive
8–16	Extra sensitive
>16	Quick

1.5 PHYSICAL PROPERTIES OF SOILS

Introduction

In general, soil is a three-phase material consisting of a skeleton of solid particles encompassing voids filled with water and air. In order to describe fully the characteristics of a soil deposit it is necessary that the constitution of the solids–water–air mixture can be expressed quantitatively in terms of some standard physical properties. Definitions of these standard physical properties can be introduced with reference to Fig. 1.4, which represents schematically the proportions by volume and by mass of the constituent phases in a typical element of the soil deposit in which

total volume of soil element = V		total mass of soil element = M	
volume of solids	= V_s	mass of solids	= M_s
volume of voids	= V_v	mass of voids	= M_v
volume of pore water	= V_w	mass of pore water	= M_w
volume of pore air	= V_a	mass of pore air assumed to be zero	

It follows that

$$V = V_s + V_v = V_s + V_w + V_a \tag{1.2}$$

and

$$M = M_s + M_v = M_s + M_w \tag{1.3}$$

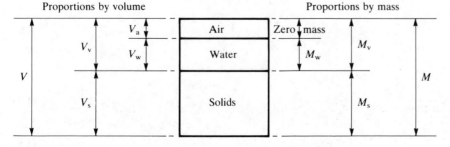

Figure 1.4 Schematic representation of constituent phases of a soil element.

Table 1.3 Typical values of particle specific gravity

Soil type	G_s
Gravel, sand and silt	2.65
Inorganic clay	2.70
Organic clay	2.60
Fen peat	2.00
Bog peat	1.50

Particle Specific Gravity

One fundamental property required in the definition of some of the physical properties of soils is the specific gravity of the soil particles, or *particle specific gravity*, denoted by G_s. This is defined as

$$G_s = \frac{\text{density of soil particles}}{\text{density of water}}$$

Thus

$$G_s = \frac{M_s}{V_s \rho_w} \tag{1.4}$$

where

$$\rho_w = \text{density of water} = 1000 \text{ kg/m}^3 \text{ or } 1 \text{ Mg/m}^3$$

The value of G_s depends on the mineralogical composition of the constituent soil particles, typical values being given in Table 1.3.

Void Ratio and Porosity

The proportion of void space in the soil element is expressed in terms of either the *void ratio*, denoted by e, or alternatively the *porosity*, denoted by n. These are defined with reference to Fig. 1.4 as

$$e = \frac{V_v}{V_s} \tag{1.5}$$

and

$$n = \frac{V_v}{V} \tag{1.6}$$

Both e and n are dimensionless parameters, and values of n are frequently expressed as a percentage. Note that n cannot exceed 100 per cent.

Now

$$\frac{V_v}{V_s} = \frac{V_v}{V - V_v} = \frac{\dfrac{V_v}{V}}{1 - \dfrac{V_v}{V}}$$

Thus

$$e = \frac{n}{1 - n} \tag{1.7}$$

and

$$n = \frac{e}{1 + e} \tag{1.8}$$

Granular soils The ranges of values of void ratio and porosity commonly found in granular soils are limited by the state of packing of the grains in the soil skeleton. This can be illustrated by considering the limiting conditions possible in an ideal soil consisting of uniformly sized spherical particles.

The *loosest* state (corresponding to maximum void space) is obtained when the spheres are arranged in a cubic packing with six points of contact per sphere, as in Fig. 1.5a. Calculation then gives

$$\text{maximum } e = 0.91, \qquad \text{maximum } n = 47.6 \text{ per cent}$$

The *densest* state (corresponding to minimum void space) is obtained when the spheres are arranged in a rhombic packing with twelve points of contact per sphere, as in Fig. 1.5b. Calculation now gives

$$\text{minimum } e = 0.35, \qquad \text{minimum } n = 26 \text{ per cent}$$

In practice, it is found that the limiting values for granular soils lie remarkably close to these theoretical values, typical ranges being

$$\text{well-graded sands} \quad e = 0.43\text{–}0.67, \quad n = 30\text{–}40 \text{ per cent}$$
$$\text{uniform-sized sands} \quad e = 0.51\text{–}0.85, \quad n = 34\text{–}46 \text{ per cent}$$

Well-graded soils can achieve a denser packing and hence lower void ratios than uniform soils, as a result of the finer particles occupying the voids between coarser particles.

It is clear then that a knowledge of the void ratio of a granular soil in its natural state will not in itself be an absolute indication of whether the soil deposit is in a loose or dense state. This information can be obtained only if the *in situ* void ratio e is compared with the maximum and minimum void ratios, e_{max} and e_{min}, which can be achieved with that soil. Such a comparison may be expressed numerically in terms of the *relative density*, D_r, of the soil deposit, which is defined as

$$D_r = \frac{e_{max} - e}{e_{max} - e_{min}} \tag{1.9}$$

The form of Eq. (1.9) indicates that $0 \leqslant D_r \leqslant 1$. Low values of relative density are indicative of a granular soil existing naturally in a loose state, while high values are indicative of a granular soil existing in a dense state.

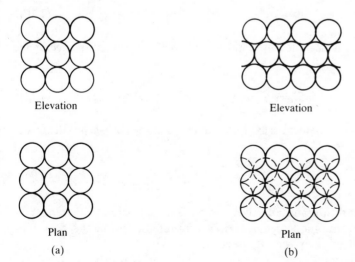

Elevation   Elevation

Plan   Plan

(a)   (b)

Figure 1.5 Ideal granular soil of uniform spherical particles: (a) cubic packing, (b) rhombic packing.

Relative density may also be known as *density index*, I_D.

In the laboratory, the maximum void ratio condition may be achieved by pouring an oven-dried sample of the soil from a fixed height into a standard mould. Alternatively, about 1 kg of the dry soil may be placed in a 2-litre measuring cylinder which is then closed, shaken a few times and inverted. On quickly tilting the cylinder upright again, the sand takes up what may be assumed to be its loosest packing.

The minimum void ratio condition is obtained by compacting an oven-dried sample of the soil into a standard mould, the method being either (1) to fill the mould in three equal layers, each layer being compacted using a vibrating hammer, or (2) to fill the mould in a single layer, apply a surcharge weight to the surface of the sand and compact on a vibrating table.

Details of how these tests are carried out can be found in ASTM D–2049–69, BS 5930: 1981, Table 4, and Akroyd (1957). The calculations involved are illustrated in Example 1.2.

Cohesive soils Because of the electro-chemical activity associated with clay mineral particles, cohesive soils frequently possess a much higher proportion of void space than is possible in granular soils. For clays, typical values of void ratio and porosity may be in the range

$$e = 0.55\text{--}5, \qquad n = 35\text{--}83 \text{ per cent}$$

Thus, as first formed, clay deposits are generally very compressible materials. They are naturally less compressible if they have been overconsolidated either by glaciation or erosion.

Peat Peat soils are characterized by a high organic content and a great capacity for holding and storing water, with associated values of void ratio often in the range 10–15. Thus, in a typical peat deposit having a thickness of 3 m, there may be less than 300 mm of actual solid matter. Consequently, peats are highly compressible materials and surface deposits may undergo strains of the order of 50 per cent or more under the action of loads equivalent to only a metre or so of fill.

Water Content, Degree of Saturation and Air Voids Content

The proportion of water present in a soil element is expressed in terms of the *water content, w*, defined with reference to Fig. 1.4 as

$$w = \frac{M_w}{M_s} \qquad (1.10)$$

The proportion of void space that is occupied by water is expressed in terms of the *degree of saturation, S_r*, and is defined as

$$S_r = \frac{V_w}{V_v} \qquad (1.11)$$

The proportion of air present in a soil element is expressed in terms of the *air voids content, A_r*, defined as

$$A_r = \frac{V_a}{V} \qquad (1.12)$$

The water content, degree of saturation and air voids content are dimensionless parameters and are normally expressed in the form of a percentage. However, note that while $0 \leqslant S_r \leqslant 100$ per cent and $0 \leqslant A_r \leqslant n$, values of w may exceed 100 per cent.

Below the water table soils will generally be *saturated*, i.e., all the voids will be occupied by water and $S_r = 100$ per cent. Fine-grained soils may also be saturated above the water table,

Table 1.4 Typical properties of some natural soils (based on Terzaghi and Peck, 1967)

Description	Porosity n (%)	Void ratio e	Water content at $S_r = 1$ w (%)	Density (Mg/m³) ρ_d	Density (Mg/m³) ρ_s
Loose uniform sand	46	0.85	32	1.44	1.89
Dense uniform sand	34	0.51	19	1.75	2.08
Loose well-graded sand	40	0.67	25	1.59	1.98
Dense well-graded sand	30	0.43	16	1.86	2.16
Well-graded glacial till	20	0.25	9	2.11	2.32
Soft glacial clay	55	1.20	45	1.21	1.76
Stiff glacial clay	37	0.60	22	1.69	2.06
Soft slightly organic clay	66	1.9	70	0.92	1.57
Soft very organic clay	75	3.0	110	0.68	1.43
Soft montmorillonite clay (bentonite)	84	5.2	194	0.44	1.28
Fen peat	91	10	500	0.18	1.09
Bog peat	94	15	1000	0.09	1.03

owing principally to the effects of capillary rise in the very fine pores. However, coarse-grained soils will probably be only partly saturated above the water table with $S_r < 100$ per cent.

Water contents vary considerably from one soil to another and indeed may vary throughout the same deposit, and will of course depend on the degree of saturation. Typical values for various soils at full saturation are given in Table 1.4 together with other basic data.

A useful expression relating w, S_r, e and G_s is obtained from Eqs (1.4), (1.5), (1.10) and (1.11) as follows:

$$\frac{M_w}{M_s} = \frac{V_w \rho_w}{V_s \rho_w G_s} = \frac{V_w}{V_v} \cdot \frac{V_v}{V_s} \cdot \frac{1}{G_s}$$

$$\therefore \qquad w = \frac{S_r e}{G_s} \qquad (1.13)$$

Similarly Eqs (1.6), (1.11) and (1.12) yield an expression relating A_r, S_r and n as follows:

$$\frac{V_a}{V} = \frac{V_v - V_w}{V} = \frac{V_v}{V}\left[1 - \frac{V_w}{V_v}\right]$$

$$\therefore \qquad A_r = n(1 - S_r) \qquad (1.14)$$

Density

The *bulk density*, ρ, of a soil element is defined fundamentally as its mass per unit volume, and hence with reference to Fig. 1.4 bulk density is expressed as

$$\rho = \frac{M}{V} \qquad (1.15)$$

Alternatively, expanding and substituting from Eqs (1.4), (1.5) and (1.10) we get

$$\rho = \frac{M}{V} = \frac{M_s + M_w}{V_s + V_v} = \frac{M_s\left[1 + \dfrac{M_w}{M_s}\right]}{V_s\left[1 + \dfrac{V_v}{V_s}\right]}$$

$$\therefore \qquad \rho = \frac{G_s(1 + w)}{(1 + e)}\rho_w \qquad (1.16)$$

and on substituting for w from Eq. (1.13)

$$\rho = \left[\frac{G_s + S_r e}{1 + e}\right]\rho_w \qquad (1.17)$$

If the soil element were to be saturated at the same void ratio then $S_r = 1$ (i.e., 100 per cent), and we obtain the corresponding *saturated density*, ρ_s, as

$$\rho_s = \left[\frac{G_s + e}{1 + e}\right]\rho_w \qquad (1.18)$$

On the other hand, if the soil element were to exist in a dry condition at the same void ratio then $S_r = 0$, and we obtain the corresponding *dry density*, ρ_d, as

$$\rho_d = \left[\frac{G_s}{1 + e}\right]\rho_w \qquad (1.19)$$

or from first principles with $M_w = 0$ in Fig. 1.4:

$$\rho_d = \frac{M_s}{V} \qquad (1.20)$$

If the soil element is situated below the water table, the soil particles will experience an upthrust U so that their effective weight W'_s is given by

$$W'_s = W_s - U$$

Thus $\qquad W'_s = (W - W_w) - \rho_w g V_s = W - \rho_w g (V_w + V_s)$

Since the voids will be completely filled with water, $V_w = V_v$ and therefore $V_w + V_s = V$. Hence

$$W'_s = W - \rho_w g V$$

Thus $\qquad \dfrac{W'_s}{gV} = \dfrac{W}{gV} - \rho_w$

Now the effective weight of the soil particles W'_s also denotes the effective weight of the soil element and therefore W'_s/gV defines the *effective density* ρ' of the element. Also, the total weight W of the element is the saturated weight and therefore W/gV represents the saturated density ρ_s. We thus obtain

$$\rho' = \rho_s - \rho_w \qquad (1.21)$$

Substituting for ρ_s from Eq. (1.18) then gives

$$\rho' = \left[\frac{G_s - 1}{1 + e}\right]\rho_w \qquad (1.22)$$

The effective density is also referred to as the *submerged density* or the *buoyant density*.

We can derive two further relationships for density which have particular relevance in the analysis of compaction test results (Sec. 9.2). From Eq. (1.15)

$$\rho = \frac{M}{V} = \frac{M_s + M_w}{V} = \frac{M_s}{V}\left[1 + \frac{M_w}{M_s}\right]$$

$$\therefore \qquad \rho = \rho_d(1 + w) \qquad (1.23)$$

From Eq. (1.2)

$$V - V_a = V_s + V_w$$

$$\therefore \quad V\left[1 - \frac{V_a}{V}\right] = \frac{M_s}{G_s\rho_w} + \frac{M_w}{\rho_w} = \frac{M_s}{G_s\rho_w}\left[1 + G_s\frac{M_w}{M_s}\right]$$

$$\therefore \quad \frac{M_s}{V} = \frac{G_s\left[1 - \dfrac{V_a}{V}\right]}{\left[1 + G_s\dfrac{M_w}{M_s}\right]}\rho_w$$

$$\therefore \quad \rho_d = \frac{G_s(1 - A_r)}{(1 + G_s w)}\rho_w \qquad (1.24)$$

The most convenient units for soil density in the SI system are Mg/m^3 and some typical values for various soils are given in Table 1.4.

Unit Weight

As an alternative to density, one may work in terms of unit weight. This is defined fundamentally as the weight per unit volume, and can be obtained by multiplying the density by the gravitational acceleration term g. Now in the SI system $1\,N \equiv 1\,kg \times 1\,m/s^2$ and therefore $1\,kN \equiv 1\,Mg \times 1\,m/s^2 = 1\,Mg\,m/s^2$. Thus, with $g = 9.81\,m/s^2$, a soil having a bulk density of $2.0\,Mg/m^3$ will therefore have a *bulk unit weight*, γ, given by

$$\gamma = \rho g = 2.0 \times 9.81 \frac{Mg}{m^3}\cdot\frac{m}{s^2} = 19.62\,kN/m^3$$

Similarly we have *saturated unit weight*, γ_s, *dry unit weight*, γ_d, and *effective unit weight*, γ'.

Particle specific gravity, water content and bulk density can be determined directly using standard test procedures, full details of which can be found in the following:

	BS 1377: 1975	ASTM
Specific gravity	Test 6	D–854–58
Water content	Test 1	D–2216–71
Bulk density	Test 15	D–1556–64: D–2167–66
		D–2922–78: D–2937–71

The other properties are normally obtained by calculation, as illustrated in Examples 1.2 and 1.3.

Example 1.1 The following results were obtained from a laboratory test to determine the particle specific gravity of a medium sand.

Mass of density bottle, M_1	= 35.825 g
Mass of density bottle + dry sand, M_2	= 63.761 g
Mass of density bottle + sand + distilled water, M_3	= 103.619 g
Mass of density bottle + distilled water, M_4	= 86.365 g

Calculate the specific gravity of the sand particles.

SOLUTION The tabulated weighings give

$$M_2 - M_1 = \text{mass of dry sand particles (g)}$$
$$M_4 - M_1 = \text{mass of water required to fill density bottle (g)}$$
$$M_3 - M_2 = \text{mass of water in density bottle with sand particles (g)}$$

$\therefore$

$$(M_4 - M_1) - (M_3 - M_2)$$
$$= \text{mass of water displaced by sand particles (g)}$$
$$= \text{volume of water displaced by sand particles (cm}^3\text{)}$$
$$= \text{volume of sand particles (cm}^3\text{)}$$

Therefore density of sand particles $= \dfrac{M_2 - M_1}{(M_4 - M_1) - (M_3 - M_2)}$ (g/cm^3)

Specific gravity of sand particles $= \dfrac{\text{density of sand particles}}{\text{density of water}}$

and as the density of water $= 1$ g/cm^3 then

Specific gravity of sand particles $G_s = \dfrac{M_2 - M_1}{(M_4 - M_1) - (M_3 - M_2)}$

Thus we obtain $G_s = \dfrac{63.761 - 35.825}{(86.365 - 35.825) - (103.619 - 63.761)} = \underline{2.62}$

Example 1.2 An investigation at a particular site revealed a deposit of sand overlying bedrock. A sample of the sand taken from above the water table had a total mass of 2205 g and was found to have occupied in its natural state a volume of 1125 cm^3. After oven-drying the mass of the sample was 1970 g, and its particle specific gravity was found to be 2.65.

(a) For the sand above the water table, calculate
    (i) bulk density   (ii) water content   (iii) void ratio
    (iv) degree of saturation   (v) air voids content
(b) For the sand below the water table, calculate
    (i) water content   (ii) saturated density
(c) After oven-drying, 1000 g of the sand was poured into a 2-litre measuring cylinder. The cylinder was then closed, inverted, and quickly tilted upright again, at which time the sand was found to occupy a volume of 641.5 cm^3.

    The dry sand was then compacted into a 100-mm diameter by 120-mm deep mould in three approximately equal layers using a Kango hammer, vibrating each layer for $1\frac{1}{2}$ minutes. The mass of sand required to fill the mould in this manner was 1746.6 g.

    Calculate the relative density of the sand deposit.

SOLUTION
(a) Total mass of sample $M = 2205$ g
    Total volume of sample $V = 1125$ cm^3
    Mass of solids in sample $M_s = 1970$ g
$\therefore$ Mass of water in sample $M_w = M - M_s = 2205 - 1970 = 235$ g
$\therefore$ Volume of water in sample $V_w = 235$ cm^3

From Eq. (1.4)

    Volume of solids in sample $V_s = \dfrac{M_s}{G_s \rho_w} = \dfrac{1970}{2.65 \times 1} = 743.4$ cm^3

$\therefore$ Volume of voids in sample $V_v = V - V_s = 1125 - 743.4 = 381.6$ cm^3

and   Volume of air in sample $V_a = V_v - V_w = 381.6 - 235 = 146.6 \text{ cm}^3$

Thus, for the sand above the water table we obtain

(i) bulk density $\rho = \dfrac{M}{V} = \dfrac{2205}{1125} = 1.96 \text{ g/cm}^3 = \underline{1.96 \text{ Mg/m}^3}$

(ii) water content $w = \dfrac{M_w}{M_s} = \dfrac{235}{1970} = 0.119 = \underline{11.9 \text{ per cent}}$

(iii) void ratio $e = \dfrac{V_v}{V_s} = \dfrac{381.6}{743.4} = \underline{0.513}$

Alternatively, by rearranging Eq. (1.16)

$$e = G_s(1 + w)\dfrac{\rho_w}{\rho} - 1 = 2.65 \times 1.119 \times \dfrac{1}{1.96} - 1 = 0.513$$

(iv) degree of saturation $S_r = \dfrac{V_w}{V_v} = \dfrac{235}{381.6} = 0.616 = \underline{62 \text{ per cent}}$

Alternatively from Eq. (1.13)

$$S_r = \dfrac{wG_s}{e} = \dfrac{0.119 \times 2.65}{0.513} = 0.615$$

(v) air voids content $A_r = \dfrac{V_a}{V} = \dfrac{146.6}{1125} = 0.130 = \underline{13 \text{ per cent}}$

Alternatively from Eqs (1.14) and (1.18)

$$A_r = n(1 - S_r) = \dfrac{e}{1 + e}(1 - S_r) = \dfrac{0.513}{1.513}(1 - 0.616) = 0.130$$

(b) Below the water table the voids will be completely filled with water. For full saturation the mass of water in the sample would be

$$M_w = 235 + 146.6 = 381.6 \text{ g}$$

and the total mass of the sample would be

$$M = M_s + M_w = 1970 + 381.6 = 2351.6 \text{ g}$$

Thus for the sand below the water table we obtain

(i) water content $w = \dfrac{M_w}{M_s} = \dfrac{381.6}{1970} = 0.194 = \underline{19.4 \text{ per cent}}$

Alternatively from Eq. (1.13) with $S_r = 1$

$$w = \dfrac{S_r e}{G_s} = \dfrac{1 \times 0.513}{2.65} = 0.194$$

(ii) saturated density $\rho_s = \dfrac{M}{V} = \dfrac{2351.6}{1125} = 2.09 \text{ g/cm}^3 = \underline{2.09 \text{ Mg/m}^3}$

Alternatively from Eq. (1.18)

$$\rho_s = \left[\dfrac{G_s + e}{1 + e}\right]\rho_w = \left[\dfrac{2.65 + 0.513}{1.513}\right] \times 1.0 = 2.09 \text{ Mg/m}^3$$

(c) For the maximum void ratio state:

Total mass of soil in cylinder $M = 1000$ g
Total volume of soil in cylinder $V = 641.5$ cm^3

The sand is dry and hence

Mass of solids in cylinder $M_s = 1000$ g

and from Eq. (1.4)

Volume of solids in cylinder $V_s = \dfrac{M_s}{G_s\rho_w} = \dfrac{1000}{2.65 \times 1} = 377.4$ cm^3

$\therefore$ Volume of voids in cylinder $V_v = V - V_s = 641.5 - 377.4 = 264.1$ cm^3

and Maximum void ratio $e_{max} = \dfrac{V_v}{V_s} = \dfrac{264.1}{377.4} = \underline{0.70}$

For the minimum void ratio state:

Total mass of soil in mould $M = 1746.6$ g

Total volume of soil in mould $V = \pi \times (5)^2 \times 12 = 942.5$ cm^3

The sand is dry and hence

Mass of solids in mould $M_s = 1746.6$ g

$\therefore$ Volume of solids in mould $V_s = \dfrac{M_s}{G_s\rho_w} = \dfrac{1746.6}{2.65 \times 1} = 659.1$ cm^3

$\therefore$ Volume of voids in mould $V_v = V - V_s = 942.5 - 659.1 = 283.4$ cm^3

and Minimum void ratio $e_{min} = \dfrac{V_v}{V_s} = \dfrac{283.4}{659.1} = \underline{0.43}$

Therefore from Eq. (1.9), relative density of the sand deposit is given by

$$D_r = \frac{e_{max} - e}{e_{max} - e_{min}} = \frac{0.70 - 0.51}{0.70 - 0.43} = 0.70 = \underline{70 \text{ per cent}}$$

Example 1.3 A road embankment is constructed of clay fill compacted to a bulk density of 2.05 Mg/m^3 at a water content of 18 per cent. The specific gravity of the soil particles is 2.70. Calculate the porosity, degree of saturation, air voids content and dry density of the clay fill.

SOLUTION Consider a sample of the soil having a mass M (g) and a total volume V (cm^3). Then for a specified bulk density of 2.05 g/cm^3 and water content of 18 per cent, we have

$M = 2.05V$ and $M_w = 0.18M_s$

Now $M = M_s + M_w$

$\therefore$ $2.05V = M_s + 0.18M_s = 1.18M_s$

Thus $M_s = 1.737V$

Hence $V_s = \dfrac{M_s}{G_s\rho_w} = \dfrac{1.737V}{2.70 \times 1} = 0.643V$

Also $\qquad M_{\text{w}} = M - M_{\text{s}} = 2.05V - 1.737V = 0.313V$

$\therefore \qquad V_{\text{w}} = 0.313V$

$\qquad V_{\text{v}} = V - V_{\text{s}} = V - 0.643V = 0.357V$

and $\qquad V_{\text{a}} = V_{\text{v}} - V_{\text{w}} = 0.357V - 0.313V = 0.044V$

Hence we obtain:

Porosity $\qquad n = \dfrac{V_{\text{v}}}{V} = \dfrac{0.357V}{V} = 0.357 = \underline{35.7 \text{ per cent}}$

Degree of saturation $S_{\text{r}} = \dfrac{V_{\text{w}}}{V_{\text{v}}} = \dfrac{0.313V}{0.357V} = 0.877 = \underline{87.7 \text{ per cent}}$

Air voids content $\quad A_{\text{r}} = \dfrac{V_{\text{a}}}{V} = \dfrac{0.044V}{V} = 0.044 = \underline{4.4 \text{ per cent}}$

Dry density $\qquad \rho_{\text{d}} = \dfrac{M_{\text{s}}}{V} = \dfrac{1.737V}{V} = 1.737 \text{ g/cm}^3 = \underline{1.737 \text{ Mg/m}^3}$

1.6 CLASSIFICATION AND DESCRIPTION OF ENGINEERING SOILS

Introduction

The object of soil classification is to provide a basis whereby engineers can group soils according to their physical characteristics and appearance for the purposes of comparing different soils, communicating their properties and to a limited extent assessing their suitability for a particular engineering use.

The physical characteristics and appearance of a granular soil are influenced mainly by the distribution of the various particle sizes in the soil deposit, and of a clay soil by the stiction and plasticity properties associated with its mineralogical composition and water content, and also by its natural fabric or macrostructure. The granular fraction of a soil deposit is therefore classified according to its *particle size distribution*, while the clay fraction is classified according to its plasticity characteristics in terms of what are known as its *Atterberg Limits*.

Particle Size Distribution

The distribution of particle size in a soil mass is usually expressed in terms of a *grading curve* or *particle size distribution curve*, in which the percentage by mass of particles finer than any particular size is plotted against particle size to a logarithmic base; some typical grading curves are shown in Fig. 1.6.

The grading curve is obtained by examining the particle size distribution within a representative sample of the soil mass, this being done for the sand and gravel fractions in the form of a *sieve analysis* and for the silt fraction in the form of a *sedimentation analysis*.

Sieve analysis A representative sample of the soil of known mass is passed through a series of standard sieves having successively finer aperture size, and the mass of soil retained on each sieve is measured. This enables the cumulative percentage by mass of the soil sample passing through each sieve to be calculated and plotted against the relevant aperture size. Sieves of appropriate size for the material being tested are selected from the range of test sieves commonly used for particle size analysis given in Table 1.5.

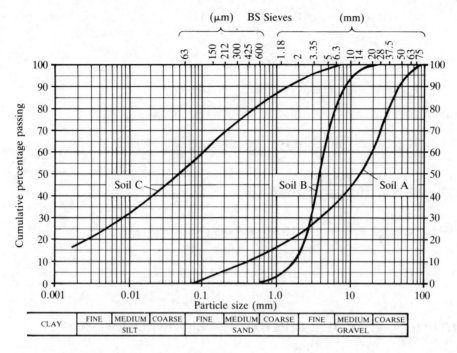

Figure 1.6 Typical grading curves (Example 1.4).

Table 1.5 Range of test sieves commonly used for particle size analysis

British Standard† (designation by aperture size)	ASTM Standard‡	
	Designation	Aperture size
75 mm	3 inch	75 mm
63 mm	2 inch	50 mm
50 mm	1½ inch	37.5 mm
37.5 mm	1 inch	25 mm
28 mm	¾ inch	19 mm
20 mm	⅜ inch	9.5 mm
14 mm	No. 4	4.75 mm
10 mm	No. 8	2.36 mm
6.3 mm	No. 10	2 mm
5 mm	No. 16	1.18 mm
3.35 mm	No. 20	850 μm
2 mm	No. 30	600 μm
1.18 mm	No. 40	425 μm
600 μm	No. 50	300 μm
425 μm	No. 60	250 μm
300 μm	No. 100	150 μm
212 μm	No. 140	106 μm
150 μm	No. 200	75 μm
63 μm		

† BS 1377: 1975.
‡ ASTM D–422–63.

If the soil contains silt and clay-sized particles, the sample is first treated with a deflocculating agent and washed through selected sieves to isolate the fines. The coarse-grained material is then dried and sieved as described above.

Details of the standard test procedures are given in BS 1377: 1975, Tests 7(A) and 7(B), and ASTM D–422–63.

Sedimentation analysis The size of silt particles places them beyond the practical limits of sieve analysis and so the size distribution over the silt range is determined by observing the sedimentation characteristics of the particles as they settle out of suspension in water.

The sedimentation analysis is carried out on material which has passed through the 63 μm BS sieve (No. 10 US sieve). A suspension of known concentration is prepared using distilled water to which a deflocculating agent has been added to ensure that the particles settle out separately. After being thoroughly shaken in a sedimentation cylinder, the suspension is set down and the sedimentation process allowed to begin.

Interpretation of the sedimentation analysis is based on Stokes' Law which expresses the terminal velocity v with which a spherical particle will fall through water as a function of the square of the particle diameter D in the form

$$v = \frac{(G_s - G_w)\rho_w}{18\eta} D^2 \qquad (1.25)$$

where η = coefficient of dynamic viscosity of water. Taking $G_s = 2.65$, $G_w = 1$, $\rho_w = 1 \text{ g/cm}^3$, $\eta = 9.12 \times 10^{-6} \text{ g s/cm}^2$ and expressing D in mm, Eq. (1.25) becomes

$$v = 100.51 D^2 \text{ cm/s}$$

Thus at a depth L (cm) within the suspension after a time t (s), there will be no particles larger than

$$D = \sqrt{\frac{L}{100.51t}} \text{ (mm)}$$

and all particles smaller than this value of D will be at a concentration unchanged from that at the start of sedimentation. This concentration is a measure of the mass of particles in the original suspension having a particle size finer than D mm.

One procedure for determining the concentration is the *pipette method* in which a small specimen of the suspension is withdrawn from a depth $L = 10$ cm at a specified time t s. The specimen is dried, and the mass of solid residue obtained and used to determine the mass of particles in the original suspension having a diameter less than

$$D = \sqrt{\frac{10}{100.51t}} \text{ (mm)}$$

The mass of particles finer than D mm in the original soil sample is then obtained by simple proportion. Repeating this procedure at various times after the start of sedimentation enables the particle size analysis to be completed and the grading curve for the soil extended through the silt range. Full details of the pipette method of sedimentation analysis are given in BS 1377: 1975, Test (C).

An alternative procedure is the *hydrometer method*, in which a special hydrometer is inserted into the suspension at various specified times after the start of sedimentation. At each time, the hydrometer reading yields the specific gravity (or concentration) of the suspension at a particular depth. Full details of the hydrometer method are given in BS 1377: 1975, Test (D) and ASTM D–422–63.

It should be noted that Stokes' Law relates particularly to spherical particles, and consequently the sedimentation analysis yields the so-called 'equivalent particle diameter', i.e., the diameter of a sphere having the same specific gravity as the actual soil particle and settling with the same terminal velocity. Also Stokes' Law is applicable only to particles which are approximately silt-sized. Coarser particles are likely to create excessive turbulence in the suspension, and with the very fine clay particles the influence of Brownian movement precludes the application of Stokes' Law.

Description of grading The shape of the particle size distribution curve indicates whether a soil contains a wide range or only a limited range of particle size, and is used to formulate a description of the grading of the soil.

A coarse-grained soil is described as *well graded* if it contains approximately equal proportions of all particle sizes, and is characterized by a relatively smooth curve covering a wide range of sizes, as soil A in Fig. 1.6. Otherwise a coarse-grained soil is said to be *poorly graded*, in one of the following ways. If a high proportion of the particles lies in a narrow size band, the grading is described as *uniform* and is characterized by a large portion of the curve being nearly vertical, as soil B in Fig. 1.6. If the soil contains large and small particles but exhibits a marked absence of particles in an intermediate size range, it may be described as *gap-graded*.

An indication of the grading may be expressed numerically in terms of the *coefficient of uniformity*, C_U, defined as

$$C_U = \frac{D_{60}}{D_{10}} \tag{1.26}$$

or the *coefficient of curvature*, C_Z, defined as

$$C_Z = \frac{D_{30}^2}{D_{10}D_{60}} \tag{1.27}$$

where D_{10} = the particle size such that 10 per cent of the material is finer than that size
and D_{30}, D_{60} = the particle sizes such that 30 per cent and 60 per cent respectively of the material is finer than these sizes.

C_U and C_Z are used as part of the Unified Soil Classification System described later in this section. In general, however, the higher the value of C_U the greater is the range of particle size in the soil. Soils are classed as well graded if $C_U > 4$ or 6 and $1 < C_Z < 3$ (see Table 1.6).

Consistency of Clays and the Atterberg Limits

One of the most important characteristics of a clay soil is its plasticity. The extent to which a natural clay exhibits plasticity depends upon its clay mineral composition and water content. Furthermore, the consistency of a natural clay is found to vary with water content, ranging from a solid state in the dry condition, through a semi-solid crumbly and non-plastic state at low water contents, to a plastic state at higher water contents, and finally an essentially liquid state at very high water contents.

The water contents at which the consistency changes from one state to another are found to differ from one clay to another, depending upon the amount and type of clay minerals present. Since water content is a readily measurable property, a simple and convenient method of classifying clays has been developed based upon these limiting water contents.

Actually, the change from one consistency state to another is gradual and therefore to meet the requirements of a standard classification it has been necessary to establish arbitrary divisions between the various states. These are referred to as the *Atterberg limits* (after the Swedish scientist who devised them), and are shown in Fig. 1.7 to consist of:

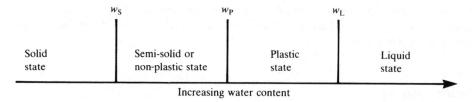

Figure 1.7 Consistency states of clay soil.

(a) the *shrinkage limit*, w_S or SL, which defines the change from the solid state to the semi-solid or non-plastic state,

(b) the *plastic limit*, w_P or PL, which defines the change from the non-plastic to the plastic state, and

(c) the *liquid limit*, w_L or LL, which defines the change from the plastic to the liquid state.

It is important to note that the Atterberg limits are simply water contents.

The range of water contents over which a clay exhibits plasticity is termed the *plasticity index*, I_P or PI, and is given by

$$I_P = w_L - w_P \tag{1.28}$$

The natural water content w at which a clay exists in the field may be compared with its liquid and plastic limits by reference to the *liquidity index*, I_L or LI, which is defined as

$$I_L = \frac{w - w_P}{w_L - w_P} = \frac{w - w_P}{I_P} \tag{1.29}$$

The liquidity index is generally expressed as a percentage and thus a value of I_L approaching 100 per cent indicates that the natural clay in the field has a consistency near to its liquid limit, while a value of I_L approaching 0 per cent indicates that it has a consistency near to its plastic limit. Most natural clays exist in the field in a plastic state and so the values of I_L will commonly fall within the range 0–100 per cent. However, it should be noted that the value of I_L can be negative.

As was discussed in Sec. 1.3, plasticity is attributed to a deformation of the adsorbed water around clay mineral particles. Therefore, the degree of plasticity exhibited by a soil is related to type and amount of clay minerals present. Skempton (1953) expressed this relationship mathematically in terms of the *activity A* of the clay which he defined as

$$A = \frac{I_P}{\text{per cent clay}} \tag{1.30}$$

where the per cent clay is taken as the percentage by mass finer than 0.002 mm. The relative values of activity are lowest for kaolinite, rather higher for illite and highest for montmorillonite.

The Atterberg limits are determined in the laboratory from empirical tests carried out on prepared samples of material passing the 425 µm test sieve. The standard methods for determining the liquid limit are described fully in BS 1377: 1975, Test 2, and ASTM D–423–66, and for the plastic limit in BS 1377: 1975, Test 3, and ASTM D–424–59. In the context of soil classification, the shrinkage limit is relatively unimportant.

It should be emphasized that where laboratory tests on soil samples are to yield parameters for use in the design of engineering works, the samples must be representative and undisturbed in order that the design parameters measured will reflect the engineering behaviour of the soil deposit in the field. The liquid and plastic limit tests, however, are carried out on remoulded samples and cannot therefore be expected to reflect characteristics of engineering behaviour which depend upon the natural macrostructure of the clay soil in the field. The prime function of these tests is to provide a basis for the classification of clay soils and not to enable predictions of engineering behaviour to be made.

Soil Classification Systems

Numerous soil classification systems have been proposed over the years, with the result that there is no internationally agreed standard. In the United States the most widely used are probably the Unified Soil Classification Sytem and the AASHTO Classification Sytem.

The AASHTO System was developed originally by the US Bureau of Public Roads in the late twenties to assess the suitability of a material for use in road construction. After some major revisions in 1945 it was adopted by the American Association of State Highway and Transportation Officials as AASHTO standard M—145.

The Unified System, developed originally by Casagrande in the forties for use in airfield construction, was modified in 1952 by the US Bureau of Reclamation and the US Corps of Engineers to extend its range of application. In 1969 it was adopted by the American Society for Testing and Materials as the standard method of classifying soils for engineering purposes, ASTM D–2487–69.

Until 1981, Britain used a classification system very similar to the Unified System. However, in that year the British Soil Classification System was published as part of BS 5930: 1981 'Code of practice for site investigations'.

Descriptions of the Unified Classification Sytem and the British Classification System are presented in the following sections.

Unified Soil Classification System A summary of the Unified Classification System is presented in Table 1.6.

Based on the particle size distribution of material passing the 75 mm sieve, the soil is first designated either as *coarse grained* if more than 50 per cent is retained on the No. 200 sieve, or as *fine grained* if 50 per cent or more passes the No. 200 sieve. These major divisions are subdivided into groups, each group being assigned a symbol consisting of a prefix and a suffix letter.

Coarse-grained soils have group symbols made up from:

Prefix letters: G—gravel, if 50 per cent or more of coarse fraction is retained on the No. 4 sieve
S—sand, if more than 50 per cent of coarse fraction passes the No. 4 sieve
Suffix letters: W—well graded
P—poorly graded } choice depends upon values of C_U and C_Z
M—silty
C—clayey } choice depends upon values of w_L and I_P

If less than 5 per cent of the material passes the No. 200 sieve the suffix letter will be W or P depending upon the values of C_U and C_Z, and if more than 12 per cent passes the No. 200 sieve the suffix letter will be M or C depending upon the values of w_L and I_P. If the percentage fines is between 5 and 12 per cent, a borderline classification is given using dual symbols.

Fine-grained soils have group symbols made up from:

Prefix letters: M—silt   C—clay   O—organic soil
Suffix letters: L—low plasticity ($w_L < 50$ per cent)   H—high plasticity ($w_L > 50$ per cent)

The classification is based solely on Atterberg limit values for the fraction passing the No. 40 sieve, and is obtained from the plasticity chart in Table 1.6. Soils which plot above the A-line are inorganic clays, and those which plot below the A-line are silts and organic clays.

Table 1.6 Unified Classification System (ASTM D-2487–69). Copyright ASTM. Reprinted with permission.

MAJOR DIVISIONS			GROUP SYMBOLS	TYPICAL NAMES	CLASSIFICATION CRITERIA
COARSE-GRAINED SOILS (More than 50% retained on No. 200 sieve)	GRAVELS (More than 50% of coarse fraction retained on No. 4 sieve)	CLEAN GRAVELS	GW	Well-graded gravels and gravel-sand mixtures, little or no fines	$C_u = D_{60}/D_{10}$ Greater than 4; $C_z = \dfrac{(D_{30})^2}{D_{10} \times D_{60}}$ Between 1 and 3
			GP	Poorly graded gravels and gravel-sand mixtures, little or no fines	Not meeting both criteria for GW
		GRAVELS WITH FINES	GM	Silty gravels, gravel-sand-silt mixtures	Atterberg limits plot below "A" line or plasticity index less than 4 — Atterberg limits plotting in hatched area are borderline classifications requiring use of dual symbols
			GC	Clayey gravels, gravel-sand-clay mixtures	Atterberg limits plot above "A" line and plasticity index greater than 7
	SANDS (More than 50% of coarse fraction passes No. 4 sieve)	CLEAN SANDS	SW	Well-graded sands and gravelly sands, little or no fines	$C_u = D_{60}/D_{10}$ Greater than 6; $C_z = \dfrac{(D_{30})^2}{D_{10} \times D_{60}}$ Between 1 and 3
			SP	Poorly graded sands and gravelly sands, little or no fines	Not meeting both criteria for SW
		SANDS WITH FINES	SM	Silty sands, sand-silt mixtures	Atterberg limits plot below "A" line or plasticity index less than 4 — Atterberg limits plotting in hatched area are borderline classifications requiring use of dual symbols
			SC	Clayey sands, sand-clay mixtures	Atterberg limits plot above "A" line and plasticity index greater than 7
FINE-GRAINED SOILS (50% or more passes No. 200 sieve)	SILTS AND CLAYS (Liquid limit 50% or less)		ML	Inorganic silts, very fine sands, rock flour, silty or clayey fine sands	*See PLASTICITY CHART*
			CL	Inorganic clays of low to medium plasticity, gravelly clays, sandy clays, silty clays, lean clays	
			OL	Organic silts and organic silty clays of low plasticity	
	SILTS AND CLAYS (Liquid limit greater than 50%)		MH	Inorganic silts, micaceous or diatomaceous fine sands or silts, elastic silts	
			CH	Inorganic clays of high plasticity, fat clays	
			OH	Organic clays of medium to high plasticity	
Highly Organic Soils			PT	Peat, muck and other highly organic soils	

Classification on basis of percentage of fines

- Less than 5% Pass No. 200 sieve: GW, GP, SW, SP
- More than 12% Pass No. 200 sieve: GC, GM, SM, SC
- 5% to 12% Pass No. 200 sieve: Borderline Classification requiring use of dual symbols

PLASTICITY CHART

For classification of fine-grained soils and fine fraction of coarse-grained soils.

Atterberg Limits plotting in hatched area are borderline classifications requiring use of dual symbols.

Equation of A-line: $PI = 0.73 (LL - 20)$

Axes: Plasticity Index (vertical), Liquid Limit (horizontal). Regions: CL-ML, ML or OL, CL, MH or OH, CH. A-Line.

Visual-Manual Identification, See ASTM Designation D 2488

31

Table 1.7 British Soil Classification System (BS 5930: 1981)

Soil groups			Group symbol	Subgroup symbol		Fines (% less than 0.06 mm)	Liquid limit %	Name
GRAVEL and SAND may be qualified Sandy GRAVEL and Gravelly SAND, etc. where appropriate (see note 1)								
COARSE SOILS less than 35% of the material is finer than 0.06 mm	GRAVELS More than 50% of coarse material is of gravel size (coarser than 2 mm)	Slightly silty or clayey GRAVEL	G	GW	GW	0 to 5		Well graded GRAVEL
				GP	GPu GPg			Poorly graded/Uniform/Gap graded GRAVEL
		Silty GRAVEL	G-F	G-M	GWM GPM	5 to 15		Well graded/Poorly graded silty GRAVEL
		Clayey GRAVEL		G-C	GWC GPC			Well graded/Poorly graded clayey GRAVEL
		Very silty GRAVEL	GF	GM	GML, etc	15 to 35		Very silty GRAVEL; subdivide as for GC
		Very clayey GRAVEL		GC	GCL GCI GCH GCV GCE			Very clayey GRAVEL (clay of low, intermediate, high, very high, extremely high plasticity)
	SANDS More than 50% of coarse material is of sand size (finer than 2 mm)	Slightly silty or clayey SAND	S	SW	SW	0 to 5		Well graded SAND
				SP	SPu SPg			Poorly graded/Uniform/Gap graded SAND
		Silty SAND	S-F	S-M	SWM SPM	5 to 15		Well graded/Poorly graded silty SAND
		Clayey SAND		S-C	SWC SPC			Well graded/Poorly graded clayey SAND
		Very silty SAND	SF	SM	SML, etc	15 to 35		Very silty SAND; subdivided as for SC
		Very clayey SAND		SC	SCL SCI SCH SCV SCE			Very clayey SAND (clay of low, intermediate, high, very high, extremely high plasticity)
FINE SOILS more than 35% of the material is finer than 0.06 mm	Gravelly or sandy SILTS and CLAYS 35% to 65% fines (see note 2)	Gravelly SILT	FG	MG	MLG, etc			Gravelly SILT; subdivide as for CG
		Gravelly CLAY		CG	CLG CIG CHG CVG CEG		< 35 / 35 to 50 / 50 to 70 / 70 to 90 / > 90	Gravelly CLAY of low plasticity / of intermediate plasticity / of high plasticity / of very high plasticity / of extremely high plasticity
		Sandy SILT	FS	MS	MLS, etc			Sandy SILT; subdivide as for CG
		Sandy CLAY		CS	CLS, etc			Sandy CLAY; subdivide as for CG
	SILTS and CLAYS 65% to 100% fines	SILT (M-SOIL)	F	M	ML, etc			SILT; subdivide as for C
		CLAY		C	CL CI CH CV CE		< 35 / 35 to 50 / 50 to 70 / 70 to 90 / > 90	CLAY of low plasticity / of intermediate plasticity / of high plasticity / of very high plasticity / of extremely high plasticity
ORGANIC SOILS			Descriptive letter 'O' suffixed to any group or sub-group symbol.			Organic matter suspected to be a significant constituent. Example MHO: Organic SILT of high plasticity.		
PEAT			Pt Peat soils consist predominantly of plant remains which may be fibrous or amorphous.					

Note 1. GRAVEL qualifies as 'very sandy' if over 20 per cent, 'sandy' if between 5 and 20 per cent, and 'slightly sandy' if less than 5 per cent of the coarse material is of sand size. Similarly SAND may be qualified as 'very gravelly', 'gravelly', or 'slightly gravelly'.

Note 2. 'Gravelly' if more than 50 per cent of the coarse material is of gravel size; 'sandy' if more than 50 per cent of the coarse material is of sand size.

Peat and other highly organic soils are classified by visual inspection (ASTM D–2488–69) and have the group symbol Pt.

Use of the Unified Classification System is illustrated in Example 1.4.

British Soil Classification System A summary of the British Classification System is presented in Table 1.7.

On the basis of the particle size distribution of material passing the 63 mm BS sieve, a soil is described either as *coarse* if less than 35 per cent is finer than 0.06 mm, or as *fine* if more than 35 per cent is finer than 0.06 mm. Within these broad divisions, the soil is placed in one of a number of groups according to the grading of the coarse fraction and the plasticity characteristics of the fraction passing the 425 μm BS sieve. Each group has a descriptive name and a group symbol made up of letters which indicate the main soil type and the grading or plasticity characteristics as follows:

G—gravel   S—sand   F—fine soil, fines
M—silt (M-soil)   C—clay   Pt—peat

W—well graded
P—poorly graded
Pu—uniformly graded
Pg—gap graded
O—organic

L—low plasticity ($w_L < 35$)
I—intermediate plasticity ($w_L = 35$–50)
H—high plasticity ($w_L = 50$–70)
V—very high plasticity ($w_L = 70$–90)
E—extremely high plasticity ($w_L > 90$)
U—in upper plasticity range ($w_L > 35$)

In the group symbols the letter describing the dominant size fraction is placed first, followed by other letters indicating such features as a secondary size fraction, the grading or plasticity characteristics, and the presence of organic material. For example

GWM—well-graded silty GRAVEL
MLG—gravelly SILT of low plasticity
CHSO—organic sandy CLAY of high plasticity

Note that the name of the group should show the main soil component in capitals.

For coarse-grained soils the particle size distribution curve will assist in designating the grading characteristics, while for fine-grained soils the plasticity chart shown in Fig. 1.8 is used in conjunction with values of liquid limit and plasticity index to obtain the appropriate soil name and group symbol.

Peat soils are classified solely by the visual predominance of organic material, the dark brown or black colour and the distinctive odour.

Use of the British Classification System is illustated in Example 1.4.

Example 1.4 The grading curve for a soil A is shown in Fig. 1.6. The results of a dry sieve analysis on a sample of a soil B of mass 1211 g are shown in columns 1 and 2 in Table 1.8. A soil C has $w_L = 40$ and $w_P = 18$ and the grading curve shown in Fig. 1.6.

Classify the three soils according to the British Soil Classification System and the Unified Classification System.

SOLUTION
British Classification System
Soil A: The grading curve shows that this soil has 72 per cent gravel and 23 per cent sand, thus it is a very sandy gravel. It contains a significant proportion of all particle sizes in the sand and gravel ranges, and is therefore well graded.

Thus soil A is classified as a well-graded very sandy GRAVEL, GWS.

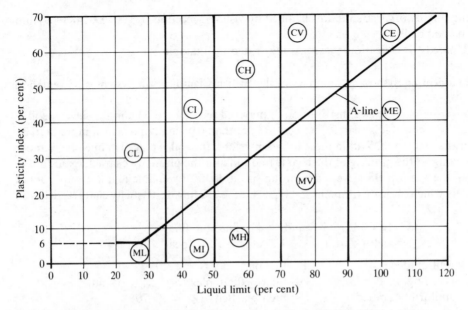

Figure 1.8 Plasticity chart for British Classification System. (From BS 5930: 1981.)

Soil B: The particle size analysis is obtained by completing Table 1.8.
The grading curve is now plotted as in Fig. 1.6 and shows the material to be 88 per cent medium and fine gravel and 12 per cent coarse sand, essentially uniform in particle size.
Thus soil B is classified as a uniform sandy GRAVEL, GPuS.
Soil C: The grading curve indicates that this material is 53 per cent fines, 40 per cent sand and 7 per cent fine gravel. For $w_L = 40$ and $w_P = 18$, $I_P = w_L - w_P = 22$. These values plot above the A-line in Fig. 1.8, so soil is designated as clay.
Thus soil C is classified as a sandy CLAY of intermediate plasticity, CIS.

Unified Classification System
Soil A: The grading curve indicates a coarse-grained soil with no fines and 67 per cent of the coarse fraction retained on the No. 4 (4.75 mm) sieve. From Fig. 1.6, $D_{10} = 0.4$, $D_{30} = 4$ and $D_{60} = 20$. Hence, from Eqs (1.26) and (1.27), $C_U = 50$ and $C_Z = 2$.
Thus soil A is classified as a well-graded gravel, GW.

Table 1.8 Results of sieve analysis on soil B

BS sieve	Mass retained (g)	Percentage retained	Cumulative per cent passing
20 mm	0	0	100.0
14 mm	33.3	2.7	97.3
10 mm	41.2	3.4	93.9
6.3 mm	157.1	13.0	80.9
5 mm	144.3	11.9	69.0
3.35 mm	407.4	33.6	35.4
2 mm	287.6	23.7	11.7
1.18 mm	88.4	7.3	4.4
600 μm	37.3	3.1	1.3

Soil B: The grading curve is plotted from Table 1.8 and indicates a coarse-grained soil with no fines and 67 per cent passing the No. 4 (4.75 mm) sieve. From Fig. 1.6, $D_{10} = 1.8$, $D_{30} = 2.9$ and $D_{60} = 4.4$; hence $C_U = 2.4$ and $C_Z = 1.06$.

Thus soil B is classified as a poorly-graded sand, SP.

Soil C: The grading curve shows that 55 per cent passes the No. 200 (75 μm) sieve. The values of $w_L = 40$, $w_P = 18$ and $I_P = 22$ plot above the A-line in Table 1.6, with $w_L < 50$ and $I_P > 7$.

Thus soil C is classified as an inorganic clay of low to medium plasticity, CL.

Description of Soils

A distinction between what is meant by 'soil classification' and 'soil description' is very important. Classification places a soil in one of a limited number of groups on the basis of the grading and plasticity characteristics of a disturbed sample of the soil, and ignores the particular conditions in which the soil was found in the field. However, a full soil description will include information not only on the particle size, grading and plasticity characteristics of the soil but also details on the colour, compactness or strength, macrostructure and state of weathering of the soil in its natural undisturbed condition. Thus, when a soil is to be employed in its natural state, for example, as a foundation stratum, a full soil description will probably give the best assessment of its likely engineering behaviour. However, if the soil is being considered as a construction material, for example, as an embankment fill, the soil classification may give a better guide to its suitability for such earthworks.

A full description of the soil will require careful visual inspection and manual examination of the material in the field and probably also of undisturbed samples in the laboratory. Coarse-grained soils will consist predominantly of particles that are visible and easily distinguishable to the naked eye, and therefore a visual inspection of such soils will probably yield most of the soil description. However, the limit of visibility of the naked eye corresponds roughly with the size division between the sand and silt particles, and thus difficulties of visual identification arise primarily in the distinction between fine sands, silts and clays. A number of simple tests have been devised which enable rapid assessments to be made of particle size and plasticity. Details of these tests and full recommendations for soil description are given in BS 5930: 1981 and ASTM D–2488–69.

PROBLEMS

1.1 A sample of clay having a length of 100 mm was extracted from a U 100 sampling tube, the internal diameter being 100 mm. The sample had a mass of 1531 g and after drying 1178 g. If the specific gravity of the soil particles is 2.75 calculate the bulk density, water content, void ratio, dry density, degree of saturation and air voids content.

[Ans.   1.95 Mg/m^3;   30.0 per cent;   0.83;   1.50 Mg/m^3;   98.9 per cent;   0.5 per cent]

1.2   A sample of soil remoulded at a water content of 11 per cent was compacted into a cylindrical mould 100 mm diameter, 115 mm deep and mass 4706 g. When filled with the compacted soil the total mass was 6331 g. If the specific gravity of the soil particles is 2.75 calculate the dry density, degree of saturation and air voids content. What additional mass of remoulded soil at the same water content would have to be compacted into the mould in order to achieve a degree of saturation of 70 per cent?

[Ans.   1.62 Mg/m^3;   43.4 per cent;   23.2 per cent;   300 g]

1.3 A road embankment is constructed of fill material compacted to a density of 2.15 Mg/m^3 at a water content of 11.5 per cent. The specific gravity of the soil grains is 2.70. Calculate the dry density, porosity, degree of saturation and air voids content of the fill material.

[Ans.   1.93 Mg/m^3;   28.6 per cent;   77.6 per cent;   6.4 per cent]

1.4 Samples of a soil deposit were recovered from the sea-bed at the proposed site of a new tanker jetty. The saturated density was found to be 2.08 Mg/m³ and the specific gravity of the soil particles to be 2.70. If the specific gravity of the seawater was 1.03, calculate the void ratio, dry density and effective density of the soil deposit.
[Ans. 0.59; 1.70 Mg/m³; 1.05 Mg/m³]

1.5 An undisturbed sample of moist sand was obtained from the base of an excavation using a thin-walled sampling tube. In the undisturbed state the sample had a mass of 884 g and a volume of 478 cm³. After oven-drying, the mass of the sample was found to be 829 g. Given that the specific gravity of the sand particles was 2.67, calculate the bulk density, void ratio, water content, air voids content and the degree of saturation of the moist sand in its *in situ* conditions.

Tests to determine the maximum and minimum void ratios for the sand gave $e_{max} = 0.98$ and $e_{min} = 0.34$. Calculate the relative density of the sand deposit.
[Ans. 1.85 Mg/m³; 0.54; 6.6 per cent; 23.5 per cent; 32.8 per cent; 68.8 per cent]

STRESSES AND DEFORMATIONS IN A SOIL MASS

To explain the engineering behaviour of soils we must understand the concept of stress in relation to a mass of soil, and in particular the way in which the stress acting on the soil mass as a whole is related to the stress that develops within the soil skeleton and that which exists within the pore fluid.

In order to solve engineering problems we must understand how to evaluate the stresses acting at a point in a soil mass due to its self-weight and also the change in stress that results from any external loading (or unloading) of the soil from the construction of engineering works. Also of importance are the deformations of the soil mass, particularly the settlements, that result from such stress changes.

The stress at a point is generally not the same in all directions and it is therefore relevant to examine the general state of stress that exists at a point in a soil mass and to consider the relationship between the stresses acting in different directions. However, in many engineering problems we are interested mainly in the stresses acting in a particular direction; for example, a consideration of the bearing capacity and settlement of foundations principally involves the stresses acting in a vertical direction, whereas a study of the earth pressures on retaining walls requires a knowledge of the horizontal stresses in the soil mass.

2.1 PRINCIPLE OF EFFECTIVE STRESS

In a soil mass there will be stresses within the soil skeleton as a result of the forces acting at the points of contact between individual particles and there will be stresses within the pore fluid occupying the voids of the soil. To study the engineering behaviour of soils we need to be able to distinguish between these two types of stress and also understand the relationship between them. For this purpose, consider a saturated mass of soil having a horizontal surface (Fig. 2.1) and let the water table be at ground level. Considering a horizontal plane XX of area A at depth z, the vertical column of soil above XX will have a total weight W given by

$$W = W_s + W_w \tag{2.1}$$

where W_s is the weight of the soil particles and W_w is the weight of the water in the voids.

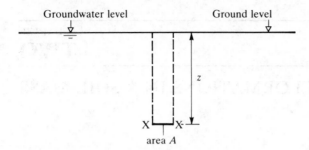

Figure 2.1

The soil particles below the water table are subject to an upthrust U so that their effective weight W'_s is given by

$$W'_s = W_s - U$$

Thus
$$W_s = W'_s + U$$

and on substituting in Eq. (2.1)

$$W = W'_s + U + W_w$$

If V_s denotes the volume of soil particles in the column and V_w the volume of water then $U = \rho_w g V_s$ (Archimedes' Principle) and $W_w = \rho_w g V_w$. Hence

$$W = W'_s + \rho_w g(V_s + V_w)$$

Since the soil is saturated, the volume of water V_w is equal to the volume of voids V_v. Therefore $V_s + V_w$ denotes the total volume V of the column. Thus

$$W = W'_s + \rho_w g V$$

And as $V = Az$ then

$$\frac{W}{A} = \frac{W'_s}{A} + \rho_w g z$$

Now W/A defines the stress on XX as a result of the total weight of the column and is referred to as the *total stress*, denoted by σ. W'_s/A defines the stress on XX as a result of the effective weight of the soil particles and is referred to as the *effective stress, σ' (or sometimes $\bar{\sigma}$)*. Plane XX being depth z below the water table, the term $\rho_w g z$ defines the hydrostatic *porewater pressure* at XX, denoted by u. Thus we obtain the relationship

$$\sigma = \sigma' + u \qquad (2.2)$$

Equation (2.2) is found to be generally true for a saturated soil, irrespective of the groundwater conditions and the stress direction and notwithstanding the influence of external loads. The relationship is known as the *principle of effective stress* and was first postulated by Karl Terzaghi in 1923. It states simply that *at any point in a saturated soil mass the total stress in any direction is equal to the algebraic sum of the effective stress in that direction and the porewater pressure.*

Despite its extremely simple algebraic form, the principle of effective stress is probably the most fundamentally important relationship in the study of Soil Mechanics and its publication by Terzaghi marked the emergence of the subject as a separate engineering discipline.

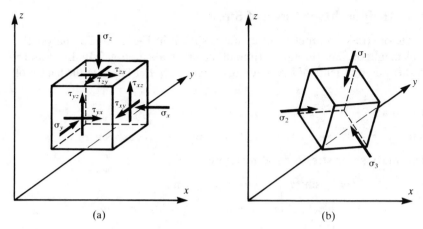

Figure 2.2 (a) General state of stress on a soil element, (b) principal stresses.

2.2 STRESSES AT A POINT IN A SOIL MASS

The general state of stress on an element within a soil mass is shown with reference to total stresses in Fig. 2.2a. On each face the resultant stress is represented by one component of normal stress σ and two components of shear stress τ, each identified by a directional suffix related to the three reference directions x, y, z. However, for this state of stress there must exist three mutually perpendicular planes in the element on which the resultant stress is the normal stress, with the components of shear stress being zero. These are the *principal planes* and the associated normal stresses are the *principal stresses*. In descending order of magnitude we have the *major* principal stress σ_1 which acts on the *major* principal plane, the *intermediate* principal stress σ_2 acting on the *intermediate* principal plane and the *minor* principal stress σ_3 which acts on the *minor* principal plane. If the faces of the element are oriented in the directions of the principal planes, the state of stress on the element is as represented in Fig. 2.2b. If the element is considered to be infinitesimally small, the stresses shown on the faces of the element in Fig. 2.2 can be taken to represent the stresses acting on different planes through a *point* in the soil mass.

In the case of retaining walls, embankments, cuttings and strip foundations, the mass of soil under stress is often very long in one direction, as illustrated in Fig. 2.3. For this typical geometry, deformations of the soil mass in the y direction occur only locally at the ends of the structure and conditions over most of the soil mass approximate to those of *plane strain*, with σ_y being the intermediate principal stress. Thus, by treating unit thickness of the soil mass in the y direction we can reduce the problem to one involving two-dimensional stress analysis in which we need to consider stresses in the x, z plane only.

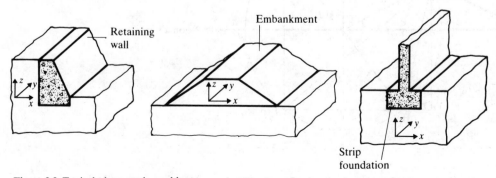

Figure 2.3 Typical plane-strain problems.

Two-dimensional Stress Analysis: Mohr Circle of Stress

The two-dimensional state of stress on an element of soil is shown in Fig. 2.4a. To analyse the stress conditions in the element consider the equilibrium of the prism abc in Fig. 2.4b. Let σ and τ denote the normal and shear components of stress acting on plane ab. Let l denote the length of ab. Thus:

Resolving forces normal to ab

$$\sigma l = \sigma_x l \sin \alpha \sin \alpha + \sigma_z l \cos \alpha \cos \alpha - \tau_{xz} l \sin \alpha \cos \alpha - \tau_{zx} l \cos \alpha \sin \alpha$$

Now $\tau_{xz} = \tau_{zx}$ (complementary shear stresses) and therefore

$$\sigma = \sigma_x \sin^2 \alpha + \sigma_z \cos^2 \alpha - \tau_{xz} \sin 2\alpha$$

$$\therefore \qquad \sigma = \tfrac{1}{2}\sigma_x(1 - \cos 2\alpha) + \tfrac{1}{2}\sigma_z(1 + \cos 2\alpha) - \tau_{xz} \sin 2\alpha$$

$$\therefore \qquad \sigma = \tfrac{1}{2}(\sigma_x + \sigma_z) - \tfrac{1}{2}(\sigma_x - \sigma_z) \cos 2\alpha - \tau_{xz} \sin 2\alpha \qquad (2.3)$$

and

$$[\sigma - \tfrac{1}{2}(\sigma_x + \sigma_z)]^2 = [\tfrac{1}{2}(\sigma_x - \sigma_z) \cos 2\alpha + \tau_{xz} \sin 2\alpha]^2 \qquad (2.4)$$

Resolving forces parallel to ab

$$\tau l = \sigma_x l \sin \alpha \cos \alpha - \sigma_z l \cos \alpha \sin \alpha + \tau_{xz} l \sin \alpha \sin \alpha - \tau_{zx} l \cos \alpha \cos \alpha$$

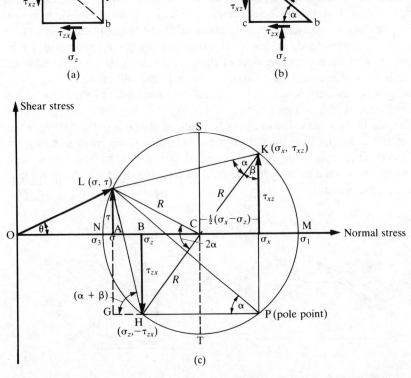

(a)　　　　　(b)

(c)

Figure 2.4 (a) and (b) Two-dimensional state of stress on a soil element, (c) Mohr Diagram and Mohr circle of stress.

$$\therefore \qquad \tau = \tfrac{1}{2}(\sigma_x - \sigma_z)\sin 2\alpha - \tau_{xz}\cos 2\alpha \qquad (2.5)$$

and

$$\tau^2 = [\tfrac{1}{2}(\sigma_x - \sigma_z)\sin 2\alpha - \tau_{xz}\cos 2\alpha]^2 \qquad (2.6)$$

Adding Eqs (2.4) and (2.6)

$$[\sigma - \tfrac{1}{2}(\sigma_x + \sigma_z)]^2 + \tau^2 = [\tfrac{1}{2}(\sigma_x - \sigma_z)]^2 + \tau_{xz}^2 \qquad (2.7)$$

A plot of shear stress τ against normal stress σ is thus defined by a circle of radius $R = \sqrt{[\tfrac{1}{2}(\sigma_x - \sigma_z)]^2 + \tau_{xz}^2}$ with its centre on the σ axis at $\sigma = \tfrac{1}{2}(\sigma_x + \sigma_z)$. This is illustrated in Fig. 2.4c, with the sign convention that compressive normal stresses and anti-clockwise shear stresses are positive. The plot of shear stress against normal stress is known as a *Mohr Diagram* and the circle as the *Mohr circle of stress*.

On the circumference of every Mohr circle there exists a particular point called the *pole* point which has a unique feature:

> *A line drawn from the pole point parallel to a given plane in the soil will intersect the circle again at a point the coordinates of which represent the normal and shear components of stress on that plane.*

Thus there is a correlation between (i) the stress conditions on any plane in the soil element, (ii) the direction of that plane and (iii) the position of the pole point. If any two of these are known, a simple construction on the Mohr circle yields the third. For example, in Fig. 2.4c point H has coordinates $(\sigma_z, -\tau_{zx})$ defining the stress conditions on plane cb in the soil element, and point K has coordinates (σ_x, τ_{xz}) defining the stress conditions on ac. Thus, the pole point P is found by drawing a line through H parallel to plane cb in the element (or a line through K parallel to ac) to intersect the circle at point P. A line through P parallel to plane ab in the element cuts the circle at point L, the coordinates of which must be (σ, τ).

The validity of this construction can be verified from the geometry of the Mohr circle in Fig. 2.4c. Thus, applying the cosine rule to triangle LHC gives

$$LH = 2R \sin \alpha$$

Also

$$\angle LHG = \alpha + \beta$$

$$\therefore \qquad AB = GH = LH \cos(\alpha + \beta)$$

Thus

$$OA = OB - AB = OB - LH \cos(\alpha + \beta)$$

$$\therefore \qquad \sigma = \sigma_z - 2R \sin \alpha [\cos \alpha \cos \beta - \sin \alpha \sin \beta]$$

$$\therefore \qquad \sigma = \sigma_z - 2R \sin \alpha \left[\cos \alpha \frac{\tau_{xz}}{R} - \sin \alpha \frac{\tfrac{1}{2}(\sigma_x - \sigma_z)}{R} \right]$$

from which

$$\sigma = \tfrac{1}{2}(\sigma_x + \sigma_z) - \tfrac{1}{2}(\sigma_x - \sigma_z)\cos 2\alpha - \tau_{xz}\sin 2\alpha \qquad (2.3 \text{ bis})$$

which re-establishes Eq. (2.3).

Also

$$LG = LH \sin(\alpha + \beta)$$

$$\therefore \qquad \tau + \tau_{xz} = 2R \sin \alpha [\sin \alpha \cos \beta + \cos \alpha \sin \beta]$$

$$\therefore \qquad \tau = 2R \sin \alpha \left[\sin \alpha \frac{\tau_{xz}}{R} + \cos \alpha \frac{\tfrac{1}{2}(\sigma_x - \sigma_z)}{R} \right] - \tau_{xz}$$

from which

$$\tau = \tfrac{1}{2}(\sigma_x - \sigma_z)\sin 2\alpha - \tau_{xz}\cos 2\alpha \qquad (2.5 \text{ bis})$$

which re-establishes Eq. (2.5).

Thus, the coordinates of point L define σ and τ, the components of normal and shear stress on plane ab. We see then that the resultant stress on ab, which acts at an obliquity θ measured clockwise from the normal in Fig. 2.4b, is represented on the Mohr Diagram by the vector OL drawn at angle θ anti-clockwise from the normal stress axis.

By definition, the principal planes are planes of zero shear stress and must therefore be represented by the points where the circle cuts the normal stress axis. Thus in Fig. 2.4c point M gives the major principal stress σ_1 acting on the major principal plane and point N the minor principal stress σ_3 acting on the minor principal plane. The angle subtended at the pole point is equal to 90° and therefore the principal planes are at right angles to each other. Similarly, the maximum values of shear stress are represented by points S and T and are associated with a normal stress of magnitude $\frac{1}{2}(\sigma_1 + \sigma_3)$. We see that the planes of maximum shear stress lie at 45° to the principal planes.

The Mohr circle of stress is therefore an extremely useful expedient in performing two-dimensional stress analysis. Furthermore, by considering the soil element in Fig. 2.4a to be extremely small, we can use a Mohr circle to represent the stress conditions at a particular point in a soil mass, each position around the circumference of the circle giving the components of stress on a different plane through the point.

Although illustrated here with reference to total stresses in the soil, the concept of Mohr circles is equally applicable to two-dimensional *effective stress* analysis. This can be done by drawing Mohr circles of *effective stress* on an *effective stress* Mohr Diagram of shear stress against normal effective stress.

2.3 STRESSES DUE TO SELF-WEIGHT

The vertical stresses that exist in a soil mass due only to its self-weight are referred to as *overburden* stresses.

Figure 2.5 shows a homogeneous deposit of soil having a horizontal surface. For these conditions the shear stress on all vertical planes is zero and the vertical and horizontal stresses are therefore principal stresses. The vertical total stress σ_v (or total overburden pressure) at any point is simply the stress derived from the weight of all the material above the point. Thus, considering the horizontal plane XX of area A at depth z, the total weight of the vertical column of soil above XX is given by

$$W = \rho g(z - z_w)A + \rho_s g z_w A$$

where ρ is the bulk density of the soil, ρ_s is the saturated density and g is the gravitational

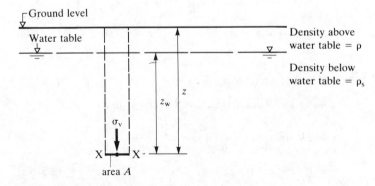

Figure 2.5

acceleration. Hence the vertical total stress σ_v on XX, defined as W/A, is given by

$$\sigma_v = \rho g(z - z_w) + \rho_s g z_w \tag{2.8}$$

With density in Mg/m^3, $g = 9.81$ m/s^2 and depth in m, σ_v has the units of kN/m^2.

The porewater pressure u at any point in the soil mass will have an equilibrium value compatible with the hydraulic boundary conditions existing in the soil mass. The simplest conditions are those of a static groundwater level (as considered here), in which case the porewater pressures are referred to as *hydrostatic* pressures. Being a fluid pressure, the porewater pressure at any point is the same in all directions and there is therefore no need to attribute a directional suffix. Thus in Fig. 2.5, the hydrostatic porewater pressure at XX depth z_w below the water table is given by

$$u = \rho_w g z_w \tag{2.9}$$

The associated vertical effective stress (or effective overburden pressure) on XX is obtained from the principle of effective stress using Eq. (2.2) in the form

$$\sigma'_v = \sigma_v - u \tag{2.10}$$

Thus substituting for σ_v and u from Eqs (2.8) and (2.9)

$$\sigma'_v = [\rho g(z - z_w) + \rho_s g z_w] - \rho_w g z_w$$
$$= \rho g(z - z_w) + (\rho_s - \rho_w) g z_w$$

From Eq. (1.21), $(\rho_s - \rho_w)$ defines the effective density ρ' and therefore we obtain

$$\sigma'_v = \rho g(z - z_w) + \rho' g z_w \tag{2.11}$$

Thus, under hydrostatic conditions the effective overburden pressure in a soil mass is a function of the total density of the soil over the depth above the water table and the effective density of the soil over the depth below the water table.

The horizontal stress at a point in a soil mass is strongly influenced by the stress history of the deposit and as such cannot be calculated in a simple manner as for overburden pressures. A full discussion on this is deferred until Chapter 6.

Example 2.1 A soil profile consists of 5 m of sand overlying 4 m of gravel resting on bedrock. Groundwater level (GWL) is 2 m below the horizontal surface of the sand.
(a) Determine the distributions of total vertical stress, porewater pressure and effective vertical stress with depth down to bedrock, given that the bulk density of the sand above GWL = 1.70 Mg/m^3, the saturated density of the sand below GWL = 2.05 Mg/m^3 and the saturated density of the gravel = 2.15 Mg/m^3.
(b) How do these distributions change if the groundwater level is lowered to the sand/gravel interface?

SOLUTION (a) The soil profile is as shown in Fig. 2.6.
We start by calculating the stresses at the boundaries of the three zones.

At the surface of the sand: $\sigma_v = 0$, $u = 0$ and $\sigma'_v = \sigma_v - u = 0$
At a depth of 2 m: $\sigma_v = 1.70 \times 9.81 \times 2 = 33.35$ kN/m^2,
$\qquad\qquad u = 0$, $\sigma'_v = \sigma_v - u = 33.35$ kN/m^2
At a depth of 5 m: $\sigma_v = 33.35 + 2.05 \times 9.81 \times 3 = 93.69$ kN/m^2,
$\qquad\qquad u = 1 \times 9.81 \times 3 = 29.43$ kN/m^2, $\sigma'_v = 93.69 - 29.43 = 64.26$ kN/m^2
At a depth of 9 m: $\sigma_v = 93.69 + 2.15 \times 9.81 \times 4 = 178.05$ kN/m^2,
$\qquad\qquad u = 1 \times 9.81 \times 7 = 68.67$ kN/m^2, $\sigma'_v = 178.05 - 68.67 = 109.38$ kN/m^2

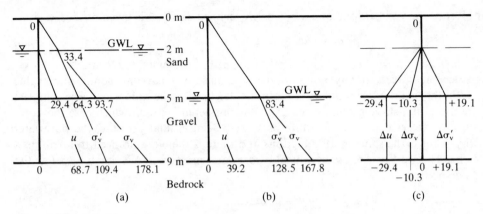

Figure 2.6 Example 2.1.

If the soil density in each zone is constant, the relationship $\sigma_v = \rho g z$ predicts a linear variation of σ_v with depth through each zone. Similarly, the variation of $u = \rho_w g z_w$ is linear with depth below the water table. Thus it follows that σ_v' varies linearly through each zone. The distributions of σ_v, u and σ_v' are therefore as shown in Fig. 2.6a.

(b) With the water table at the sand/gravel interface we have

At the surface of the sand: $\sigma_v = 0$, $u = 0$ and $\sigma_v' = 0$
At a depth of 5 m: $\sigma_v = 1.70 \times 9.81 \times 5 = 83.39$ kN/m²,
$$u = 0, \ \sigma_v' = 83.39 \text{ kN/m}^2$$
At a depth of 9 m: $\sigma_v = 83.39 + 2.15 \times 9.81 \times 4 = 167.75$ kN/m²,
$$u = 1 \times 9.81 \times 4 = 39.24 \text{ kN/m}^2, \ \sigma_v' = 167.75 - 39.24 = 128.51 \text{ kN/m}^2$$

The distributions of σ_v, u and σ_v' are now as shown in Fig. 2.6b. Comparing the results of (a) and (b), we can determine the changes in stress $\Delta\sigma_v$, Δu and $\Delta\sigma_v'$ with depth (Fig. 2.6c). This indicates that on lowering the water table in a soil mass the total vertical stress decreases at all points below the original GWL, but by less than the decrease in porewater pressure, with the result that there is an *increase* in effective vertical stress in the soil, this increase being constant at all depths below the lowered position of the water table. We see that these changes in stress are compatible with the principle of effective stress; for example, at any point below the lowered water table

$$\Delta\sigma_v = -10.3 \text{ kN/m}^2 \quad \text{and} \quad \Delta u = -29.4 \text{ kN/m}^2$$

and therefore from the principle of effective stress

$$\Delta\sigma_v' = \Delta\sigma_v - \Delta u = -10.3 - (-29.4) = +19.1 \text{ kN/m}^2$$

as shown in Fig. 2.6c.

2.4 STRESSES DUE TO APPLIED LOADS

The stress distributions that result in a soil mass due to loads applied by the construction of engineering works are influenced by the thickness and uniformity of the soil mass, the size and shape of the loaded area, and the stress–strain properties of the soil. Now the stress–strain behaviour of real materials is seldom simple and in the case of engineering soils it is frequently very complex indeed. By way of illustration, we can refer to Fig. 2.7 (reproduced from Bishop, 1972) and compare the stress–strain relationships for a number of ideal materials with that of a

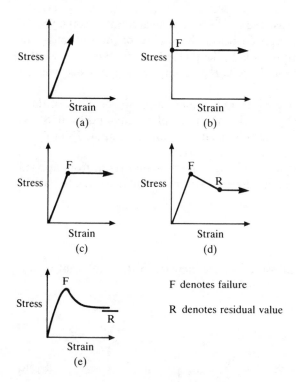

F denotes failure

R denotes residual value

Figure 2.7 Stress–strain relationships for ideal materials: (a) elastic, (b) rigid plastic, (c) elastic–plastic, (d) elastic–plastic work softening; (e) typical stress–strain relationship for a real soil. (From Bishop, 1972. Reprinted with permission of G. T. Foulis & Co. Ltd.)

real soil. Further examples of the stress–strain relationships for real soils are given in Figs 5.1b,d and 5.3.

However, in the context of investigating the stresses and deformations in a soil mass, we can identify two categories of engineering problem. One category consists of *stability* problems, which are analysed by considering the limiting equilibrium of a mass of soil which is on the point of failure by shear along a potential slip surface. The soil in the failure zone is assumed to be in a state of *plastic equilibrium* and in the analysis the soil behaviour is defined by a value of shear strength for the soil along the slip surface. A comparison of the actual stresses on the potential slip surface with those required to generate failure yields a factor of safety against instability. The limiting equilibrium approach to stability analyses is presented in detail in Chapters 6 to 8 when considering the earth pressures on retaining walls, the stability of slopes and the bearing capacity of foundations.

The second category consists of *stress distribution and deformation* problems, in which we are primarily interested in predicting stresses and deformations (usually settlements) in the soil when the stress levels are restricted to a working range well below the failure value and lie within the approximately linear initial portion of the stress–strain curve. For these conditions the soil is assumed to be in a state of *elastic equilibrium* and the stress distributions and deformations are determined on the assumption that the soil behaves as a homogeneous, isotropic, linearly elastic material whose properties are defined by a modulus of elasticity, E, and a Poisson's ratio, v. It is this category of problem that is considered in this chapter and later in Chapter 4 when considering the settlement analysis of structures.

Many of the solutions obtained for stress distributions have been derived from the work of Boussinesq who in 1885 developed mathematical expressions for the increase in stress in a semi-infinite† mass of soil due to a point load at its surface (Fig. 2.8a). The Boussinesq expressions have

† A semi-infinite mass is one which is bounded by a horizontal surface and extends to infinity vertically downwards and in all directions horizontally.

been integrated to yield solutions for loaded areas, and modified to take account of soil layers of finite thickness, multi-layer systems and loads applied below the surface of the soil mass. An extensive review of the many published solutions is given by Scott (1963), Harr (1966) and Poulos and Davis (1974). However, only those commonly required in engineering practice will be presented here.

Complex loading conditions can often be treated as a combination of two or more of these simple loading cases and a solution obtained by applying the principle of superposition. Stress changes due to unloading, in excavations and cuttings for example, can be computed simply on the basis of a negative loading applied over the area of the excavation.

It must be remembered that the solutions yield the changes in stress that result from applied loads, and do not take into account the stresses that already exist in the soil mass due to its self-weight.

(a) Vertical Point Load

With reference to Fig. 2.8a, the Boussinesq expressions for the increase in stress at point N in a semi-infinite soil mass due to a point load Q at its surface are

$$\Delta\sigma_v = \frac{3Q}{2\pi} \frac{z^3}{(r^2 + z^2)^{5/2}} \tag{2.12a}$$

$$\Delta\sigma_r = \frac{Q}{2\pi} \left[\frac{3r^2 z}{(r^2 + z^2)^{5/2}} - \frac{1 - 2v}{r^2 + z^2 + z\sqrt{r^2 + z^2}} \right] \tag{2.12b}$$

$$\Delta\sigma_\theta = -\frac{Q}{2\pi}(1 - 2v)\left[\frac{z}{(r^2 + z^2)^{3/2}} - \frac{1}{r^2 + z^2 + z\sqrt{r^2 + z^2}} \right] \tag{2.12c}$$

$$\Delta\tau_{rz} = \frac{3Q}{2\pi} \frac{rz^2}{(r^2 + z^2)^{5/2}} \tag{2.12d}$$

where z = depth from soil surface to point N
  r = radial distance from N to the line of action Q
and v = Poisson's ratio.

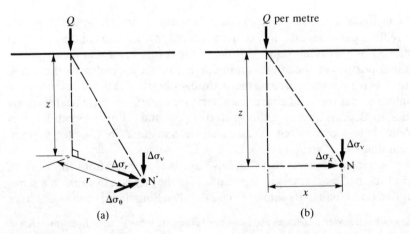

(a)   (b)

Figure 2.8

(b) Vertical Line Load of Infinite Length

With reference to Fig. 2.8b, the increases in stress at N due to a line load of Q per metre run are

$$\Delta\sigma_v = \frac{2Q}{\pi} \frac{z^3}{(x^2 + z^2)^2} \tag{2.13a}$$

$$\Delta\sigma_x = \frac{2Q}{\pi} \frac{x^2 z}{(x^2 + z^2)^2} \tag{2.13b}$$

$$\Delta\tau_{xz} = \frac{2Q}{\pi} \frac{xz^2}{(x^2 + z^2)^2} \tag{2.13c}$$

(c) Uniform Pressure on an Infinite Strip

The increases in stress at point N due to a uniform pressure q acting over an infinitely long flexible strip of width B are given with reference to Fig. 2.9a as

$$\Delta\sigma_v = \frac{q}{\pi} [\alpha + \sin\alpha \cos(\alpha + 2\beta)] \tag{2.14a}$$

$$\Delta\sigma_x = \frac{q}{\pi} [\alpha - \sin\alpha \cos(\alpha + 2\beta)] \tag{2.14b}$$

$$\Delta\tau_{xz} = \frac{q}{\pi} \sin\alpha \sin(\alpha + 2\beta) \tag{2.14c}$$

(d) Triangular Pressure Distribution on an Infinite Strip

When the applied pressure increases linearly across the width of the strip to give a triangular distribution as in Fig. 2.9b, the increases in stress at point N are given by

$$\Delta\sigma_v = \frac{q}{\pi} \left[\frac{x}{B} \alpha - \frac{1}{2} \sin 2\beta \right] \tag{2.15a}$$

$$\Delta\sigma_x = \frac{q}{\pi} \left[\frac{x}{B} \alpha - \frac{z}{B} \ln \frac{R_1^2}{R_2^2} + \frac{1}{2} \sin 2\beta \right] \tag{2.15b}$$

$$\Delta\tau_{xz} = \frac{q}{2\pi} \left[1 + \cos 2\beta - \frac{2z}{B} \alpha \right] \tag{2.15c}$$

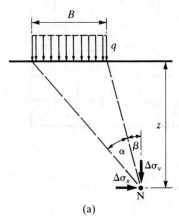

(a)

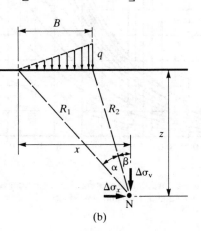

(b)

Figure 2.9

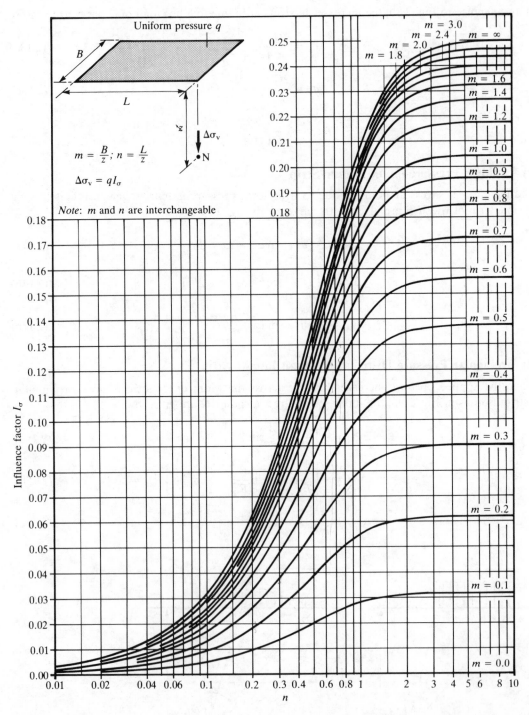

Figure 2.10 Values of influence factor I_σ for calculating increase in total vertical stress $\Delta\sigma_v$ under the corner of a uniformly loaded rectangular area. (After Fadum, 1948 and reproduced with permission of Professor Fadum.)

Cases (c) and (d) can be superimposed in order to estimate the stress changes that result from the construction of embankments or the formation of cuttings in a soil mass.

(e) Uniform Pressure on a Rectangular Area

In this case we present the solution for the increase in total vertical stress at a point N below one *corner* of a uniformly loaded flexible rectangular area. The solution can be expressed in the form

$$\Delta\sigma_v = qI_\sigma \tag{2.16}$$

where I_σ is an *influence factor of stress* which depends on the length L and width B of the rectangular area and the depth z to the point N. Values of I_σ in terms of parameters $m = B/z$ and $n = L/z$ are given in Fig. 2.10 after Fadum (1948).

The merit of presenting a solution for a corner point is that by simple superposition $\Delta\sigma_v$ can then readily be computed for any point in the soil mass due to any uniformly loaded area which can be subdivided into rectangles. For example, under point X in Fig. 2.11a, the increase in stress due to the loaded area $L \times B$ is calculated from

$$\Delta\sigma_v = \Delta\sigma_{v(area\,1)} + \Delta\sigma_{v(area\,2)} + \Delta\sigma_{v(area\,3)} + \Delta\sigma_{v(area\,4)}$$

Similarly under point Y in Fig. 2.11b, the increase in stress due to loading over the shaded area is calculated from

$$\Delta\sigma_v = \Delta\sigma_{v(area\,b \times b)} - \Delta\sigma_{v(area\,a \times a)}$$

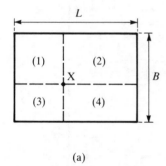

(a)

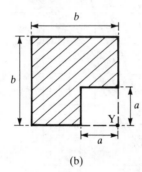

(b)

Figure 2.11

(f) Uniform Pressure on a Circular Area

At depth z below the centre of a flexible circular area of radius R and carrying a uniform pressure q, the increase in total vertical stress is given by

$$\Delta\sigma_v = q\left\{1 - \left[\frac{1}{1 + (R/z)^2}\right]^{3/2}\right\} \tag{2.17}$$

However, for points other than those under the centre, the solutions have an extremely complex form (Harr, 1966) and are generally presented in the form of charts (Foster and Ahlvin, 1954) or tables (Ahlvin and Ulery, 1962). With reference to point N in Fig. 2.12, we can write the increase in total vertical stress as

$$\Delta\sigma_v = qI_\sigma \tag{2.18}$$

where the influence factor I_σ depends on R, z and r. Values of I_σ as a function of the parameters z/R and r/R can be obtained from Fig. 2.13 (after Foster and Ahlvin, 1954).

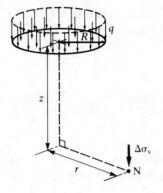

Figure 2.12

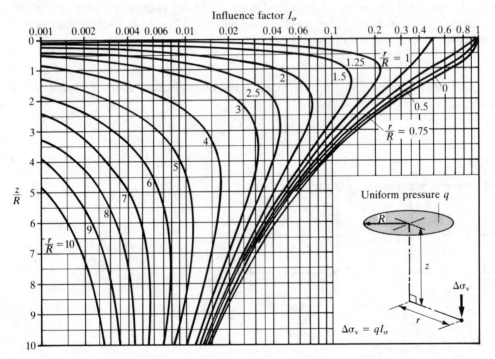

Figure 2.13 Values of influence factor I_σ for calculating increase in total vertical stress $\Delta\sigma_v$ under a uniformly loaded circular area. (After Foster and Ahlvin, 1954. Reprinted with permission of the Transportation Research Board.)

(g) Newmark's Influence Chart

A graphical procedure for determining the increase in total vertical stress under any shape of flexible uniformly loaded area was devised by Newmark (1942).

The Newmark chart, shown in Fig. 2.14, consists of a number of influence areas formed by the intersection of a series of concentric circles with radial lines emanating from the origin. The chart is constructed such that each influence area when loaded with a uniform pressure q will produce the same increase in total vertical stress at a depth AB below the origin of the chart. Thus, if as in this case the total number of influence areas on the chart is 200, each will represent a stress change of 0.005 q, thus defining an *influence value* I for this chart of 0.005.

To use the chart, an outline of the shape of the loaded area is drawn to a scale compatible with

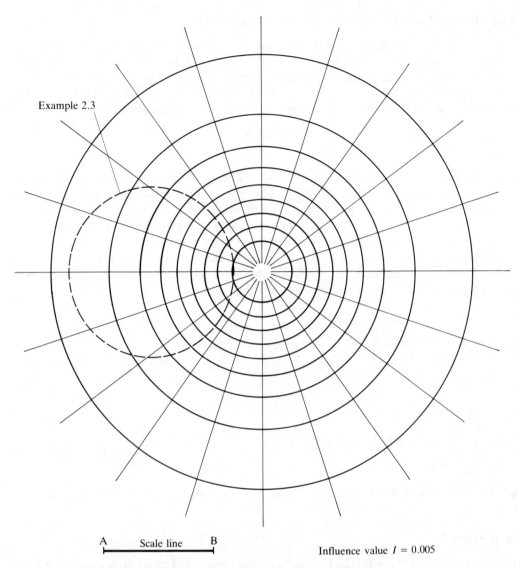

Example 2.3

A   Scale line   B

Influence value $I = 0.005$

Figure 2.14 Newmark's influence chart for calculating increase in total vertical stress $\Delta\sigma_v$ under a uniformly loaded area. (After Newmark, 1942. Reprinted with permission of the University of Illinois.)

that at which the chart has been produced; that is such that the length of the scale line **AB** on the chart represents the depth z at which the stress increase is to be found. The scaled outline is located so that the point under which the stress is to be determined lies directly over the origin of the chart. The number of influence areas enclosed by the outline is estimated and denoted as n. The increase in total vertical stress is then given by

$$\Delta\sigma_v = qIn \tag{2.19}$$

By moving the scaled outline around on the chart, it is possible to determine $\Delta\sigma_v$ for all points in the soil at the one depth z. To investigate $\Delta\sigma_v$ at any other depth, the process is repeated with the outline redrawn to a new scale.

The Newmark chart is particularly useful for irregularly shaped loaded areas and as an alternative means of evaluating stresses under circular loaded areas.

(h) Approximate Estimates of Increase in Vertical Stress

For uniformly loaded circular or rectangular areas, an approximate estimate of the increase in total vertical stress can be obtained by assuming the applied loading to be distributed within a truncated cone or pyramid formed with its sides sloping at 2 vertical to 1 horizontal in the manner illustrated in Fig. 2.15. For example, if the loaded area is a rectangle of length L and width B, the average increase in total vertical stress at depth z will be given approximately by

$$\Delta\sigma_v = \frac{qLB}{(L+z)(B+z)} \tag{2.20}$$

Alternatively, any loaded area can be considered as a number of discrete subareas, each contributing a point load to the soil surface through its centre point. The increase in stress in the soil due to the full area is then obtained using the appropriate Boussinesq equation for a point load and invoking the principle of superposition. Provided that the depth at which the stress is to be found is at least 3 times the width chosen for the subareas, only slight inaccuracies result. Indeed with the availability of desk top computers, it is a simple matter to consider sufficient subareas to ensure precision in the calculations, in which case this approach may prove more expedient than one which relies on the use of charts or tables of influence factors.

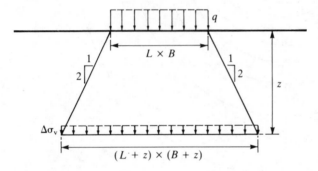

Figure 2.15 Approximate method for calculating average increase in total vertical stress under a uniformly loaded area.

Bulbs of Stress

The solutions presented in (a)–(g) can be used to obtain contours of equal stress increase in a soil mass due to a load applied at its surface. For example, contours of equal increase in total vertical stress expressed as a proportion of the applied pressure q are shown for a section through an infinitely long strip in Fig. 2.16a and a section through the centre-line of a square area in Fig. 2.17a. The contours form what is referred to as the *bulb of stress* for the loaded area, and give a useful visual representation of the manner in which the stress increase is distributed through the soil mass. We see, for instance, that at any depth the maximum stress increase occurs under the centre. Distributions of $\Delta\sigma_v$ under centre points are therefore of particular interest and are shown separately for the strip and the square area in Figs 2.16b and 2.17b respectively. Under the centre of a square loaded area of width B, $\Delta\sigma_v$ at a depth of about $3B$ is only about 5 per cent of the surface pressure q. On the other hand, under the centre-line of a strip of width B, a comparable reduction in $\Delta\sigma_v$ is not achieved until the depth exceeds $10B$. Thus, the depth over which the stress increase is significant, referred to as the *zone of influence*, can be taken to extend to some 10 times the width in the case of an infinitely long strip and about 3 times the width in the case of a square loaded area. In a similar manner, we find the zone of influence of a circular loaded area extends to a depth of about 3 times its diameter.

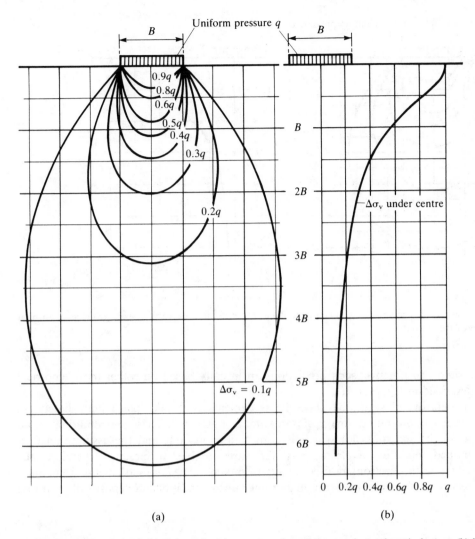

Figure 2.16 Uniformly loaded infinite strip: (a) contours of equal increase in total vertical stress, (b) increase in total vertical stress under the centre.

2.5 SETTLEMENTS BASED ON ELASTIC THEORY

The theory of elasticity on which the solutions given in Sec. 2.4 are based may also be used to obtain expressions for the deformations that result in a soil mass when subjected to an applied load. Of particular interest in practice are the vertical deformations, that is *settlements*, that occur at the surface of the soil mass when the load is applied over the area of a foundation. The solutions for settlement based on elastic theory involve the modulus of elasticity E and Poisson's ratio v. However, a soil mass does not possess unique values of E and v, and the difficulty of determining appropriate values of these parameters for particular field problems limits the application of these solutions in practice.

In deposits of sand the modulus value varies not only with depth but also across the width of the loaded area, and over the initial 'elastic' range of deformation the value of Poisson's ratio varies with strain. Consequently, solutions based on elasticity are seldom used in the prediction of

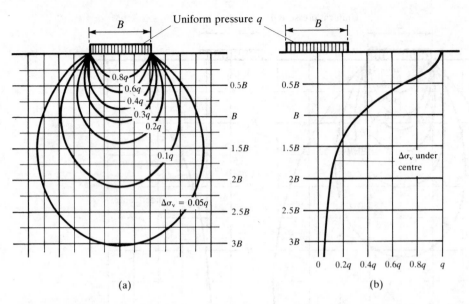

Figure 2.17 Uniformly loaded square area: (a) contours of equal increase in total vertical stress, (b) increase in total vertical stress under the centre.

settlements in sands. In practice, such predictions are usually based on rather more empirical methods, as described in Chapter 8.

However, in deposits of saturated clay, the settlements that take place immediately on construction occur without any drainage of porewater from the soil. These are conditions of no volume change in the soil mass for which Poisson's ratio $v = 0.5$, and the assumption of a constant undrained modulus of elasticity is not unreasonable. In practice, therefore, the solutions presented in this section are used mainly to predict *immediate* settlements (sometimes referred to as *elastic* settlements) occurring under undrained conditions in deposits of saturated clay.

Uniformly Loaded Rectangular Area

The settlement at a *corner* of a flexible rectangular area of length L and width B applying a uniform pressure q to the surface of a semi-infinite soil mass is given by

$$S_i = \frac{qB(1 - v^2)}{E} I_s \tag{2.21}$$

where I_s is an *influence factor of settlement* which depends on the length/width ratio of the rectangular area. The relationship between I_s and L/B was given by Terzaghi (1943) and is shown in Fig. 2.18.

If the rectangular area is at the surface of a soil layer of finite thickness D resting on a rigid base, the settlement at a *corner* can be obtained from the approximate solution presented by Steinbrenner in 1934. In this case the influence factor I_s can be expressed in terms of two functions F_1 and F_2 in the form

$$I_s = F_1 + \left[\frac{1 - 2v}{1 - v}\right] F_2 \tag{2.22}$$

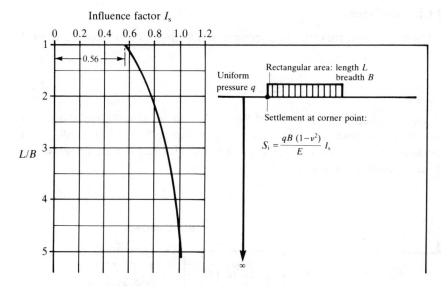

Figure 2.18 Values of influence factor I_s for calculating the immediate surface settlement S_i under the corner of a uniformly loaded flexible rectangular area on a semi-infinite mass of soil. (After Terzaghi, 1943.)

Both functions F_1 and F_2 depend on the ratios L/B and D/B, and are presented in graphical form in Fig. 2.19.

Surface settlements at points other than corner points, or due to loaded areas consisting of a combination of rectangular shapes, can be determined by applying the principle of superposition in the manner explained for stress calculations in Sec. 2.4e.

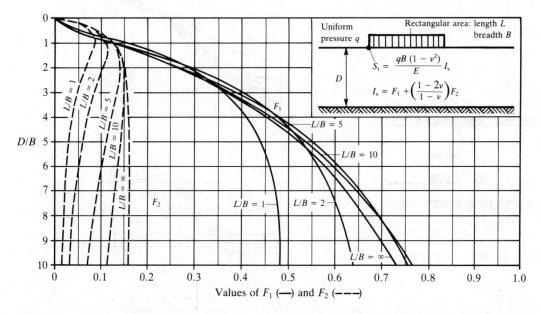

Figure 2.19 Values of functions F_1 and F_2 for calculating the immediate surface settlement S_i under the corner of a uniformly loaded flexible rectangular area on a soil layer of finite thickness. (After Steinbrenner.)

Uniformly Loaded Circular Area

The surface settlements due to a uniform pressure q acting over a flexible circular area of radius R are given by

$$S_i = \frac{qR}{E} I_s \qquad (2.23)$$

where the influence factor I_s depends on the value of Poisson's ratio and on the radial distance from the centre of the area to the point at which the settlement is to be found. Values of I_s for a semi-infinite soil mass and for two cases of a soil layer of finite thickness D were presented by Terzaghi (1943) and are reproduced in Fig. 2.20.

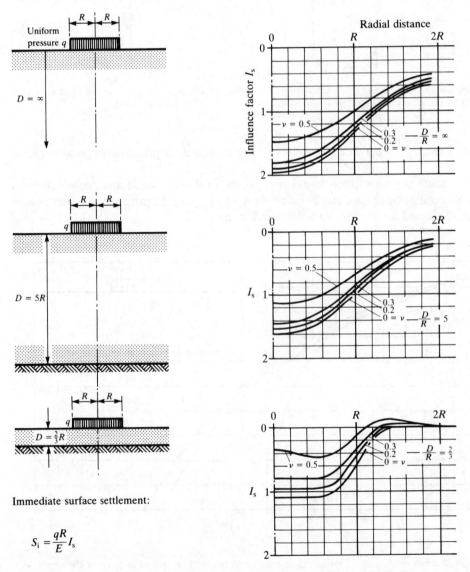

Figure 2.20 Values of influence factor I_s for calculating the immediate surface settlement S_i under a uniformly loaded flexible circular area. (After Terzaghi, 1943.)

Example 2.2 A flexible rectangular area 8 m long by 4 m wide applies a uniform pressure of 40 kN/m^2 to the surface of a 20-m thick layer of saturated clay overlying bedrock. Calculate the increase in total vertical stress at a depth of 5 m in the clay below the centre and below one of the corners of the loaded area. Estimate also the immediate differential settlement between the centre and a corner of the loaded area.

The properties of the clay are: undrained modulus of elasticity $= 3500 \text{ kN/m}^2$ and Poisson's ratio $= 0.5$.

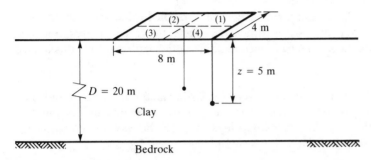

Figure 2.21 Example 2.2.

SOLUTION To determine increases in total vertical stress under a rectangular loaded area we use the Fadum chart in Fig. 2.10. For stresses under the centre point, we must divide the loaded area into four subareas and apply the principle of superposition. Thus with reference to Fig. 2.21:

Area	B (m)	L (m)	z (m)	$m = B/z$	$n = L/z$	I_σ
Whole	4	8	5	0.8	1.6	0.175
Subarea (1)	2	4	5	0.4	0.8	0.093

Using Eq. (2.16) we obtain the increase in total vertical stress at a depth of 5 m below a corner of the loaded area as:

$$\Delta\sigma_v = qI_\sigma = 40 \times 0.175 = \underline{7 \text{ kN/m}^2}$$

and below the centre as

$$\Delta\sigma_v = 4 \times qI_\sigma = 4 \times 40 \times 0.093 = \underline{14.9 \text{ kN/m}^2}$$

To determine the immediate surface settlements of a flexible rectangular area on a layer of finite thickness we use the Steinbrenner chart in Fig. 2.19. For the settlement at the centre, we again divide the loaded area into four subareas and apply the principle of superposition.

The saturated clay has Poisson's ratio $v = 0.5$ and hence the influence factor I_s, given by Eq. (2.22), reduces to $I_s = F_1$. Thus with reference to Fig. 2.21:

Area	L (m)	B (m)	D (m)	L/B	D/B	$I_s = F_1$
Whole	8	4	20	2	5	0.525
Subarea (1)	4	2	20	2	10	0.64

Using Eq. (2.21) we obtain the immediate settlement at a corner of the loaded area as

$$S_i = \frac{qB(1 - v^2)}{E} I_s = \frac{40 \times 4 \times 0.75 \times 0.525}{3500} = 0.018 \text{ m} = \underline{18 \text{ mm}}$$

and at the centre as

$$S_i = 4 \times \frac{qB(1 - v^2)}{E} I_s = \frac{4 \times 40 \times 2 \times 0.75 \times 0.64}{3500} = 0.044 \text{ m} = \underline{44 \text{ mm}}$$

Hence the immediate differential settlement $= 44 - 18 = \underline{26 \text{ mm}}$.

It can readily be verified that the maximum settlement of a flexible loaded area occurs under its centre and the minimum settlement under a corner (the edge in the case of a circular loaded area). Hence 26 mm represents the *maximum* immediate differential settlement for this loaded area.

Example 2.3 Figure 2.22 shows the plan dimensions of an existing factory building founded on the surface of a thick deposit of homogeneous clay. The foundation pressure from the building is 30 kN/m². Also shown is the line of an existing tunnel through the clay, the crown of the tunnel being at an average depth of 12 m below ground level.

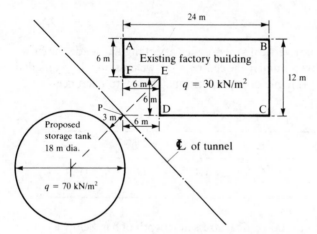

Figure 2.22 Example 2.3.

It is proposed to construct a storage tank in the position shown, having an 18 m diameter flexible foundation which will transmit a pressure of 70 kN/m² to the surface of the clay. If this proposed construction is carried out, estimate:

(a) the total vertical stress in the soil 12 m below point P and
(b) the immediate surface settlement which will occur at P and the edge and centre of the circular foundation.

The properties of the clay are $\rho_s = 1.90 \text{ Mg/m}^3$, $E = 5500 \text{ kN/m}^2$ and $v = 0.5$.

SOLUTION (a) The total vertical stress in the soil 12 m below P will be given by

$$\sigma_v = \text{total overburden pressure} + \text{increase in stress due to the existing building} + \text{increase in stress due to the proposed storage tank}$$

Total overburden pressure $\sigma_{vo} = 1.90 \times 9.81 \times 12 = 223.67 \text{ kN/m}^2$

The increase in stress due to the existing building is obtained using the Fadum chart shown in Fig. 2.10. From the principle of superposition, the increase in total vertical stress under point P is given by

$$\Delta\sigma_v = \Delta\sigma_{v_{ABCP}} - \Delta\sigma_{v_{FEDP}}$$

and from Eq. (2.16)

$$\Delta\sigma_v = (qI_\sigma)_{ABCP} - (qI_\sigma)_{FEDP}$$

With reference to Fig. 2.22:

Area	B (m)	L (m)	z (m)	m = B/z	n = L/z	I_σ
ABCP	12	24	12	1	2	0.198
FEDP	6	6	12	0.5	0.5	0.083

Thus

$$\Delta\sigma_v = 30 \times 0.198 - 30 \times 0.083 = \underline{3.45\ kN/m^2}$$

The increase in stress due to the storage tank may be calculated using an influence factor obtained from Fig. 2.13, or using the Newmark chart in Fig. 2.14.

With reference to Fig. 2.13, the radial distance to P is $r = 12$ m, the radius $R = 9$ m and the depth $z = 12$ m. Therefore $z/R = 1\frac{1}{3}$, $r/R = 1\frac{1}{3}$ and $I_\sigma = 0.18$. From Eq. (2.18)

$$\Delta\sigma_v = qI_\sigma = 70 \times 0.18 = \underline{12.60\ kN/m^2}$$

For the Newmark chart, a plan showing the circular foundation and point P is drawn to a scale such that the scale line AB in Fig. 2.14 represents the depth $z = 12$ m. This plan is then superimposed on Fig. 2.14 with point P positioned over the origin of the chart. The number of influence areas enclosed by the loaded area is assessed as $n = 35.4$. Thus, from Eq. (2.19)

$$\Delta\sigma_v = qIn = 70 \times 0.005 \times 35.4 = \underline{12.39\ kN/m^2}$$

Thus, the total vertical stress in the soil 12 m below point P is given by

$$\sigma_v = 223.67 + 3.45 + 12.60 = \underline{239.72\ kN/m^2}$$

(b) We assume that any settlements due to the existing structures will already have occurred and hence immediate settlements will result only from the additional load imposed by the tank. The surface settlements can be estimated from Eq. (2.23):

$$S_i = \frac{qR}{E} I_s$$

where herein $q = 70$ kN/m^2, $R = 9$ m, $E = 5500$ kN/m^2 and I_s is obtained from Fig. 2.20. Assuming the clay layer to be infinitely thick we have $D/R = \infty$, and given that $v = 0.5$ we obtain influence factors and immediate settlements as follows:

At the centre of the foundation, radial distance $= 0$, $I_s = 1.50$ and

$$S_i = \frac{70 \times 9 \times 1.5}{5500} = 0.172\ m = \underline{172\ mm}$$

At the edge of the foundation, radial distance $= R$, $I_s = 1.0$ and

$$S_i = \frac{70 \times 9 \times 1.0}{5500} = 0.115\ m = \underline{115\ mm}$$

At point P, radial distance $= 1\frac{1}{3}R$, $I_s = 0.75$ and

$$S_i = \frac{70 \times 9 \times 0.75}{5500} = 0.086\ m = \underline{86\ mm}$$

PROBLEMS

2.1 An investigation at a particular site revealed a deep deposit of sand with the water table at a depth of 2 m. Calculate the total vertical stress, porewater pressure and effective vertical stress at a depth of 10 m, given that the density of the sand above the water table is 1.80 Mg/m^3 and below the water table is 2.0 Mg/m^3.
[Ans.   192.3 kN/m^2;   78.5 kN/m^2;   113.8 kN/m^2]

2.2 Boreholes at a proposed construction site revealed the sequence of strata described in the table below. Equilibrium groundwater level was encountered at a depth of 2 m and bedrock at a depth of 15 m.

Depth	Soil description	Soil properties
0–3 m	Alluvial sand	$G_s = 2.63$ Above GWL, $w = 11.2\%$ Below GWL, $w = 22\%$
3–11 m	Post-glacial silty clay	$G_s = 2.74$, $w = 36.5\%$
11–15 m	Stiff boulder clay	$G_s = 2.69$, $w = 16\%$

Determine the distributions of total vertical stress, porewater pressure and effective vertical stress over the depth of 15 m.

Ans.	Depth (m)	0	2	3	11	15
	σ_v (kN/m^2)	0	36.3	56.2	203.0	288.5
	u (kN/m^2)	0	0	9.8	88.3	127.5
	σ_v' (kN/m^2)	0	36.3	46.4	114.7	161.0

2.3 A rectangular water tank of width 6 m and length 8 m and having a flexible base is to be founded on the surface of a deposit of stiff clay 18 m thick and overlying bedrock. The tank imposes a pressure of 40 kN/m^2 on the soil.

(a) Determine the increase in total vertical stress with depth in the clay layer under the centre and under a corner of the tank.
(b) Calculate the immediate settlements under the centre, a corner and the mid-points of the length and width of the foundation. Hence estimate the maximum differential immediate settlement.

The properties of the clay are $E = 7200$ kN/m^2 and $v = 0.5$.

Ans. (a)										
Depth (m)		2	4	6	8	10	12	14	16	18
	Centre	35.8	24.8	16.2	10.9	7.5	5.6	4.2	3.4	2.7
$\Delta\sigma_v$ (kN/m^2)										
	Corner	9.8	9.0	7.6	6.2	5.0	4.0	3.3	2.7	2.2

(b) 25.3 mm;   9.7 mm;   15.7 mm;   14.5 mm;   15.6 mm

2.4 An oil tank 14 m in diameter and having a flexible base is to be founded on the surface of a deposit of soft estuarine clay and will impose a pressure of 50 kN/m^2 on the soil. The clay is 25 m thick and overlies bedrock.

(a) Determine the increase in total vertical stress with depth in the clay layer under the centre and under the edge of the tank.
(b) Calculate the immediate surface settlement at the centre of the tank and at radial distances of 4 m, 7 m and 10 m.
Hence estimate the maximum differential immediate settlement of the tank.

The properties of the clay are $E = 2800$ kN/m^2 and $v = 0.5$.

Ans. (a)						
Depth (m)		4	8	12	16	20	25
	Centre	43.0	28.8	17.5	11.3	8.0	5.0
$\Delta\sigma_v$ (kN/m^2)						
	Edge	20.0	15.3	10.3	8.3	6.0	4.4

(b) 110 mm;   103 mm;   59 mm;   23 mm;   51 mm

2.5 A circular loaded area of diameter B applies a uniform pressure q to the surface of a semi-infinite mass of soil. By drawing contours of constant stress increase equal to $0.05\,q$, $0.1\,q$, $0.2\,q$, $0.3\,q$, $0.4\,q$, $0.6\,q$ and $0.8\,q$, establish the bulb of stress for the loaded area. Plot also the increase in total vertical stress on horizontal planes at depths of $0.5\,B$, B and $2\,B$ below the loaded area.

THREE

SEEPAGE THEORY AND GROUNDWATER FLOW

3.1 INTRODUCTION

Frequently, the porewater pressures that prevail in a soil mass in the field are not those associated with hydrostatic conditions but are such as to cause flow of the groundwater through the pores of the soil. For example, consider the case of a concrete dam founded on a soil deposit as shown in Fig. 3.1a. If water is impounded to some depth on the upstream side, the difference in water level across the dam will cause seepage to occur through the foundation soil from the upstream side of the structure to the downstream side. As the seepage flow develops the porewater pressures throughout the soil mass adjust from their initial values to final values compatible with the new hydraulic boundary conditions, and volume changes occur in the soil mass. During this period the seepage flow is a function of time and is referred to as *transient flow*. When the porewater pressures are everywhere in equilibrium with the new boundary conditions, the seepage flow is then independent of time and is therefore referred to as *steady state flow*.

The rate at which the porewater pressures adjust to their new equilibrium values is controlled principally by the soil type. The free-draining sands and gravels readily allow the flow of water, and the porewater pressures are able to adjust very rapidly. Therefore, following any change in hydraulic boundary conditions it can be assumed that steady state conditions in sands and gravels are achieved virtually instantaneously. In contrast, steady state conditions in slow-draining clay soils may not be achieved for several years and the period of transient flow is of particular importance, principally in the study of consolidation and swelling of clay soils considered in Chapter 4. This chapter, however, is concerned with the theory of steady state flow and its application to field problems of groundwater flow, typically of the type illustrated in Fig. 3.1:

(a) flow under concrete dams and weirs founded on permeable soils
(b) flow under cofferdams in permeable soils
(c) flow through earth dams
(d) flow to wells or well-points in permeable soils.

According to the classical experiments of Osborne Reynolds in the late 1800s, the flow of water may assume either of two distinctly characteristic states, referred to as *laminar flow* or *turbulent*

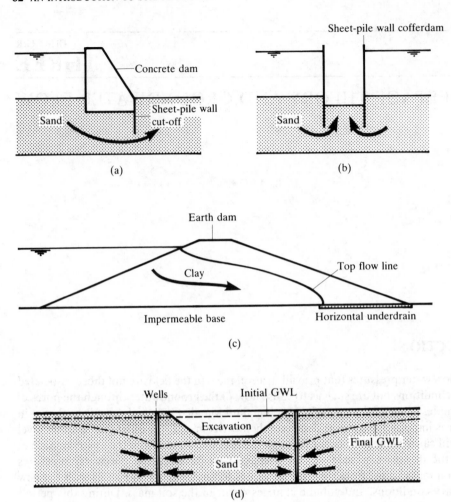

Figure 3.1 Typical seepage flow problems.

flow. Laminar flow is orderly and in layers, each particle of water flowing along a definite path which never intersects the path of any other particle. Within the range of laminar flow, the hydraulic gradient (i.e., the head lost due to friction per unit length of flow path) is found to be proportional to the velocity of flow. Such flow occurs typically at low velocities. At higher velocities a more irregular or turbulent flow pattern is observed in which the flow paths cross and recross each other at random. The hydraulic gradient is now found to vary with the square of the velocity.

The pores of most soils are relatively small and seepage velocities are low, so that in almost all cases the flow of groundwater is *laminar flow*.

3.2 THEORY OF STEADY STATE FLOW

Darcy's Law for Flow through Soils

The pores of a soil mass are interconnected in an extremely complex but entirely random manner and form numerous narrow, irregularly shaped, twisting flow channels within the soil mass.

Consequently, an analysis of the flow through individual pores is impossible. However, in engineering problems involving seepage through soils it is not the micro-flow through individual pores that is of interest, but rather the combined macro-flow through all the pores of an element of soil which is sufficiently large to be typically representative of the soil mass as a whole. Studies of such flow were carried out about 1856 by the Frenchman Henry Darcy as part of a series of experiments on sand filter beds for the public water supply system for the city of Dijon.

The form of Darcy's experiment is shown in Fig. 3.2 where a vertical column of sand of length ΔD and cross-sectional area A is connected to upper and lower water reservoirs to produce

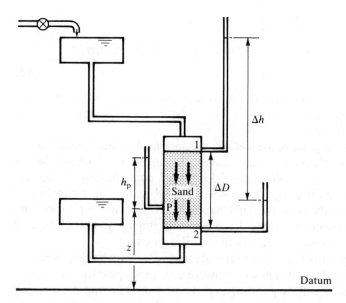

Figure 3.2 Darcy's experiment.

downward flow through the sand. Considering any point P in the sand, the *total head h* in the water is the sum of the *elevation head* h_{el}, the *pressure head* h_p and the *velocity head* h_v:

$$h = h_{el} + h_p + h_v \tag{3.1}$$

The elevation head h_{el} is the height above an arbitrary datum level and is denoted herein by z. The pressure head $h_p = u/\rho_w g$ and is the height of water supported in a stand-pipe or piezometer tube. The velocity head $h_v = v^2/2g$ and in most groundwater flow problems is small enough to be neglected. For example, a seepage velocity of 0.1 m/s produces a velocity head of only 0.5 mm. Thus, neglecting h_v, Eq. (3.1) becomes

$$h = h_{el} + h_p = z + \frac{u}{\rho_w g} \tag{3.2}$$

Since the sum of the elevation head and the pressure head in a fluid is the *piezometric head*, then we see that in groundwater flow the piezometric head and the total head may be taken to be the same.

Viscous resistance to flow through the pore channels results in a loss of energy or drop in total head in the water as it flows through the sand. The piezometric heads at the top and bottom of the sand column are measured by piezometer tubes inserted at points 1 and 2, and the *difference in piezometric level* between the two tubes therefore defines the *difference in total head* Δh across the sand column.

As a result of his experiments Darcy observed that the flow rate Q through the sand was directly proportional to the cross-sectional area A and the difference in total head Δh, and inversely proportional to the length ΔD. Expressed mathematically this gives

$$Q = kA \frac{\Delta h}{\Delta D} \tag{3.3}$$

where k is a constant of proportionality referred to as the *coefficient of permeability*, and $\Delta h/\Delta D$ denotes the rate of head loss through the sand and is referred to as the *hydraulic gradient i*. That is

$$i = \frac{\Delta h}{\Delta D} \tag{3.4}$$

The quantity Q/A denotes the *discharge velocity v* and so Eq. (3.3) can be written as

$$v = ki \tag{3.5}$$

Equation (3.5) is Darcy's Law for flow through soils and states that the discharge velocity is directly proportional to the hydraulic gradient. As noted later by Reynolds, this is a distinguishing characteristic of laminar flow.

The coefficient of permeability is a property of the soil and is determined by test. Because of the difficulty in obtaining undisturbed samples of sands and gravels, the coefficient of permeability of the free-draining cohesionless soils is usually determined from field pumping tests. These are discussed later in this chapter when considering flow to wells. The laboratory determination of the coefficient of permeability of clay soils is discussed in Chapter 4 when considering vertical and radial consolidation tests. In the meantime, Table 3.1 presents a summary of the order of magnitude of the coefficient of permeability of some natural soil deposits.

Figure 3.2 illustrates a particularly simple case of steady state seepage in which the direction of flow at all points in the soil is immediately known. However, in most problems involving groundwater flow, the direction of flow will vary throughout the flow domain and determining the direction of flow becomes part of the problem. Therefore it is usually more convenient to express the discharge velocity at any point in terms of components with reference to a pre-selected coordinate system. Thus, if the orthogonal cartesian coordinate system x, y, z defines the principal directions of permeability in a soil mass with z taken as the vertical axis and x, y to define the horizontal plane, then the components of discharge velocity in the three reference directions are

$$v_x = k_x i_x = -k_x \frac{\partial h}{\partial x} \tag{3.6a}$$

$$v_y = k_y i_y = -k_y \frac{\partial h}{\partial y} \tag{3.6b}$$

Table 3.1 Coefficients of permeability of some natural soils

Soil type	Coefficient of permeability (m/s)
Clay	$< 10^{-9}$
Sandy clay	10^{-9} to 10^{-8}
Silt	10^{-8} to 10^{-7}
Peat	10^{-9} to 10^{-6}
Fine sand	10^{-6} to 10^{-4}
Coarse sand	10^{-4} to 10^{-3}
Gravelly sand	10^{-3} to 10^{-2}
Gravel	$> 10^{-2}$

and
$$v_z = k_z i_z = -k_z \frac{\partial h}{\partial z} \qquad (3.6c)$$

where k_x, k_y, k_z are the coefficients of permeability and $i_x = -\partial h/\partial x$, $i_y = -\partial h/\partial y$, $i_z = -\partial h/\partial z$ are the components of hydraulic gradient in the three reference directions respectively. The negative signs simply indicate that v_x, v_y and v_z are taken to be positive in the directions of flow. That is, in the directions of decreasing total head.

Equation (3.6) represents the *generalized form of Darcy's Law* for flow in three dimensions.

Governing Equation for Steady State Flow

Consider the flow of water through a saturated elemental cube of soil located in the x, y, z coordinate system as shown in Fig. 3.3.

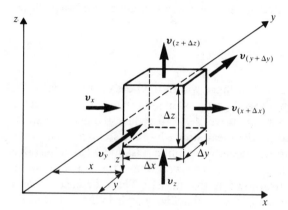

Figure 3.3 Components of discharge velocity into and out of a soil element.

For flow in the x direction:

quantity of flow into element per unit time $= v_x \, \Delta y \, \Delta z$

and quantity of flow out of element per unit time $= v_{x+\Delta x} \, \Delta y \, \Delta z$

Now by Taylor's theorem

$$v_{x+\Delta x} = v_x + \frac{\partial v_x}{\partial x} \Delta x + \frac{1}{2!} \frac{\partial^2 v_x}{\partial x^2} \Delta x^2 + \frac{1}{3!} \frac{\partial^3 v_x}{\partial x^3} \Delta x^3 + \cdots$$

Taking only the first two terms on the right-hand side, since the higher-derivative terms may be considered second order, then

$$v_{x+\Delta x} = v_x + \frac{\partial v_x}{\partial x} \Delta x$$

Hence quantity of flow out of element per unit time $= \left[v_x + \frac{\partial v_x}{\partial x} \Delta x \right] \Delta y \Delta z$

Similar expressions obtain for flow in the y and z directions.

For conditions of steady state flow, conservation of matter requires that the total quantity of water flowing out of the element per unit time equals the total quantity of water flowing into the element per unit time. We thus obtain

$$\left[v_x + \frac{\partial v_x}{\partial x} \Delta x \right] \Delta y \Delta z + \left[v_y + \frac{\partial v_y}{\partial y} \Delta y \right] \Delta x \Delta z + \left[v_z + \frac{\partial v_z}{\partial z} \Delta z \right] \Delta x \Delta y$$

$$= v_x \, \Delta y \Delta z + v_y \, \Delta x \Delta z + v_z \, \Delta x \Delta y$$

whence
$$\frac{\partial v_x}{\partial x} + \frac{\partial v_y}{\partial y} + \frac{\partial v_z}{\partial z} = 0 \qquad (3.7)$$

Equation (3.7) is known as the *equation of continuity* in three dimensions.
Substituting Eq. (3.6) into Eq. (3.7) gives

$$\frac{\partial}{\partial x}\left[-k_x \frac{\partial h}{\partial x}\right] + \frac{\partial}{\partial y}\left[-k_y \frac{\partial h}{\partial y}\right] + \frac{\partial}{\partial z}\left[-k_z \frac{\partial h}{\partial z}\right] = 0 \qquad (3.8)$$

For steady state conditions, no volume changes occur in the soil element and the permeability can be assumed constant. Equation (3.8) then becomes

$$k_x \frac{\partial^2 h}{\partial x^2} + k_y \frac{\partial^2 h}{\partial y^2} + k_z \frac{\partial^2 h}{\partial z^2} = 0 \qquad (3.9)$$

Equation (3.9) is the governing equation for three-dimensional steady state groundwater flow.

3.3 UPWARD SEEPAGE FLOW

When water flows through a soil mass, the viscous resistance within the pore channels results in seepage forces being transmitted by the water to the soil particles. In areas where the flow occurs predominantly in an upward direction, these seepage forces tend to reduce the effective stress between the soil particles and hence tend to reduce the shear strength of the soil mass. This may be demonstrated with reference to the simple arrangement of a column of sand and an adjustable water reservoir, shown in Fig. 3.4. On positioning the water reservoir above the top of the sand, water flows upwards through the sand and overflows at the surface. The difference in level between the surface of the reservoir and the surface of the sand defines the drop in total head Δh during flow through the sand column of length ΔD. The hydraulic gradient across the sand is then given by

$$i = \frac{\Delta h}{\Delta D}$$

At the base of the sand the total vertical stress σ_v is given by

$$\sigma_v = \rho_s g \, \Delta D$$

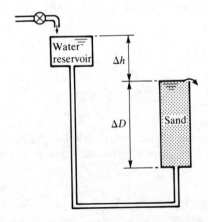

Datum

Figure 3.4 Upward seepage flow through soil.

The associated porewater pressure u is

$$u = \rho_w g(\Delta D + \Delta h)$$

From the principle of effective stress, the effective vertical stress σ'_v is then

$$\sigma'_v = \sigma_v - u = \rho_s g \, \Delta D - \rho_w g(\Delta D + \Delta h) = \rho' g \, \Delta D - \rho_w g \, \Delta h$$

where ρ' = the effective density of the sand = $\rho_s - \rho_w$.

Thus
$$\sigma'_v = \rho' g \, \Delta D \left[1 - \frac{\rho_w}{\rho'} \frac{\Delta h}{\Delta D} \right] = \rho' g \, \Delta D \left[1 - \frac{\rho_w}{\rho'} i \right] \qquad (3.10)$$

On raising the water reservoir, the hydraulic gradient i across the sand increases and from Eq. (3.10) the effective vertical stress is seen to decrease. The form of this equation indicates that the effective vertical stress is reduced to zero if the hydraulic gradient reaches a value of ρ'/ρ_w. This value is referred to as the *critical hydraulic gradient*, i_c. Thus

$$i_c = \frac{\rho'}{\rho_w}$$

The ratio ρ'/ρ_w is defined by Eq. (1.22) in terms of the particle specific gravity G_s and the void ratio e. We thus obtain

$$i_c = \frac{\rho'}{\rho_w} = \frac{G_s - 1}{1 + e} \qquad (3.11)$$

At the critical condition of zero effective stress, the sand particles become separated from one another and appear to be in suspension in the pore water, and the soil mass begins to 'boil'. The sand is then said to be in a *quick* condition in which it has no shear strength and is highly unstable.

For the simple arrangement shown in Fig. 3.4 a quick condition could equally well be produced by maintaining the reservoir level constant and decreasing the thickness of the sand. Thus, in practice, if an excavation is made in a deposit of sand below groundwater level, the resulting upward seepage flow through the base of the excavation could result in a quick condition being formed. This mechanism of instability is examined in detail in Example 3.3. In a similar manner, the base of an excavation in a deposit of clay overlying water-bearing sand or gravel may heave if the total weight of clay, decreasing by virtue of excavation, becomes equal to the upthrust on the clay due to the porewater pressure in the sand or gravel. This condition is illustrated in Example 3.1.

To maintain the stability of such excavations it is often necessary to install well-points or pumping wells around the perimeter of the excavation and reduce the pressure head in the sand. This constitutes the problem of flow to wells and is considered in Secs 3.6 and 3.7.

Equation (3.11) indicates that the critical hydraulic gradient is independent of particle size and therefore a quick condition is possible in all types of soil. However, in practice, a quick condition is most likely to arise in silts and fine-to-medium sands. For clay soils the stiction between the clay mineral particles tends to resist separation, and with the highly permeable coarse sands and gravels it is unlikely that the large volumes of water needed to maintain a quick condition would be encountered.

Using the typical void ratio values for sands given in Table 1.4 and taking $G_s = 2.65$, Eq. (3.11) yields the values of i_c given in Table 3.2 (overleaf). This indicates that for the majority of sands the critical hydraulic gradient is approximately 1.

68 AN INTRODUCTION TO SOIL MECHANICS

Table 3.2 Values of critical hydraulic gradient in sands

| | Density | |
Grading	Loose	Dense
Uniform sand	$i_c = 0.89$	$i_c = 1.09$
Well-graded sand	$i_c = 0.99$	$i_c = 1.15$

Example 3.1 A layer of uniform clay 8 m thick overlies 1 m of dense sand resting on bedrock. The groundwater level in the clay is at the soil surface and the piezometric level for the sand is 2 m above the top of the clay. The density of the clay is 2 Mg/m³.

(a) Assuming steady state conditions to prevail, calculate the distributions of total vertical stress, porewater pressure and effective vertical stress throughout the clay layer.

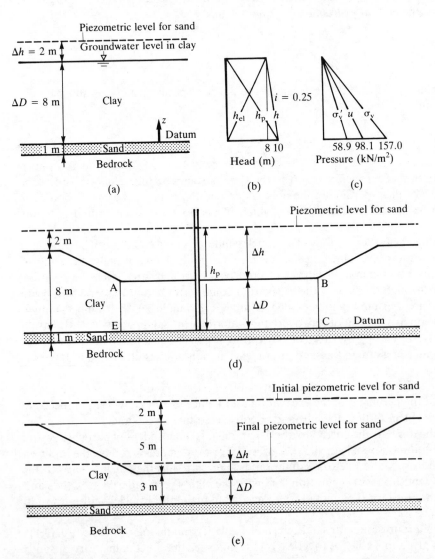

Figure 3.5 Example 3.1.

(b) Calculate the depth to which a wide excavation can be made in the clay before failure occurs by base heave.

(c) If an excavation is to be made to a depth of 5 m in the clay with a factor of safety of 3 against base heave, calculate the required reduction in piezometric level for the sand.

SOLUTION (a) The problem is illustrated in Fig. 3.5a.

Taking the base of the clay layer as the datum for measuring elevation head, then

At the base of the clay: $h_{el} = 0$, $h_p = 10$ m, $h = h_{el} + h_p = 10$ m
At the surface of the clay: $h_{el} = 8$ m, $h_p = 0$, $h = h_{el} + h_p = 8$ m

Thus seepage flow occurs vertically upwards through the clay under this difference in total head of 2 m. The hydraulic gradient across the clay layer is given by

$$i = \frac{\Delta h}{\Delta D} = \frac{2}{8} = \underline{0.25}$$

Since flow occurs in the vertical direction z only, there can be no hydraulic gradient in the horizontal x and y directions so that

$$\frac{\partial h}{\partial x} = 0 \quad \text{and} \quad \frac{\partial h}{\partial y} = 0$$

and the governing flow equation (3.9) reduces to the one-dimensional form

$$\frac{d^2 h}{dz^2} = 0$$

On integration this gives

$$h = az + b$$

where a and b are constants of integration which can be determined from the boundary conditions. The total head h is a linear function of z and therefore varies linearly through the clay layer. Also, since

$$h_p = h - h_{el}$$

then

$$h_p = (az + b) - z = (a - 1)z + b$$

and the pressure head also varies linearly through the clay layer. The distributions of elevation head, pressure head and total head are then as shown in Fig. 3.5b.

The total vertical stress at any depth d is given by $\sigma_v = \rho g d$ and therefore increases linearly with depth. The porewater pressure at any depth d is given by $u = \rho_w g (h_p)_d$ and, like h_p, must increase linearly with depth. Since the effective vertical stress $\sigma'_v = \sigma_v - u$, then σ'_v also increases linearly with depth. We thus obtain

At the surface of the clay: $\sigma_v = 0$, $u = 0$, $\sigma'_v = 0$
At the base of clay: $\sigma_v = 2 \times 9.81 \times 8 = 157.0$ kN/m^2,

$$u = 1 \times 9.81 \times 10 = 98.1 \text{ kN/m}^2, \quad \sigma'_v = 58.9 \text{ kN/m}^2$$

The distributions of σ_v, u and σ'_v are then as shown in Fig. 3.5c.

(b) For a wide excavation in the clay, the problem is as illustrated in Fig. 3.5d.

Neglecting the shear strength of the clay on AE and BC, heave of the base of the excavation is imminent when the total weight of the soil block ABCE (diminished by excavation) becomes equal to the upthrust on the base of the block due to the porewater pressure in the sand. We thus have

Total weight of soil block $= \rho g \, \Delta D \times$ base area
Upthrust on base of block $= \rho_w g h_p \times$ base area

Equating these gives

$$\rho \, \Delta D = \rho_w h_p \tag{3.12}$$

and with $\rho = 2$ Mg/m^3 and $h_p = 10$ m, we obtain $\Delta D = 5$ m. Therefore, excavation fails by base heave at a depth of 3 m.

(c) Referring to Fig. 3.5d:

Total head on EC $= h_{el} + h_p = 0 + (\Delta D + \Delta h) = \Delta D + \Delta h$
Total head on AB $= h_{el} + h_p = \Delta D + 0 = \Delta D$

Thus difference in total head across the soil block $= \Delta D + \Delta h - \Delta D = \Delta h$. From Eq. (3.12), the failure condition is given by

$$\rho \, \Delta D = \rho_w h_p = \rho_w(\Delta D + \Delta h)$$

Thus
$$\rho' \, \Delta D = \rho_w \, \Delta h$$

whence
$$\frac{\Delta h}{\Delta D} = \frac{\rho'}{\rho_w}$$

But $\Delta h/\Delta D$ denotes the hydraulic gradient across the soil block and ρ'/ρ_w is the expression for critical hydraulic gradient given by Eq. (3.11). Thus base heave occurs when the hydraulic gradient i across the clay (increasing with excavation) becomes equal to the critical hydraulic gradient i_c, a criterion similar to that which produces the quick condition in sands. The factor of safety F against base heave is therefore given by dividing the critical gradient i_c by the actual gradient i. Thus

$$F = \frac{i_c}{i} \tag{3.13}$$

For an excavation depth of 5 m, shown in Fig. 3.5e, the thickness of clay above the sand is $\Delta D = 3$ m. We thus have

$$i = \frac{\Delta h}{3} \quad \text{and} \quad i_c = \frac{\rho'}{\rho_w} = \frac{2 - 1}{1} = 1$$

Therefore, for the specified factor of safety of 3

$$3 = \frac{1}{\Delta h/3}$$

giving
$$\Delta h = 1 \text{ m}$$

Thus, the required reduction in piezometric level for the sand is 6 m.

3.4 FLOW UNDER RETAINING STRUCTURES

This section considers particularly the case of flow under concrete dams, weirs and cofferdams, but has applications to groundwater flow behind and under retaining walls. As illustrated in Fig. 3.6, such structures tend to be very long in the y direction so that seepage flow occurs essentially in the x, z plane with three-dimensional flow occurring only locally at the ends of the structure. Thus we can treat a unit length in the y direction as typical of the flow pattern under the structure as a whole.

For no flow in the y direction, $\partial h/\partial y = 0$ and the governing flow equation (3.9) reduces to the two-dimensional form:

$$k_x \frac{\partial^2 h}{\partial x^2} + k_z \frac{\partial^2 h}{\partial z^2} = 0 \tag{3.14}$$

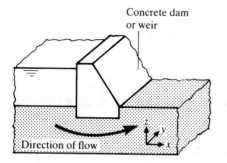
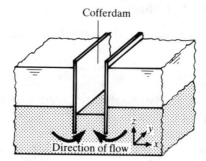

Figure 3.6 Typical two-dimensional flow problems.

If the soil is *isotropic*, its permeability in all directions is the same and $k_x = k_z$, and Eq. (3.14) becomes

$$\frac{\partial^2 h}{\partial x^2} + \frac{\partial^2 h}{\partial z^2} = 0 \tag{3.15}$$

which is a two-dimensional Laplace equation in the x, z domain.

However, because of their mode of deposition, many sedimentary deposits have a higher permeability in the horizontal direction than that in the vertical direction. Even with such *anisotropic* soils, Eq. (3.14) can nevertheless be reduced to Laplacian form by rearranging as follows:

$$\frac{k_x}{k_z}\frac{\partial^2 h}{\partial x^2} + \frac{\partial^2 h}{\partial z^2} = 0 \tag{3.16}$$

Defining a new horizontal space variable x_t as

$$x_t = \sqrt{\frac{k_z}{k_x}}\, x \tag{3.17}$$

then we have

$$\partial x_t^2 = \frac{k_z}{k_x} \partial x^2$$

which on substitution into Eq. (3.16) gives

$$\frac{\partial^2 h}{\partial x_t^2} + \frac{\partial^2 h}{\partial z^2} = 0 \tag{3.18}$$

which is a two-dimensional Laplace equation in the x_t, z domain. The effect of anisotropy is therefore taken into account by transforming the horizontal coordinates according to Eq. (3.17), and the problem then again becomes one of solving a two-dimensional Laplace equation.

Analytical solutions of the two-dimensional Laplace equation can be obtained for only the simplest of problems (Harr, 1962; Verruijt, 1970) and require an understanding of the theory of complex variables and techniques of conformal mapping. With the aid of computers, numerical solutions using finite element techniques can be obtained for problems with complex boundary geometry and highly variable permeability characteristics (Desai, 1977). However, it is important for engineers to be able to obtain rapid and relatively accurate solutions to problems of this type. For this purpose a graphical method of solution is commonly used which utilizes certain special characteristics of the two-dimensional Laplace equation to produce a flow net for the particular problem. We consider these characteristics in the following section.

Elements of Flow Net Theory

For flow in the x, z plane only, the continuity equation (3.7) reduces to

$$\frac{\partial v_x}{\partial x} + \frac{\partial v_z}{\partial z} = 0 \tag{3.19}$$

The components of discharge velocity v_x and v_z can be related to two functions, a potential function ϕ and a stream function ψ.

Potential function ϕ For two-dimensional flow in an isotropic soil, the generalized form of Darcy's Law, Eq. (3.6), reduces to

$$v_x = -k \frac{\partial h}{\partial x} \qquad v_z = -k \frac{\partial h}{\partial z} \tag{3.20}$$

where the coefficient of permeability is constant in all directions.

Equation (3.20) may be rewritten as

$$v_x = -\frac{\partial \phi}{\partial x} \qquad v_z = -\frac{\partial \phi}{\partial z} \tag{3.21}$$

where $\phi = kh$ and is referred to as the *potential* or *groundwater potential*. Note that the potential ϕ is directly proportional to the total head h.

Substituting Eq. (3.21) into (3.19) gives

$$\frac{\partial^2 \phi}{\partial x^2} + \frac{\partial^2 \phi}{\partial z^2} = 0 \tag{3.22}$$

which is a two-dimensional Laplace equation in terms of the potential ϕ. The solution of this equation would permit us to draw contours of constant ϕ in the x, z plane. These contours are called *equipotential lines*, and we are particularly interested in equipotential lines drawn at equal intervals of potential $\Delta\phi$, as in Fig. 3.7. The direction of flow at any point will be in the direction of maximum hydraulic gradient, and therefore maximum potential gradient, and thus at right angles to the equipotential lines.

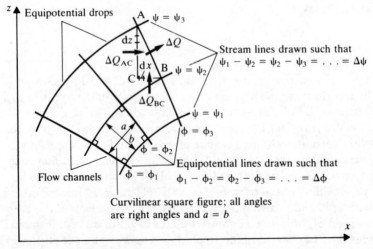

Figure 3.7 Element of flow net.

Stream function ψ Since the components of discharge velocity v_x and v_z must satisfy the continuity equation (3.19), v_x and v_z may also be derived from a second function ψ defined by

$$v_x = -\frac{\partial \psi}{\partial z} \qquad v_z = \frac{\partial \psi}{\partial x} \qquad (3.23)$$

Simple substitution confirms that these definitions satisfy Eq. (3.19).
  Differentiation of Eq. (3.20) leads to

$$\frac{\partial v_z}{\partial x} - \frac{\partial v_x}{\partial z} = 0 \qquad (3.24)$$

and substitution of Eq. (3.23) into (3.24) gives

$$\frac{\partial^2 \psi}{\partial x^2} + \frac{\partial^2 \psi}{\partial z^2} = 0 \qquad (3.25)$$

Thus the function ψ also satisfies a two-dimensional Laplace equation. The solution of this equation would permit us to draw contours of constant ψ in the x, z plane, and of particular interest again is the case where these lines are drawn at equal intervals $\Delta\psi$, as in Fig. 3.7.
  It can be shown (see, for example, Verruijt, 1970) that the lines of constant ϕ and the lines of constant ψ intersect everywhere at right angles. Since the flow direction is always at right angles to the equipotential lines, the lines of constant ψ are *stream lines* denoting the direction of flow throughout the x, z plane, and ψ is called the *stream function*. Moreover, if the interval of potential $\Delta\phi$ is taken equal to the interval of stream function $\Delta\psi$ then, as shown in Fig. 3.7, the intersecting equipotential lines and stream lines form a system of curvilinear 'square' figures, referred to as a *flow net*. The flow region is divided by the equipotential lines into a number of *equipotential drops* and by the stream lines into a number of *flow channels* or *stream lanes*.
  The stream function has a particularly important relationship with the quantity of seepage flow. Consider points A, B and C in the upper flow channel in Fig. 3.7. Continuity requires that the seepage flow across AB, which denotes the quantity of seepage in the flow channel, ΔQ, must equal the combined flow across the horizontal and vertical sections BC and AC, which can be obtained by integrating the vertical and horizontal components of discharge velocity respectively. That is

$$\Delta Q = \Delta Q_{BC} + \Delta Q_{AC} = \int_C^B v_z \, dx + \int_C^A v_x \, dz$$

Substituting for v_x and v_z from Eq. (3.23) we obtain

$$\Delta Q = \int_C^B \frac{\partial \psi}{\partial x} \, dx - \int_C^A \frac{\partial \psi}{\partial z} \, dz = [\psi]_C^B - [\psi]_C^A$$

Therefore $\qquad \Delta Q = (\psi_2 - \psi_c) - (\psi_3 - \psi_c) = \psi_2 - \psi_3 = \Delta\psi \qquad (3.26)$

Thus, the quantity of seepage through any flow channel is equal to the difference in value of stream function across the flow channel.

Graphical Solution by Flow Net Construction

It has been established that equipotential lines and stream lines which are drawn at constant intervals such that the interval of potential $\Delta\phi$ equals the interval of stream function $\Delta\psi$ will intersect everywhere at right angles and form a system of curvilinear 'square' figures. The converse of this statement must also be true. That is, *if equipotential lines and stream lines are constructed throughout a flow domain such that they intersect everywhere at right angles and form a* *system of curvilinear 'square' figures, then the interval of potential $\Delta\phi$ and the interval of stream function $\Delta\psi$ must be constant and equal.* It is upon this characteristic that the graphical method of solving two-dimensional steady state flow problems is based. The method is best explained by means of an example.

Example 3.2 Figure 3.8a shows the cross-section through a long concrete dam founded in sand which is isotropic with $k_x = k_z = 10^{-4}$ m/s and has a saturated density of 2 Mg/m^3. Calculate:

(a) the steady state seepage loss beneath the dam,
(b) the upthrust on the base of the dam, and
(c) the maximum exit hydraulic gradient.

SOLUTION In problems of this type the boundaries of the flow region usually define certain known equipotential and stream lines. Taking the surface of the bedrock as datum, the total head at all points on AB is given by $h_1 = h_{el} + h_p = 14$ m $+ 10$ m $= 24$ m, and on CD by $h_2 = h_{el} + h_p = 14$ m $+ 1$ m $= 15$ m. Thus, the boundaries AB and CD are lines of constant total head and, since $\phi = kh$, AB and CD are therefore boundary equipotential lines. The flow is confined between the base of the impervious structure and the top of the impermeable bedrock. Thus, the top and bottom boundary stream lines are BEFGC and HK respectively.

In the graphical method of solution, a knowledge of these boundary equipotential and stream lines enables intermediate equipotential and stream lines to be constructed, which intersect each other at right angles and form a flow net of curvilinear 'square' figures. Having first drawn the boundaries of the flow region to a suitable scale, the flow net is constructed by a process of trial and error. The first step is to draw an initial trial stream line at some distance from the top stream line boundary. A series of trial equipotential lines is then drawn in from the boundary stream line through the trial stream line, forming right-angled intersections and, as far as possible, 'square' figures. These equipotential lines are extended far enough into the flow region to allow a second trial stream line to be drawn in, and the process is repeated in this manner until the bottom stream line boundary is reached. Usually the position of the last trial stream line will not be compatible with the known position of the bottom stream line boundary and therefore the position of the first trial stream line and all subsequent intermediate equipotential and stream lines will require to be adjusted (probably a number of times) before the correct form of flow net is established. Thus, from the first attempt the flow net is adjusted in successive stages until it satisfies the requirements of right-angled intersections and curvilinear 'square' figures, and is compatible with the imposed boundary conditions.

Using this sketching technique the final form of the flow net in Fig. 3.8b was obtained. Solution of the problem is then obtained as follows.

(a) *Seepage loss.* If Δh denotes the drop in total head between the upstream and downstream boundary equipotential lines, then the corresponding drop in potential is given by $k\,\Delta h$. For a flow net of 'square' figures the interval of potential $\Delta\phi$ is constant and will be equal to

$$\Delta\phi = \frac{k\,\Delta h}{N_d}$$

where N_d is *the number of equipotential drops* in the completed flow net. Moreover, the interval of potential $\Delta\phi$ is equal to the interval of stream function $\Delta\psi$, and from Eq. (3.26) the interval of stream function $\Delta\psi$ defines the quantity of seepage ΔQ in any one flow channel. Thus

$$\Delta Q = \Delta\psi = \Delta\phi = \frac{k\,\Delta h}{N_d}$$

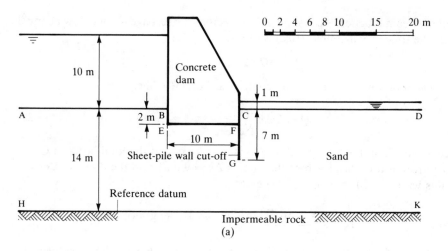

(a)

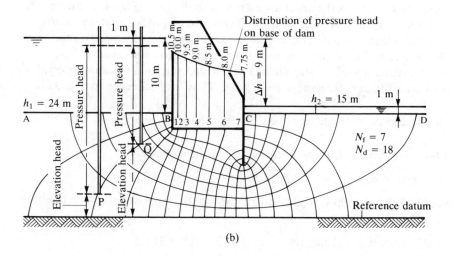

(b)

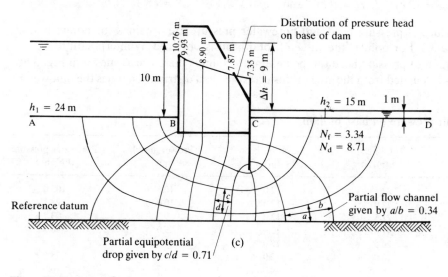

(c)

Figure 3.8 Example 3.2.

Since the interval of stream function is constant, it follows that the seepage in each flow channel is the same. Thus the total seepage flow Q is given by

$$Q = \Delta Q N_f$$

where N_f is *the number of flow channels* in the completed flow net. Therefore

$$Q = k \, \Delta h \frac{N_f}{N_d} \qquad (3.27)$$

With reference to Fig. 3.8b, the total head on AB is $h_1 = 24$ m and the total head on CD is $h_2 = 15$ m. Hence drop in total head across the dam is $\Delta h = 9$ m. From the flow net, $N_f = 7$ and $N_d = 18$. Thus with $k = 10^{-4}$ m/s, Eq. (3.27) gives

$$Q = 10^{-4} \times 9 \times \frac{7}{18} = \underline{3.5 \times 10^{-4} \text{ m}^3/\text{s}} \text{ per metre length of dam}$$

(b) *Upthrust on base of dam.* In analysing the stability of concrete dams subject to underseepage, an important factor is the uplift force applied to the base of the structure by the groundwater. This upthrust is the force arising from the distribution of porewater pressure on the base of the dam, and is therefore a function of the distribution of pressure head on the base. This can readily be determined from the flow net as described in the following.

Each equipotential line is a line of constant total head. Moreover, for a constant interval of potential there must be a constant interval of total head. Thus with reference to Fig. 3.8b:

$$\text{drop in total head between adjacent equipotential lines} = \frac{\Delta h}{N_d} = \frac{9}{18} = 0.5 \text{ m}$$

whence the total head on each equipotential line can be defined. Also,

$$\text{pressure head } h_p = \text{total head } h - \text{elevation head } h_{el}$$

and so the pressure head at any point is readily calculated. For example, at point 4 on the base of the dam in Fig. 3.8b

$$h = 24 - 6 \times 0.5 = 21 \text{ m} \quad \text{(or } h = 15 + 12 \times 0.5 = 21 \text{ m)}$$

$$h_{el} = 12 \text{ m} \quad \therefore \; h_p = 9 \text{ m} \quad \text{and} \quad u = 1 \times 9.81 \times 9 = 88.3 \text{ kN/m}^2$$

In this way, values of pressure head and porewater pressure are obtained for points 1–7, as shown in Table 3.3. For point 7 the value of total head is obtained by interpolation.

The distribution of pressure head on the base of the dam is therefore as shown in Fig. 3.8b. The upthrust is calculated from the area of this pressure head distribution times the unit weight

Table 3.3 Uplift pressure on base of dam

Point	Total head (m)	Elevation head (m)	Pressure head (m)	Porewater pressure (kN/m²)
1	22.5	12.0	10.5	103.0
2	22.0	12.0	10.0	98.1
3	21.5	12.0	9.5	93.2
4	21.0	12.0	9.0	88.3
5	20.5	12.0	8.5	83.4
6	20.0	12.0	8.0	78.5
7	19.75	12.0	7.75	76.0

of water. (Alternatively, we could plot the distribution of porewater pressure on the base and calculate the upthrust directly from the area of the porepressure diagram.) We thus obtain:

$$\text{Upthrust} = 1 \times 9.81[\tfrac{1}{2}(10.5 + 10.0) \times 0.85 + \tfrac{1}{2}(10.0 + 9.5) \times 1.30 + \tfrac{1}{2}(9.5 + 9.0) \times 1.40$$
$$+ \tfrac{1}{2}(9.0 + 8.5) \times 1.80 + \tfrac{1}{2}(8.5 + 8.0) \times 2.25 + \tfrac{1}{2}(8.0 + 7.75) \times 2.40]$$
$$= \underline{859 \text{ kN}} \text{ per metre length of dam}$$

Plotting the distribution to scale in Fig. 3.8b shows that in this case the variation in pressure head is approximately linear across the base of the dam. Thus, a close approximation of the upthrust is obtained from

$$\text{Upthrust} = 1 \times 9.81 \times \tfrac{1}{2}(10.5 + 7.75) \times 10 = \underline{895 \text{ kN/m}}$$

By definition, the pressure head at any point is the height to which water would rise in a standpipe with its tip placed at the point in question. Consider then the height to which water would rise in standpipes placed on the same equipotential line, as at points P and Q in Fig. 3.8b. The total head on this equipotential line is given by $24 - 2 \times 0.5 = 23$ m, which must equal the sum of the elevation head and the pressure head at all points on the line. Therefore, the vertical distance from the bedrock datum to the water level in the standpipes must be the same, so that the water level in the two standpipes must be the same, in this case 1 m below the upstream water surface. *Thus, when standpipes are placed at different points on the same equipotential line, water rises to the same level in each.*

(c) *Maximum exit hydraulic gradient.* With reference to Fig. 3.8b, the maximum exit hydraulic gradient i_e occurs at point C, the exit point of the top stream line. If the value of i_e approaches the critical hydraulic gradient i_c given by Eq. (3.11), fine particles in the soil near the downstream surface may be washed out. The enlarged voids which result lead locally to even higher gradients, which in turn lead to more soil particles being washed out. If unchecked, this erosion may progress down the side of the sheet pile cut-off or under the base of the dam, creating large cavities or pipe-shaped holes in the foundation soil. Eventually a surge of water and soil bursts through, completely undermining the structure and causing catastrophic failure. This mechanism of failure is referred to as *piping*, and to safeguard against such events the value of the exit hydraulic gradient at C should not exceed 0.5.

The value of i_e at point C is given approximately by the hydraulic gradient across the last equipotential drop on the top stream line. For this, the drop in total head of 0.5 m is lost over a vertical length of 1.67 m (as scaled from the figure) so that we obtain

$$i_e = \frac{0.5}{1.67} = \underline{0.30}$$

This value may therefore be considered acceptable.

As a further precaution against piping, a graded filter may be constructed at the downstream surface to prevent the washing-out of fines (Terzaghi and Peck, 1967). Modern practice may involve the use of geotextile fabrics to achieve the same effect.

When drawing a flow net it is advisable in the first instance to aim for a relatively coarse net with not more than five flow channels rather than a very fine one, otherwise the trial and error method becomes tedious and much more difficult. In any case, once the net has been established correctly in coarse form it can easily be refined by subdivision. However, in a coarse net N_f and N_d will not necessarily have integer values. This is perfectly acceptable as the form of Eq. (3.27) indicates; the seepage flow is determined not by the absolute values of N_f and N_d but by the ratio N_f/N_d. Thus, there is no unique flow net for any problem; on the contrary, there are an infinite number of correct flow nets all of which have the same N_f/N_d ratio. By way of illustration of this, a coarser net for the problem is shown in Fig. 3.8c. The solution based on this net is compared with that previously obtained in Table 3.4.

Table 3.4 Comparison of solutions for Example 3.2 based on fine and coarse flow nets

Flow net	N_f	N_d	N_f/N_d	Q (m³/s per m)	Upthrust (kN/m)	i_e
Fig. 3.8b	7	18	0.389	3.50×10^{-4}	859	0.30
Fig. 3.8c	3.34	8.71	0.383	3.45×10^{-4}	844	0.30

Provision of the sheet-pile wall cut-off has the effect of reducing the seepage loss beneath the dam and the value of the exit hydraulic gradient. This can be verified by reworking Example 3.2 with the cut-off omitted.

Example 3.3 Figure 3.9 shows a sheet-pile wall cofferdam 6 m wide and 60 m long driven to a depth of 5 m in a 9-m thick deposit of sand overlying impermeable bedrock. The water level outside the pile is 3 m above the sand, and 1 m of sand is excavated from within the cofferdam. The properties of the sand are $\rho_s = 2\ \text{Mg/m}^3$ and $k_x = k_z = 7 \times 10^{-5}$ m/s. Calculate:

(a) the steady state seepage flow into the excavation,
(b) the exit hydraulic gradient, and
(c) the factor of safety against base heave.

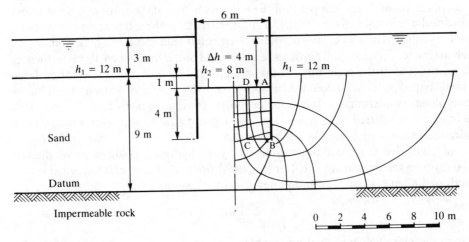

Figure 3.9 Example 3.3

SOLUTION The seepage flow will be symmetrical about the centre-line of the cofferdam and therefore we need draw the flow net for only half of the flow domain, taking the centre-line of the cofferdam and the surface of the bedrock as the bottom boundary stream line. This is shown in Fig. 3.9 and has $N_f = 3.2$ and $N_d = 10$.

Taking the surface of the bedrock as datum, the total head along the surface of the sand outside the cofferdam (the upstream boundary equipotential line) is $h_1 = 9 + 3 = 12$ m, and the total head along the base of the excavation (the downstream boundary equipotential line) is $h_2 = 8 + 0 = 8$ m. Therefore, the drop in total head across the dam is $\Delta h = 4$ m.

(a) Thus with $k = 7 \times 10^{-5}$ m/s, Eq. (3.27) gives the seepage flow into one-half of the cofferdam as

$$Q = k\,\Delta h\,\frac{N_f}{N_d} = 7 \times 10^{-5} \times 4 \times \frac{3.2}{10} = 8.96 \times 10^{-5}\ \text{m}^3/\text{s per metre}$$

Now, for flow from both sides over the length of 60 m

total seepage flow into excavation $= 60 \times 2 \times 8.96 \times 10^{-5} = \underline{1.08 \times 10^2 \text{ m}^3/\text{s}}$

(b) Drop in total head between adjacent equipotential lines $= \dfrac{\Delta h}{N_d} = \dfrac{4}{10} = 0.4 \text{ m}.$

Therefore maximum exit hydraulic gradient (point A) $= \dfrac{0.4}{0.9} = \underline{0.44}$

which can be considered acceptable.

(c) In addition to the mechanism of piping, failure due to underseepage in dams and cofferdams may also occur as a heave of a block of soil due to upward seepage flow in the vicinity of the toe of the dam or in the base of the excavation within a cofferdam, as shown by the block ABCD in Fig. 3.9. A failure of this kind occurs if the upthrust on the base of the block becomes equal to its total weight, so that the effective stress is reduced to zero. This is the quick condition in which the sand appears to 'boil' (see Sec. 3.3), and the surface of the sand heaves. In this condition, the soil supporting the sheet piles loses its strength and collapse of the cofferdam results.

To ensure against failure by this mechanism we require to have an adequate *factor of safety against heave* of the soil block ABCD. From Sec. 3.3, the critical hydraulic gradient at which the effective stress is reduced to zero is given by Eq. (3.11) and the factor of safety against heave is defined as in Eq. (3.13) by

$$F = \frac{i_c}{i} \qquad (3.28)$$

where i = actual hydraulic gradient acting across the block.

Model tests suggest that the width of the soil block over which heave is likely to occur is approximately half the depth of penetration. Thus, in this case AB = 4 m and BC = 2 m. We then obtain from the flow net

Total head at B $= 12 - 5 \times 0.4 = 10 \text{ m}$
Total head at C $= 12 - 6 \times 0.4 = 9.6 \text{ m}$
∴ Mean total head on BC $= 9.8 \text{ m}$
Also Total head on AD $= 8 \text{ m}$

Therefore the hydraulic gradient acting across the soil block ABCD is

$$i = \frac{9.8 - 8}{4} = 0.45$$

The critical hydraulic gradient is given by

$$i_c = \frac{\rho'}{\rho_w} = \frac{2 - 1}{1} = 1$$

Thus from Eq. (3.28) $\qquad F = \dfrac{i_c}{i} = \dfrac{1}{0.45} = \underline{2.22}$

This value can be considered acceptable.

Anisotropic Soils

We demonstrated earlier that the effect of anisotropy is taken into account by transforming the horizontal coordinates according to Eq. (3.17):

$$x_t = \sqrt{\frac{k_z}{k_x}}\, x$$

which reduces the governing flow equation to a two-dimensional Laplacian form in x_t and z [Eq. (3.18)]. The flow net is then drawn on the transformed section exactly as described for the isotropic case with equipotential and stream lines intersecting at right angles and forming 'square' figures. The seepage flow is given as previously by Eq. (3.27), but interpreted in the form

$$Q = k_e \, \Delta h \, \frac{N_f}{N_d} \tag{3.29}$$

where k_e denotes the *equivalent isotropic permeability* of the transformed section.

To obtain an expression for k_e, consider a particular 'square' figure under the base of the structure where the flow is essentially horizontal, as in Fig. 3.10. If the drop in total head across the 'square' figure is δh, then for the transformed section,

$$\Delta Q_t = k_e i A = k_e \frac{\delta h}{b} (b \times 1) = k_e \, \delta h$$

and for the natural section,

$$\Delta Q_n = k_x i A = k_x \frac{\delta h}{b\sqrt{k_x/k_z}} (b \times 1) = \sqrt{k_x k_z} \, \delta h$$

For continuity $\Delta Q_t = \Delta Q_n$ and hence it follows that $k_e = \sqrt{k_x k_z}$. Substituting into Eq. (3.29) then gives

$$Q = \sqrt{k_x k_z} \, \Delta h \, \frac{N_f}{N_d} \tag{3.30}$$

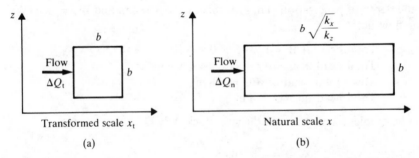

Transformed scale x_t

(a)

Natural scale x

(b)

Figure 3.10 Element of flow net for anisotropic soil: (a) on transformed section, (b) on natural section.

Example 3.4 Figure 3.11a shows a concrete dam founded on fine sand overlying impermeable bedrock. The dam is provided with an impervious apron 42 m in length constructed on the surface of the sand upstream of the dam. The sand is anisotropic with coefficients of permeability of 5.4×10^{-5} m/s and 6×10^{-6} m/s in the horizontal and vertical directions respectively. Calculate:

(a) the steady state seepage loss beneath the dam,
(b) the upthrust on the base of the dam, and
(c) the maximum exit hydraulic gradient.

SOLUTION We must transform the horizontal coordinates according to

$$x_t = \sqrt{\frac{k_z}{k_x}} \, x$$

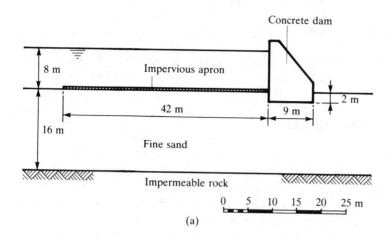

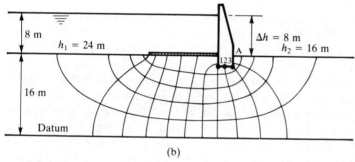

Figure 3.11 Example 3.4.

which for $k_z = 6 \times 10^{-6}$ m/s and $k_x = 5.4 \times 10^{-5}$ m/s gives $x_t = \frac{1}{3}x$. The transformed section is therefore drawn as in Fig. 3.11b with all vertical dimensions remaining the same but all horizontal dimensions reduced to one-third of those in the natural section.

The flow net drawn on the transformed section gives $N_f = 5$ and $N_d = 11$.

With the surface of the bedrock as datum:

$$\text{Total head on upstream boundary } h_1 = 16 + 8 = 24 \text{ m}$$
$$\text{Total head on downstream boundary } h_2 = 16 + 0 = 16 \text{ m}$$
$$\therefore \qquad \text{Drop in total head across the dam } \Delta h = 8 \text{ m}$$

(a) From Eq. (3.30) the seepage loss beneath the dam is then given by

$$Q = \sqrt{(5.4 \times 10^{-5} \times 6 \times 10^{-6})} \times 8 \times \tfrac{5}{11} = \underline{6.55 \times 10^{-5} \text{ m}^3/\text{s}} \text{ per metre}$$

(b) Drop in total head between adjacent equipotential lines $= \dfrac{\Delta h}{N_d} = \tfrac{8}{11} = 0.727$ m

At point 1: $h = 24 - 7 \times 0.727 = 18.91$ m, $h_{el} = 14$ m, $h_p = 4.91$ m
At point 2: $h = 24 - 8 \times 0.727 = 18.18$ m, $h_{el} = 14$ m, $h_p = 4.18$ m
At point 3: $h = 24 - 9 \times 0.727 = 17.46$ m, $h_{el} = 14$ m, $h_p = 3.46$ m

Remembering to convert horizontal distances back to the natural scale, we obtain:

$$\text{Upthrust on base of dam} = 1 \times 9.81[\tfrac{1}{2}(4.91 + 4.18) \times 4.5 + \tfrac{1}{2}(4.18 + 3.46) \times 4.5]$$

$$= \underline{369 \text{ kN/m}}$$

(c) At point A, maximum exit hydraulic gradient $i_e = \dfrac{0.727}{1.5} = \underline{0.48}$

Provision of the impervious apron on the upstream surface has the effect of reducing the seepage loss, the upthrust on the base of the dam and the exit hydraulic gradient.

3.5 FLOW THROUGH EARTH DAMS

In problems of seepage under concrete dams or sheet-pile walls, the boundary stream line positions are defined by the geometry. Such problems are in the category of *confined flow*. However, in problems of seepage through earth dams or in the slopes of cuttings, the position of the upper boundary of flow is not defined. This upper boundary of flow is at atmospheric pressure and is referred to as the *free water surface, phreatic surface* or simply as the *top stream line*. Problems in which the upper boundary of flow is a free water surface are in the category of *unconfined flow*.

Before a flow net can be drawn for an unconfined flow problem, it is necessary to determine the position of the top stream line. For flow through earth dams (Fig. 3.12), approximate mathematical solutions suggest that over much of its length the top stream line has the shape of a parabola. For the case of a horizontal underdrain (Fig. 3.12a), Casagrande (1937) proposed the following graphical method for constructing the top stream line.† Knowing the depth of water H on the upstream side and the actual entry point B, an assumed initial point A for the parabola is established such that AB = 0.3 EB. The basic parabola is then drawn which has its focus at point F and passes through the initial point A. This is done by first plotting the position of the directrix (from the fact that AF = AD), and then locating a number of points, including C, which are equidistant from the focus and the directrix. A short length of reversed curvature is then sketched in at the upstream end to satisfy the actual entry condition that the top stream line must start from B at right angles to the upstream face which is a boundary equipotential line.

Figure 3.12b shows a dam constructed without an underdrain. In this case the top stream line exits on the downstream face and the basic parabola is drawn with its focus F at the intersection of the downstream face with the impermeable base (or with the tailwater level if present). However, the top stream line deviates from the basic parabola at the discharge end where it must satisfy the exit condition of tangency to the downstream face. The method of determining the actual exit point G depends upon the slope angle α. For steep slope angles ($\alpha > 30°$) we use the relationship proposed by Casagrande (1937) and shown in Fig. 3.13 to obtain the correction Δa as a proportion of $(a + \Delta a)$ which is measured from the figure. For shallow slopes ($\alpha < 30°$) the distance a can be calculated directly from the problem geometry using the relationship‡

$$a = \frac{d}{\cos \alpha} - \sqrt{\frac{d^2}{\cos^2 \alpha} - \frac{H^2}{\sin^2 \alpha}} \qquad (3.31)$$

The discharge end of the top stream line is then sketched in by hand to be tangent to the downstream face at G.

Figure 3.12c shows an earth dam constructed with a rock fill toe drain. In this case the basic parabola is drawn with its focus F at the intersection of the discharge face with the impermeable

---

† The method is presented for an isotropic embankment where the sections are drawn to a natural scale. For an anisotropic soil, the horizontal coordinates would be transformed according to Eq. (3.17), and the top stream line (and subsequently the flow net) constructed on the transformed section.

‡ This derives from the assumption that for $\alpha < 30°$ the flow is approximately horizontal through much of the dam, and thus on any vertical section the hydraulic gradient can be taken as constant and equal to the slope of the free water surface at that section.

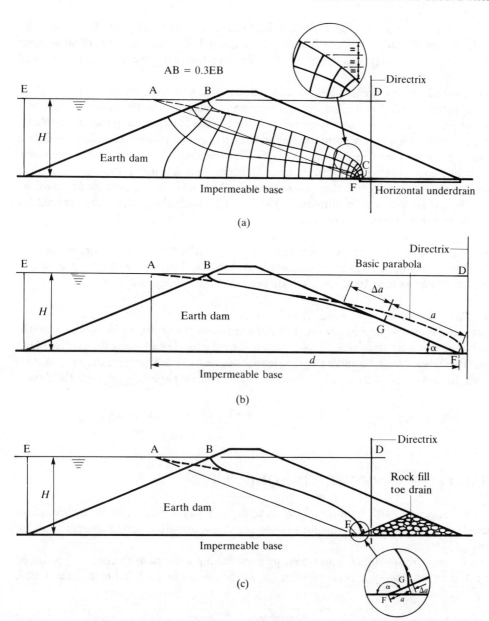

Figure 3.12 Flow through homogeneous earth dams. Construction of top stream line for (a) horizontal underdrain, (b) no drain, (c) toe drain.

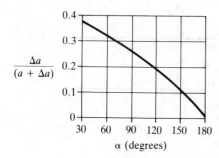

Figure 3.13 Chart for determining exit point of top stream line. (After Casagrande, 1937. Reprinted with permission of the New England Water Works Association.)

base, and the actual exit point G is located using Eq. (3.31) if $\alpha < 30°$ or Fig. 3.13 if $\alpha > 30°$. The top stream line is then sketched in to satisfy the exit condition of tangency to the vertical at point G. For this particular geometry it is apparent that the deviation from the basic parabola is of minor importance.

Having established the top stream line, the flow net can then be drawn. In addition though to the normal requirements of right-angled intersections and square figures, the flow net must also satisfy a further condition. Since the pressure head on the top stream line is zero (i.e., atmospheric pressure), then the total head at any point on the top stream line is equal to its elevation head. In a flow net of square figures, the drop in total head between adjacent equipotential lines is the same, and hence the difference in elevation head between adjacent intersections on the top stream line must be the same. Thus *the intersection of equipotential lines with the top stream line must be equidistant in the vertical direction*, as illustrated in Fig. 3.12a which shows the completed net for an earth dam with a horizontal underdrain.

Example 3.5 If the earth dam embankment shown in Fig. 3.12a is constructed of an isotropic clay fill having a coefficient of permeability of 10^{-9} m/s and retains water to a depth of $H = 27$ m, calculate the long-term steady state seepage flow through the dam.

SOLUTION From the flow net we have $N_f = 3$ and $N_d = 16$.

Taking the impermeable base as datum, the total head along the upstream face of the dam (the upstream boundary equipotential line) is $h_1 = 27$ m, and the total head along the surface of the underdrain (the downstream boundary equipotential line) is $h_2 = 0$. Therefore the drop in total head across the dam is $\Delta h = 27$ m. Thus from Eq. (3.27), the seepage flow through the dam is

$$Q = k \, \Delta h \frac{N_f}{N_d} = 10^{-9} \times 27 \times \frac{3}{16} = \underline{5 \times 10^{-9} \text{ m}^3/\text{s}} \text{ per metre length}$$

3.6 RADIAL FLOW IN CONFINED AQUIFERS

This section is concerned with confined flow to wells, and has applications in the design of pressure relief wells around excavations and in the provision of pumping or recharge wells for water supply or filtration purposes.

Consider a layer of free-draining, water-bearing sand having a constant thickness D bounded above and below by essentially impermeable strata, as shown in Fig. 3.14. If a cylindrical well is

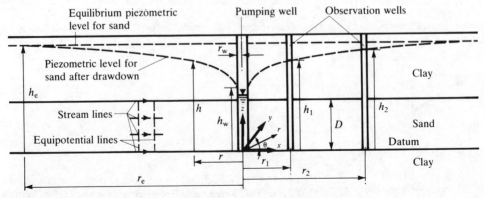

Figure 3.14 Flow in a confined aquifer from a circular source: single well.

installed such that it penetrates fully through the sand, water will initially fill the well to a height governed by the equilibrium piezometric level for the sand. On pumping from the well the water level in the well drops, the total head in the sand immediately adjacent to the well is reduced, and hence water flows through the sand from areas of higher total head to the area around the well and subsequently into the well itself. When the flow rate into the well becomes constant and equal to the rate of pumping from the well, steady state conditions prevail and there is a drawdown in piezometric level for the sand of the form shown in Fig. 3.14. Provided that the piezometric level does not drop below the top of the sand, the flow at any point in the sand occurs solely in the horizontal plane, the upper and lower boundaries of flow being defined by the top and bottom surfaces of the sand. These are the conditions of confined flow and the sand is referred to as a *confined aquifer*.

Flow from a Circular Source

Although many sedimentary deposits have a much higher permeability in the horizontal direction than the vertical, the variation in permeability within the horizontal plane is usually much less pronounced. If we can assume that the sand is isotropic in the horizontal plane, then the flow is radially symmetrical towards the well and the drawdown in piezometric level is the same at all points which are an equal distance from the well. However, as the distance from the well increases the amount of drawdown decreases, until at some radial distance r_e the well has no significant influence on the piezometric level for the sand. This distance r_e is the *radius of influence* of the well. Flow can therefore be considered as occurring from a *circular source* located at the radius of influence of the well.

As the flow at any point in the sand occurs only in the horizontal x, y plane for which we assume $k_x = k_y$, the governing steady state flow equation (3.9) reduces to the two-dimensional Laplace equation

$$\frac{\partial^2 h}{\partial x^2} + \frac{\partial^2 h}{\partial y^2} = 0 \tag{3.32}$$

For radial flow it is more convenient to operate with polar coordinates r and θ which are related to x and y in Fig. 3.14 by

$$r = \sqrt{x^2 + y^2} \qquad \theta = \tan^{-1}\left(\frac{y}{x}\right) \tag{3.33}$$

Transformed to polar coordinates, Eq. (3.32) becomes

$$\frac{\partial^2 h}{\partial r^2} + \frac{1}{r}\frac{\partial h}{\partial r} + \frac{1}{r^2}\frac{\partial^2 h}{\partial \theta^2} = 0 \tag{3.34}$$

For symmetrical flow about the z axis, h is the same at all points which are an equal distance from the well. Thus for any value of r, $\partial h/\partial \theta = 0$ and Eq. (3.34) reduces to the ordinary differential equation

$$\frac{d^2 h}{dr^2} + \frac{1}{r}\frac{dh}{dr} = 0 \Rightarrow \frac{1}{r}\frac{d}{dr}\left(r\frac{dh}{dr}\right) = 0 \tag{3.35}$$

We see that h is now a function of only one variable r, and the problem is reduced mathematically to a one-dimensional case. Solution of Eq. (3.35) to obtain values of total head throughout the flow domain and the flow into the well can now be effected directly.

Single well Taking the base of the sand as datum in Fig. 3.14, the total head h at any radius r is given by the height from the base to the piezometric level. Denoting the radius of the well as r_w, the total head in the sand at the well as h_w and the total head at the radius of influence as h_e, the boundary conditions are

$$h = h_w \text{ at } r = r_w \quad \text{and} \quad h = h_e \text{ at } r = r_e$$

Integrating Eq. (3.35) once gives

$$r \frac{dh}{dr} = c_1 \tag{3.36}$$

and a second time gives

$$h = c_1 \ln r + c_2 \tag{3.37}$$

where c_1 and c_2 are constants of integration. Substituting the boundary conditions into Eq. (3.37) and solving simultaneously we obtain

$$c_1 = \frac{h_e - h_w}{\ln r_e/r_w} \qquad c_2 = h_e - \frac{h_e - h_w}{\ln r_e/r_w} \ln r_e \tag{3.38}$$

Back substitution in Eq. (3.37) then gives

$$h = h_e - \frac{h_e - h_w}{\ln r_e/r_w} \ln \frac{r_e}{r} \tag{3.39}$$

Now continuity requires that the steady state flow into the well, Q, must equal the flow across a cylindrical section through the sand at radius r. Hence

$$Q = kiA = k \frac{dh}{dr} 2\pi r D = 2\pi k D r \frac{dh}{dr}$$

The term $r \, dh/dr = c_1$ (Eq. 3.36) and with c_1 defined by Eq. (3.38) we then obtain

$$Q = \frac{2\pi k D(h_e - h_w)}{\ln r_e/r_w} \tag{3.40}$$

Rearranging Eq. (3.40) and substituting into Eq. (3.39) gives an expression for the total head h at any radius r in terms of Q as

$$h = h_e - \frac{Q}{2\pi k D} \ln \frac{r_e}{r} \tag{3.41}$$

Equations (3.40) and (3.41) involve the radius of influence r_e. However, because of the inherent problems involved in locating the distance at which the well ceases to have an influence, an accurate determination of r_e is difficult. Moreover, the radius of influence of the well is not a constant; not only does an increase in drawdown produce an increase in r_e but the greater the permeability of the sand then the greater is the radius of influence of the well. Fortunately r_e occurs within a natural logarithm term and hence the solution is not particularly sensitive to small inaccuracies. This is illustrated in Table 3.5 which shows the effect on the value of Q of varying the r_e value typically within the range to be expected for a sand.

We see that doubling the r_e value changes the calculated Q by less than about 10 per cent. Thus small inaccuracies in r_e will be of no significance and we need to determine the radius of influence only approximately.

Because of the uncertainty associated with the value of r_e and the fact that the water level in the well will be less than h_w by an amount equal to the hydraulic head loss in the well, piezometric levels in the sand are sometimes recorded directly by installing observation wells at suitable distances from the pumping well. In Fig. 3.14, for example, observation wells at distances r_1 and r_2

Table 3.5

r_e (m)	125	250	500	1000	125	250	500	1000
r_w (m)	0.1	0.1	0.1	0.1	0.3	0.3	0.3	0.3
$\dfrac{1}{\ln r_e/r_w}$	0.1402	0.1278	0.1174	0.1086	0.1658	0.1487	0.1348	0.1238
$\dfrac{\Delta Q}{Q}$ (%)		8.8	8.1	7.5		10.3	9.3	8.5	

record piezometric levels corresponding to h_1 and h_2 respectively. Substituting these values into Eq. (3.37) and solving as before, we obtain alternative expressions for the flow Q into the well and the total head h at any radius r as

$$Q = \frac{2\pi kD(h_2 - h_1)}{\ln r_2/r_1} \tag{3.42}$$

and

$$h = h_1 - \frac{Q}{2\pi kD} \ln \frac{r_1}{r} \tag{3.43}$$

The use of observation wells in this manner forms the basis of the field pumping test carried out to determine the *in situ* permeability of the sand (see Example 3.6).

Multiple well systems Excavations in clay overlying aquifers of sand or gravel are prone to failure by base heave, as illustrated in Example 3.1, and to ensure stability it is often necessary to reduce the piezometric level in the aquifer. This can be done by pumping water out of the aquifer through a system of fully penetrating pressure relief wells installed around the perimeter of the proposed excavation in the manner shown in Fig. 3.15. Stability calculations define the minimum drawdown in piezometric level required in the area of the excavation, and to check that the proposed well system will achieve this drawdown we require an expression for the total head at any point such as P in the sand as a result of pumping from a number of wells simultaneously. Now for flow to a single well at position 1, Eq. (3.41) gives the total head at P as

$$h_{P1} = h_e - \frac{Q_1}{2\pi kD} \ln \frac{r_{e1}}{r_1}$$

and the drawdown at P as

$$h_e - h_{P1} = \frac{Q_1}{2\pi kD} \ln \frac{r_{e1}}{r_1}$$

where h_{P1} = total head at P due to pumping from well 1 only
Q_1 = steady state flow into well 1
r_1 = distance from P to the centre-line of well 1
and r_{e1} = radius of influence of well 1.

As Eq. (3.41) is the solution of a linear differential equation (a Laplace equation) we can apply the *principle of superposition* to calculate the total drawdown at P due to a number of wells acting together from the algebraic sum of the separate effects of each individual well. Thus if there are n wells, the total drawdown at P is given by

$$h_e - h_P = \frac{1}{2\pi kD}\left[Q_1 \ln \frac{r_{e1}}{r_1} + Q_2 \ln \frac{r_{e2}}{r_2} + Q_3 \ln \frac{r_{e3}}{r_3} + \cdots Q_n \ln \frac{r_{en}}{r_n} \right]$$

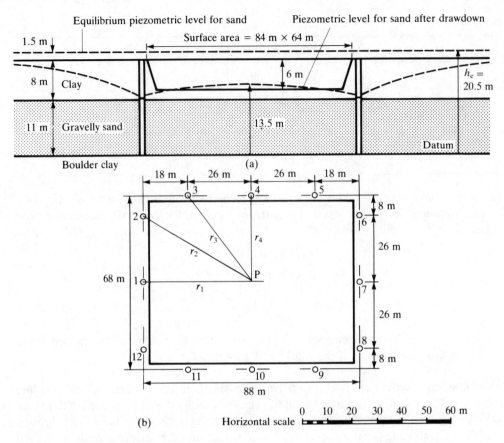

Figure 3.15 Flow in a confined aquifer from a circular source: multiple well system. (Example 3.6.)

where the subscripts $2, 3, \ldots, n$ relate to wells $2, 3, \ldots, n$ respectively. Hence

$$h_e - h_P = \frac{1}{2\pi kD} \sum_{j=1}^{n} Q_j \ln \frac{r_{ej}}{r_j} \qquad (3.44)$$

In practice, it is usually arranged for the drawdown characteristics associated with each well to be similar and hence we can take the radius of influence of each well to be the same and equal to r_e. In any case, small inaccuracies in the value of r_e are not significant. To achieve a similar drawdown at each well, we position the wells such that each intercepts approximately the same quantity of seepage and pump approximately the same quantity of water from each well. Where flow is from a circular source, correct positioning of the wells simply requires that they are spaced equally around the excavation. When pumping from deep wells it is customary to use submersible pumps located below the water level in the wells. If the same specification of pump is used throughout the system and each pump operates at the same speed under approximately the same conditions of head, then the discharge from each pump will be approximately the same. For these conditions we can assume that the flow rate Q for each well will be the same and equal to the *operating capacity of the pumps*. Thus, taking Q and r_e to be constant for each well, Eq. (3.44) becomes

$$h_e - h_P = \frac{Q}{2\pi kD} \sum_{j=1}^{n} \ln \frac{r_e}{r_j}$$

whence we obtain the total head at point P as

$$h_P = h_e - \frac{Q}{2\pi kD} \sum_{j=1}^{n} \ln \frac{r_e}{r_j} \qquad (3.45)$$

where Q is the operating capacity of the pumps and r_j is the distance from P to the centre-line of well j where $j = 1, 2, 3, \ldots, n$.

Example 3.6 An excavation is to be made to a depth of 6 m in an 8-m thick deposit of clay overlying 11 m of gravelly sand, as shown in Fig. 3.15a. At ground level the excavation will have an area of 84 m × 64 m. A site investigation revealed that the equilibrium piezometric level for the sand is 1.5 m above ground level and stability calculations indicate that this must be reduced by 7 m in the area of the excavation in order to provide an adequate factor of safety against failure by base heave.

A pumping test carried out on a 0.5-m diameter well penetrating through the sand at the centre of the proposed excavation recorded reductions in the piezometric level of 1.20 m and 0.43 m in observation wells at 12 m and 150 m from the pumping well respectively when the steady state discharge from the well was 11.4×10^{-2} m³/s.

Determine a suitable arrangement of 0.5-m diameter fully penetrating pressure relief wells to achieve the required reduction in piezometric level. Assume that submersible pumps will be used at an operating capacity of 6.5×10^{-2} m³/s and that the radius of influence of the well system is 1400 m.

SOLUTION With the base of the sand as datum, $h_e = 20.5$ m. Thus, for $Q = 11.4 \times 10^{-2}$ m³/s, the results of the pumping test are:

At $r_1 = 12$ m,   drawdown $= 1.20$ m, $\therefore$ $h_1 = 20.5 - 1.20 = 19.30$ m
At $r_2 = 150$ m,   drawdown $= 0.43$ m, $\therefore$ $h_2 = 20.5 - 0.43 = 20.07$ m

Rearranging Eq. (3.42)

$$k = \frac{Q \ln r_2/r_1}{2\pi D(h_2 - h_1)} = \frac{11.4 \times 10^{-2} \times \ln 150/12}{2 \times \pi \times 11 \times (20.07 - 19.30)} = 0.541 \times 10^{-2} \text{ m/s}$$

If the wells are installed 2 m back from the top of the slope, the system will enclose a rectangular area 88 m × 68 m. To estimate the number of wells required, we can represent this rectangular area as an equivalent circular well of radius R_w given by

$$R_w = \sqrt{\frac{88 \times 68}{\pi}} = 43.6 \text{ m}$$

For a drawdown of 7 m, the flow to this equivalent well is given by Eq. (3.40) as

$$Q = \frac{2\pi kD(h_e - h_w)}{\ln r_e/R_w} = \frac{2 \times \pi \times 0.541 \times 10^{-2} \times 11 \times 7}{\ln 1400/43.6} = 75.4 \times 10^{-2} \text{ m}^3/\text{s}$$

This is an estimate of the quantity of water that must be removed from the sand and, given a pump capacity of 6.5×10^{-2} m³/s, this suggests that we need about 12 pumps. Flow is from a circular source so we space the 12 wells equally around the perimeter of the excavation area, as shown in Fig. 3.15b. We now check that this proposal is adequate by calculating the drawdown at the centre of the proposed excavation and the total head in the sand at the wells using Eq. (3.45):

$$h_P = h_e - \frac{Q}{2\pi kD} \sum_{j=1}^{12} \ln \frac{r_e}{r_j}$$

Table 3.6

Well number	Centre of excavation		Well 3	
	r_j (m)	$\ln \dfrac{r_e}{r_j}$	r_j (m)	$\ln \dfrac{r_e}{r_j}$
1	44	3.46	38.5	3.59
2	51.1	3.31	19.7	4.26
3	42.8	3.49	0.25	8.63
4	34	3.72	26	3.99
5	42.8	3.49	52	3.29
6	51.1	3.31	70.5	2.99
7	44	3.46	77.8	2.89
8	51.1	3.31	92.2	2.72
9	42.8	3.49	85.6	2.79
10	34	3.72	72.8	2.96
11	42.8	3.49	68	3.02
12	51.1	3.31	62.6	3.11
		$\sum = 41.56$		$\sum = 44.24$

where Q is the operating capacity of the pumps, given as 6.5×10^{-2} m³/s, and r_j is the distance from P to the centre-line of well j, obtained from Fig. 3.15b. Check calculations for the centre of the excavation and well 3 are presented in Table 3.6.

Therefore at the centre of the proposed excavation

$$h_P = 20.5 - \frac{6.5 \times 10^{-2} \times 41.56}{2 \times \pi \times 0.541 \times 10^{-2} \times 11} = \underline{13.28 \text{ m}}$$

Thus the drawdown = 7.22 m. This compares favourably with the required value of 7 m.
At well 3

$$h_P = 20.5 - \frac{6.5 \times 10^{-2} \times 44.24}{2 \times \pi \times 0.541 \times 10^{-2} \times 11} = \underline{12.81 \text{ m}}$$

From symmetry of the well arrangement, this is also the total head in the sand at wells 5, 9 and 11. Similarly it can be shown that the total head at the remaining wells ranges from 12.72 m to 12.94 m. We see then that for correctly positioned wells the total head at each is approximately the same.

The total head in this case of approximately 12.8 m is satisfatory and provides an adequate depth for operation of the submersible pumps.

Flow from a Line Source

Where wells are situated near a river, a lake or the sea, the bed of which is in contact with the aquifer, this body of water will constitute the primary source of seepage towards the wells and as a result the flow pattern to the wells will not be symmetrical. In such cases the river or shoreline can be considered as an *infinite line source* of seepage.

Single well In Fig. 3.16a a well of radius r_w located at distance p from a river penetrates fully through a sand aquifer of thickness D. Initially the piezometric level for the sand is governed by the water level in the river. On pumping to achieve steady state conditions, the piezometric level

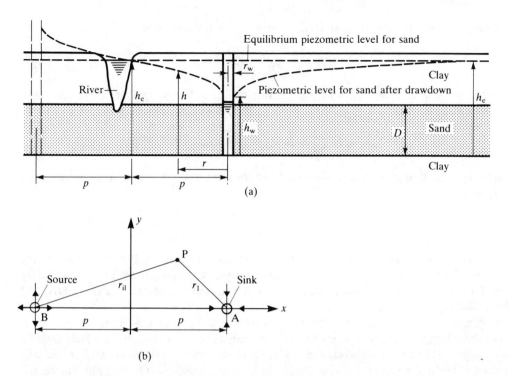

Figure 3.16 Flow in a confined aquifer from a line source: single well.

for the sand is reduced in the manner shown.† Because of the influence of the line source the flow pattern is not radially symmetrical towards the well, nor will the drawdown be the same at all points which are an equal distance from the well. The two-dimensional Laplace equation (3.34) remains the governing equation for flow to the well, but the boundary conditions are more complicated than those associated with flow from a circular source. The solution in this case is most conveniently effected using a technique known as the *method of images*. To illustrate this, consider a confined flow domain represented in plan by the x, y plane in Fig. 3.16b. If a pumping well (or *sink*) is located at position A, distance p from the y axis, and water is pumped from the sink at rate Q, then for steady state conditions the total head at point P, distance r_1 from the sink, is given by Eq. (3.41) as

$$h_{PA} = h_e - \frac{Q}{2\pi kD} \ln \frac{r_{eA}}{r_1}$$

and the drawdown in piezometric level at P is then

$$h_e - h_{PA} = \frac{Q}{2\pi kD} \ln \frac{r_{eA}}{r_1} \qquad (3.46)$$

Alternatively, if a recharge well (or *source*) is located at position B, distance p from the y axis but on the opposite side from the sink, and water is pumped in through the source at rate Q (equal to the rate of pumping from the sink), then for steady state conditions the total head at P, distance r_{i1} from the source, is given by Eq. (3.41) as

$$h_{PB} = h_e - \frac{(-Q)}{2\pi kD} \ln \frac{r_{eB}}{r_{i1}}$$

† It is assumed that the rate of pumping is not sufficient to alter the water level in the river.

and the increase in piezometric level at P (a negative drawdown) is then

$$h_e - h_{PB} = -\frac{Q}{2\pi kD} \ln \frac{r_{eB}}{r_{i1}} \tag{3.47}$$

The effect of the sink and the source acting together can be obtained by applying the principle of superposition. Thus, adding Eqs (3.46) and (3.47) the resultant drawdown at P is given by

$$h_e - h_P = \frac{Q}{2\pi kD} \ln \frac{r_{eA}}{r_1} - \frac{Q}{2\pi kD} \ln \frac{r_{eB}}{r_{i1}}$$

For the same Q, the radius of influence of the sink and the source can be taken to be the same and equal to r_e whence

$$h_e - h_P = \frac{Q}{2\pi kD} \ln \frac{r_{i1}}{r_1} \tag{3.48}$$

If P is positioned on the y axis, then $r_1 = r_{i1}$ and the drawdown is zero. If P is positioned a very long way from the well then $r_1 \to r_{i1}$ and the drawdown tends to zero. These are the boundary conditions for confined flow to a single well at A from a line source located on the y axis, and hence Eq. (3.48) represents the solution to our problem.

The pumping well at A is located in the real half of the x, y plane ($x > 0$) and the source is simply its mirror image in the imaginary half of the plane ($x < 0$). Although Eq. (3.48) yields a solution throughout the x, y plane, as shown in Fig. 3.16a, we are only concerned with predictions of drawdown in the real half of the plane. Hence for flow to a single well from a line source, the total head at any point P is given by

$$h_P = h_e - \frac{Q}{2\pi kD} \ln \frac{r_{i1}}{r_1} \tag{3.49}$$

where r_1 is the distance from P to the centre-line of the well and r_{i1} is the distance from P to the centre-line of the mirror image of the well.

If P is located at the edge of the pumping well then $r_1 = r_w$, $r_{i1} \approx 2p$ and $h_P = h_w$. Substituting these values into Eq. (3.49) and rearranging, we obtain the steady state flow into the well as

$$Q = \frac{2\pi kD(h_e - h_w)}{\ln 2p/r_w} \tag{3.50}$$

Multiple well systems If the excavation in Fig. 3.15a, is to be made adjacent to a line source of seepage through the sand, then a plan of the well system is drawn in the real half-plane and a mirror image of the system drawn on the opposite side of the line source, as shown in Fig. 3.17. In a manner similar to that presented for the circular source problem, the solution for flow to the group of wells is obtained by applying the principle of superposition, whence we obtain the total head at any point P in the sand as

$$h_P = h_e - \frac{Q}{2\pi kD} \sum_{j=1}^{n} \ln \frac{r_{ij}}{r_j} \tag{3.51}$$

where Q = operating capacity of the submersible pumps

        r_j = distance from P to the centre-line of well j ($j = 1, 2, 3, \ldots, n$)

and r_{ij} = distance from P to the centre-line of the mirror image of well j

For flow from a line source the seepage pattern is not radially symmetrical, and correct positioning of the wells around the excavation such that each intercepts the same quantity of seepage is achieved by drawing a plan flow net (this is illustrated in Example 3.7 for the

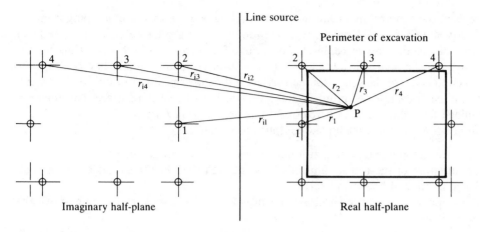

Figure 3.17 Flow in a confined aquifer from a line source: multiple well system.

unconfined flow case). The line source being the primary source of seepage, it follows that the wells must be closer together on the side of the excavation nearest to the line source.

3.7 RADIAL FLOW IN UNCONFINED AQUIFERS

Flow from a Circular Source

Consider a surface layer of free-draining, water-bearing soil, such as sand, overlying an essentially impermeable base as shown in Fig. 3.18a. If a cylindrical well of radius r_w penetrates fully to the base of the sand, water will initially flow into the well from the sand and quickly rise up the well to

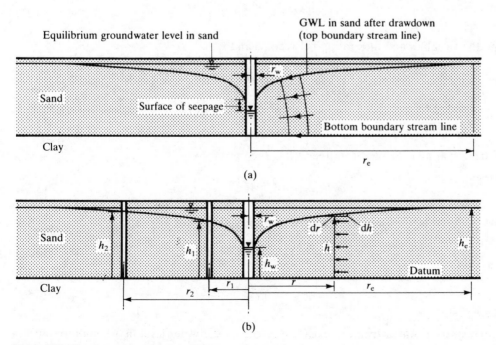

Figure 3.18 Flow in an unconfined aquifer from a circular source: single well.

a level governed by the equilibrium groundwater level in the sand. In this case pumping from the well under steady state conditions results in a drawdown in the groundwater level of the form shown, the limit of this drawdown being at the radius of influence r_e of the well. Thus flow is occurring from a *circular source* located at r_e. The bottom boundary stream line is along the interface between the base of the sand and the surface of the impermeable stratum, while the top boundary stream line is the lowered groundwater level which is a free water surface. This then is a case of unconfined flow and the sand is referred to as an *unconfined aquifer*.

The unconfined flow case has the added complications that:

1. The position of the top stream line is not defined by the problem geometry.
2. Because of curvature of the top stream line, flow through the sand is no longer horizontal, nor are the equipotential lines truly vertical.
3. A surface of seepage occurs in the well as a result of the top stream line emerging above the water level in the well.

An exact solution is available but is very complex in its derivation. However, for cases where the drawdown is not severe, an acceptable though approximate solution can be obtained very simply by assuming that:

1. There is no surface of seepage, so that the top stream line emerges at the water level in the well.
2. The hydraulic gradient at any distance r from the well is constant over the depth of flow and equal to the slope of the top stream line at distance r (the so-called Dupuit–Forchheimer assumption). Hence, the flow through the sand at distance r from the well is horizontal.

The simplified problem is illustrated in Fig. 3.18b.

Single well For continuity the flow into the well, Q, must equal the flow across any cylindrical section through the sand at radius r from the well. With the base of the sand as datum

$$Q = kiA = k\frac{dh}{dr} 2\pi rh \qquad (3.52)$$

Separating the variables and integrating between r_w and r_e

$$Q \int_{r=r_w}^{r=r_e} \frac{1}{r} dr = 2\pi k \int_{h=h_w}^{h=h_e} h \, dh$$

whence

$$Q = \frac{\pi k(h_e^2 - h_w^2)}{\ln r_e/r_w} \qquad (3.53)$$

The total head h at any radius r from the well is then given by

$$h^2 = h_e^2 - \frac{Q}{\pi k} \ln \frac{r_e}{r} \qquad (3.54)$$

Alternatively, in terms of h_1 and h_2 measured in observation wells at r_1 and r_2

$$Q = \frac{\pi k(h_2^2 - h_1^2)}{\ln r_2/r_1} \qquad (3.55)$$

and

$$h^2 = h_1^2 - \frac{Q}{\pi k} \ln \frac{r_1}{r} \qquad (3.56)$$

Multiple well systems Any attempt to excavate below groundwater level in a free-draining soil will result in water flowing into the excavation in uncontrollable quantities. Not only would this destroy working conditions in the excavation, but the associated seepage would threaten the stability of the side slopes. One solution to the problem is to lower the groundwater level to a position below the proposed base level of the excavation by pumping from a system of well-points or fully penetrating dewatering wells installed around the perimeter of the excavation, typically in the manner shown in Fig. 3.19a. The depth of the excavation relative to original groundwater level defines the minimum drawdown required.

To design a well system we require an expression for the total head at any point in the soil due to pumping from a number of wells simultaneously. In a manner similar to that described for the corresponding confined flow problem, it can be shown that for a system of n wells, the total head at point P in Fig. 3.19b is given by

$$h_P^2 = h_e^2 - \frac{Q}{\pi k} \sum_{j=1}^{n} \ln \frac{r_e}{r_j} \tag{3.57}$$

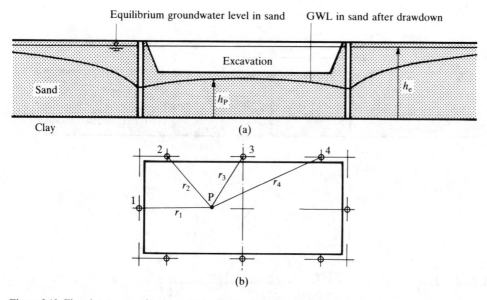

Figure 3.19 Flow in an unconfined aquifer from a circular source: multiple well system.

Flow from a Line Source

Single well This represents the case where the fully penetrating well in the unconfined aquifer is adjacent to a river or shoreline which constitutes the primary source of seepage towards the well and can be considered as an *infinite line source*. By introducing the Dupuit–Forchheimer assumption and employing the method of images in a manner similar to that described for the corresponding case of confined flow, it can be shown that under steady state conditions the flow Q into a single well at distance p from the line source is given by

$$Q = \frac{\pi k (h_e^2 - h_w^2)}{\ln 2p/r_w} \tag{3.58}$$

and the total head at any point P by

$$h_P^2 = h_e^2 - \frac{Q}{\pi k} \ln \frac{r_{i1}}{r_1} \tag{3.59}$$

Multiple well systems This is relevant in the case of dewatering wells around an excavation adjacent to a river or shoreline, as in Fig. 3.20a. Employing the principle of superposition, the total head at any point P due to pumping from a system of n wells is given by

$$h_P^2 = h_e^2 - \frac{Q}{\pi k} \sum_{j=1}^{n} \ln \frac{r_{ij}}{r_j} \qquad (3.60)$$

Example 3.7 An excavation with side slopes at 1 vertical on 3 horizontal is to be made to a depth of 12 m in a 30-m thick deposit of coarse sand overlying impervious clay. The base of the excavation measures 160 m × 40 m and its shorter axis is parallel to and at a distance of 300 m from a river, as shown in Fig. 3.20. The water level in the river and groundwater level in the sand are the same, being 1 m below the surface of the sand. If the sand has a coefficient of permeability of 1.17×10^{-3} m/s, determine a suitable arrangement of 0.5-m diameter, fully penetrating dewatering wells to lower the water table to a depth of about 1.5 m below the base level of the excavation. Assume that submersible pumps will be used, operating at a capacity of 7.6×10^{-2} m³/s.

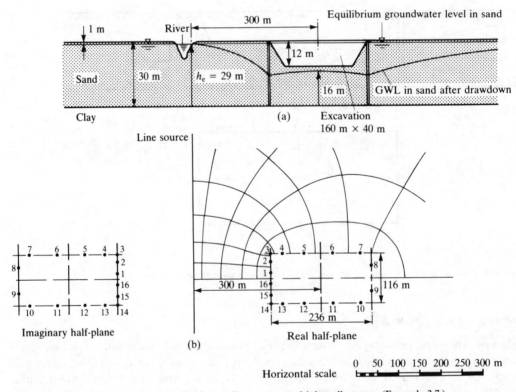

Figure 3.20 Flow in an unconfined aquifer from a line source: multiple well system. (Example 3.7.)

SOLUTION The surface area of the excavation is (160 + 2 × 36) m by (40 + 2 × 36) m, i.e., 232 m by 112 m, and if the wells are installed 2 m back from the top of the slope then the system of wells will enclose a rectangular area 236 m by 116 m. To obtain an estimate of the number of wells required, we represent this rectangular area as an equivalent circular well of radius R_w given by

$$R_w = \sqrt{\frac{236 \times 116}{\pi}} = 93.3 \text{ m}$$

With the base of the sand as datum, $h_e = 29$ m. For groundwater level at say 2 m below the base of the excavation, the total head at this equivalent well is then $h_w = 16$ m and an estimate of the total quantity of water that must be removed is the flow to the equivalent well, given by Eq. (3.58) as

$$Q = \frac{\pi k(h_e^2 - h_w^2)}{\ln 2p/R_w} = \frac{\pi \times 1.17 \times 10^{-3}(29^2 - 16^2)}{\ln (2 \times 300/93.3)} = 115.5 \times 10^{-2} \text{ m}^3/\text{s}$$

Given that the pump capacity is 7.6×10^{-2} m^3/s, this suggests that we will require about 16 pumps. Thus, we position 16 wells around the excavation such that each intercepts approximately the same quantity of seepage. Because of the influence of the river as the dominant source of seepage, the wells are not spaced equally around the excavation but are positioned with the aid of a plan flow net, as shown in Fig. 3.20b. As the flow pattern in this problem will be symmetrical about the long axis of the excavation, we need draw only half of the flow net. For a net consisting of curvilinear square figures, the quantity of seepage through each flow channel is the same and hence wells 1–8 are positioned in the centre of each of the 8 flow channels; wells 9–16 are then placed symmetrically opposite. We now check that this proposal is adequate by drawing the mirror image of the well arrangement on the opposite side of the line source, as in Fig. 3.20b, and calculating the drawdown in groundwater level at the centre of the proposed excavation and the total head in the sand at the wells using Eq. (3.60)

$$h_P^2 = h_e^2 - \frac{Q}{\pi k} \sum_{j=1}^{16} \ln \frac{r_{ij}}{r_j}$$

wherein the operating capacity Q of the pumps $= 7.6 \times 10^{-2}$ m^3/s and the values of r_j and r_{ij} are obtained from Fig. 3.20b. Table 3.7 shows check calculations for the centre of the excavation and well 3.

Table 3.7

Well number	Centre of excavation			Well 3		
	r_j (m)	r_{ij} (m)	$\ln \dfrac{r_{ij}}{r_j}$	r_j (m)	r_{ij} (m)	$\ln \dfrac{r_{ij}}{r_j}$
1	118	484	1.41	45	370	2.11
2	124	486	1.37	18	368	3.02
3	130	490	1.33	0.25	364	7.28
4	106	518	1.59	27	396	2.69
5	70	566	2.09	74	444	1.79
6	62	633	2.32	143	512	1.28
7	108	698	1.87	209	578	1.02
8	120	723	1.80	237	605	0.94
9	120	723	1.80	250	612	0.90
10	108	698	1.87	240	594	0.91
11	62	633	2.32	184	526	1.05
12	70	566	2.09	138	462	1.21
13	106	518	1.59	118	414	1.26
14	130	490	1.33	116	388	1.21
15	124	486	1.37	96	380	1.38
16	118	484	1.41	68	375	1.71
			$\sum = 27.56$			$\sum = 29.76$

Therefore at the centre of the proposed excavation

$$h_P^2 = 29^2 - \frac{7.6 \times 10^{-2} \times 27.56}{\pi \times 1.17 \times 10^{-3}} \Rightarrow h_P = \underline{16.47 \text{ m}}$$

This corresponds to a groundwater level 1.53 m below the base of the excavation and compares favourably with the required depth of about 1.5 m.

At well 3

$$h_P^2 = 29^2 - \frac{7.6 \times 10^{-2} \times 29.76}{\pi \times 1.17 \times 10^{-3}} \Rightarrow h_P = \underline{15.02 \text{ m}}$$

This is also the total head in the sand at well 14. Similarly it can be shown that the total head at the other wells ranges from 14.07 m to 14.74 m.

The total head in this case of approximately 14.5 m is satisfactory and provides an adequate depth for operation of the submersible pumps.

PROBLEMS

3.1 For the concrete dam described in Example 3.2, calculate the seepage loss, the upthrust on the base and the maximum exit gradient given that (a) the sheet-pile wall cut-off is omitted, (b) the sheet-pile wall cut-off is installed to a depth of 7 m at the upstream face of the dam.

$$\left[\begin{array}{l} \text{Ans.} \quad \text{(a)} \quad 4.5 \times 10^{-4} \text{ m}^3/\text{s per metre,} \quad 736 \text{ kN/m,} \quad 0.75 \\ \qquad \text{(b)} \quad 3.5 \times 10^{-4} \text{ m}^3/\text{s per metre,} \quad 613 \text{ kN/m,} \quad 0.56 \end{array} \right]$$

3.2 For the concrete dam described in Example 3.4, calculate the seepage loss, the upthrust on the base of the dam and the maximum exit gradient if the impervious apron is of length (a) 60 m, (b) 75 m.

$$\left[\begin{array}{l} \text{Ans.} \quad \text{(a)} \quad 6 \times 10^{-5} \text{ m}^3/\text{s per metre,} \quad 353 \text{ kN/m,} \quad 0.44 \\ \qquad \text{(b)} \quad 5.14 \times 10^{-5} \text{ m}^3/\text{s per metre,} \quad 328 \text{ kN/m,} \quad 0.38 \end{array} \right]$$

3.3 A cofferdam 4 m wide is formed in a river estuary by driving sheet-piles to a depth of 4.4 m into a 6.2 m-thick deposit of fine sand overlying impermeable bedrock. The depth of water in the river is 0.8 m and 1.5 m of sand is excavated from within the cofferdam. The sand is isotropic with $k = 8 \times 10^{-6}$ m/s and $\rho_s = 2.1$ Mg/m³. Calculate:

(i) the steady state seepage into the cofferdam,
(ii) the maximum exit hydraulic gradient,
(iii) the factor of safety against base heave in the excavation, and
(iv) the resultant horizontal water force on the sheeting.

$$\left[\begin{array}{l} \text{Ans.} \quad \text{(i)} \quad 1.1 \times 10^{-5} \text{ m}^3/\text{s per metre,} \quad \text{(ii)} \quad 0.38, \quad \text{(iii)} \quad 2.72 \\ \qquad \text{(iv)} \quad 61 \text{ kN per metre inwards} \end{array} \right]$$

3.4 Figure P3.4 shows a section through a dam constructed with a central clay core and compacted rock fill on both shoulders. If the clay is isotropic with $k = 10^{-8}$ m/s and the rock fill can be assumed to be infinitely permeable, determine the quantity of seepage through the core per metre width of the dam.

[Ans. 2.9×10^{-8} m³/s per metre]

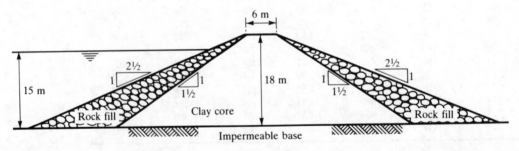

Figure P3.4

3.5 An office block with basement car park is to occupy an area of 56 m × 56 m and be founded 5 m below ground level in an 8-m thick layer of clay overlying 10 m of sand on impervious bedrock. The excavation to foundation level will be carried out with the sides supported vertically by diaphragm walls, the axis of the excavation being parallel to and at 100 m from a river, the bed of which is in contact with the sand. The piezometric level for the sand at the site of the excavation coincides with the water level in the river and is 1 m below ground level.

Calculate the required reduction in piezometric level for the sand to provide a factor of safety of 3 against base heave in the excavation. Determine a suitable installation of 0.4-m diameter, fully penetrating pressure relief wells to meet this requirement, given that the sand is isotropic with $k = 4.2 \times 10^{-3}$ m/s and $\rho_s = 2$ Mg/m³, and that submersible pumps with an operating capacity of 3.8×10^{-2} m³/s are available.

$$\left[\begin{array}{l} \text{Ans.} \quad \text{Required drawdown} = 3 \text{ m, 12 wells giving drawdown at centre} = 3 \text{ m} \\ \qquad \text{and drawdown at wells} \approx 3.4 \text{ m} \end{array} \right]$$

3.6 An excavation is to be made to a depth of 10 m in a 24-m thick deposit of sand overlying impermeable clay. The excavation will have a base area 55 m × 55 m and side slopes at 1 vertical on 3 horizontal. The site investigation revealed that the equilibrium groundwater level was 1 m below ground surface, and a pumping test carried out on a 0.5-m diameter, fully penetrating well installed at the centre of the proposed excavation produced a steady discharge of 11.4×10^{-2} m³/s with drawdowns of 1.23 and 0.39 m in observation wells at 30 m and 200 m from the pumping well respectively.

Design a fully penetrating system of 0.3-m diameter dewatering wells to bring the groundwater level down to 1.5 m below the base of the excavation, assuming that the submersible pumps to be used will operate at a capacity of 5.8×10^{-2} m³/s and that the radius of influence of the well system is 1600 m.

[Ans. 12 wells giving drawdown at centre $\approx$ 10.8 m and drawbacks at wells $\approx$ 12.4 m]

CONSOLIDATION THEORY AND SETTLEMENT ANALYSIS

4.1 INTRODUCTION

When a soil deposit is subjected to an increase in total stress, as for example from the load applied by the construction of a building or an embankment, *excess porewater pressures* are set up in the soil mass. Since water cannot sustain shear stress, these excess porewater pressures dissipate by water flowing out of the soil. The rate at which this process can occur is controlled principally by the permeability of the soil mass.

The dissipation of excess porewater pressures by the outflow of water from the soil is referred to as *consolidation* and has two important consequences:

(a) It leads to a reduction in the volume of voids and hence to a reduction in the total volume of the soil mass, which manifests itself in a settlement of the ground surface and hence a settlement of the engineering structure.

(b) As the excess porewater pressures dissipate, the effective stresses in the soil increase and hence the shear strength of the soil mass increases. Consolidation and shear strength are therefore interlinked processes.

Thus, as a soil undergoes consolidation there is a decrease in void ratio accompanied by an increase in effective stress.

For granular soils such as sands, the permeability is relatively high so that excess porewater pressures can dissipate virtually instantaneously. Consequently, settlement of a structure is generally complete by the end of construction. In contrast, clay soils generally have a very low permeability and therefore the dissipation of excess porewater pressures is a very slow process. Consequently, an engineering structure may continue to undergo settlement for many years after construction is complete.

The process of consolidation therefore applies to all soils, but in practice is only of concern in the case of structures founded on clay deposits. In such instances we require to predict:

(a) the ultimate settlement of the structure, and
(b) the rate at which the settlement will occur.

These predictions are made by means of an appropriate consolidation theory.

In general, the process of consolidation will involve the three-dimensional flow of porewater and three-dimensional strain of the soil mass. Three-dimensional theories, however, are most complex and are very difficult to apply in practice. The simplest case that can be treated mathematically is the one-dimensional case. This is the theory most frequently used in practice and forms the basis of nearly all settlement calculations.

4.2 TERZAGHI THEORY FOR VERTICAL CONSOLIDATION

Derivation of Governing Equation

Consider a deposit of homogeneous saturated soil of infinite lateral extent subject to a uniform pressure q applied over the whole of the surface area (Fig. 4.1). The soil rests on an impermeable

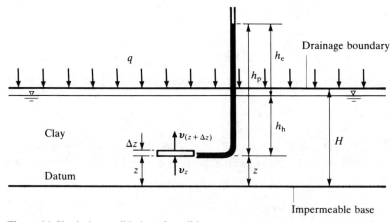

Figure 4.1 Vertical consolidation of a soil layer.

base and is free to drain from its upper face. The dissipation of excess porewater pressure at any point will involve only the upward vertical flow of porewater to the top boundary since we only have a hydraulic gradient in the vertical direction. The resulting strains will also occur solely in the vertical direction. Thus for the soil element shown let

$$v_z \qquad \text{denote the vertical velocity of flow into the element}$$

and $\qquad v_{z+\Delta z} \quad$ denote the vertical velocity of flow out of the element

Now by Taylor's theorem

$$v_{z+\Delta z} = v_z + \frac{\partial v_z}{\partial z} \Delta z + \frac{1}{2!} \frac{\partial^2 v_z}{\partial z^2} \Delta z^2 + \frac{1}{3!} \frac{\partial^3 v_z}{\partial z^3} \Delta z^3 + \cdots$$

Since Δz is taken to be very small, the second-order and higher terms may be considered negligible and hence

$$v_{z+\Delta z} = v_z + \frac{\partial v_z}{\partial z} \Delta z$$

From the principle of continuity of volume we have that

$$\begin{array}{ccc} \text{Quantity of flow out of} & \text{Quantity of flow into} & \text{Rate of change of} \\ \text{element per unit time} & - \ \text{element per unit time} & = \ \text{volume of element} \end{array}$$

Thus $\qquad \left[v_z + \dfrac{\partial v_z}{\partial z} \Delta z \right] A - v_z A = - \dfrac{\partial V}{\partial t}$

where A is the plan area of the element and V is the volume. Therefore

$$V\frac{\partial v_z}{\partial z} = -\frac{\partial V}{\partial t}$$

Assuming the soil grains and porewater to be incompressible, then the rate of change of volume of the element $\partial V/\partial t$ is equal to the rate of change of the volume of voids $\partial V_v/\partial t$. Thus

$$V\frac{\partial v_z}{\partial z} = \frac{-\partial V_v}{\partial t} \tag{4.1}$$

If V_s denotes the volume of solids in the element and e the void ratio, then by definition $V_v = eV_s$. Substituting in Eq. (4.1) and noting that V_s is a constant we obtain

$$V\frac{\partial v_z}{\partial z} = -V_s\frac{\partial e}{\partial t}$$

whence

$$\frac{\partial v_z}{\partial z} = -\frac{1}{1+e}\frac{\partial e}{\partial t} \tag{4.2}$$

For the vertical flow of porewater through the element, we have from Darcy's equation (3.6c)

$$v_z = -k_z\frac{\partial h}{\partial z}$$

where h = the total head in the element and k_z = the coefficient of vertical permeability of the soil. In Terzaghi's terminology the coefficient of vertical permeability is denoted by k_v. Adopting this notation, Eq. (4.2) becomes

$$\frac{\partial}{\partial z}\left(k_v\frac{\partial h}{\partial z}\right) = \frac{1}{1+e}\frac{\partial e}{\partial t}$$

In practice, the vertical strains are generally small and therefore it is reasonable to assume that the permeability of the soil remains constant over the applied pressure increment. We thus obtain

$$k_v\frac{\partial^2 h}{\partial z^2} = \frac{1}{1+e}\frac{\partial e}{\partial t} \tag{4.3}$$

Taking the base of the soil layer as datum, the total head h of the element is given by

$$h = z + h_h + h_e$$

where z is the elevation head, h_h is the hydrostatic pressure head and h_e denotes the excess pressure head. For small strain theory $z + h_h$ may be assumed to remain constant. Thus

$$\frac{\partial^2 h}{\partial z^2} = \frac{\partial^2 h_e}{\partial z^2}$$

The excess porewater pressure u_e in the element is given by

$$u_e = \rho_w g h_e$$

whence

$$\frac{\partial^2 h}{\partial z^2} = \frac{1}{\rho_w g}\frac{\partial^2 u_e}{\partial z^2} \tag{4.4}$$

Substituting Eq. (4.4) in (4.3) and rearranging gives

$$\frac{k_v(1+e)}{\rho_w g}\frac{\partial^2 u_e}{\partial z^2} = \frac{\partial e}{\partial t} \tag{4.5}$$

We have then one equation in two unknowns (u_e and e) and in order to define the problem completely we require a further expression relating the excess porewater pressure and void ratio. This is obtained by considering the vertical effective stress–strain behaviour for the soil. Terzaghi assumed this to be linear over a particular pressure increment, as shown in Fig. 4.2. As a change in strain is proportional to a change in void ratio, this also implies a linear e–σ'_v relationship (Fig. 4.3). Provided the pressure increment ratio is approximately unity, this is known to be quite reasonable. The slope of the line in Fig. 4.3 is denoted by a_v and is referred to as the *coefficient of compressibility*. We thus have

$$a_v = -\frac{\partial e}{\partial \sigma'_v} \tag{4.6}$$

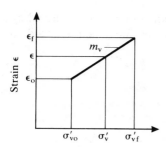

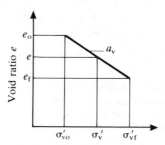

Vertical effective stress σ'_v

Figure 4.2   **Figure 4.3**

If σ_v is the total vertical stress on the element (Fig. 4.1), σ'_v the effective vertical stress in the element and u the corresponding porewater pressure, then from the principle of effective stress

$$\sigma_v = \sigma'_v + u$$

The porewater pressure u comprises a hydrostatic pressure u_h and an excess pressure u_e. That is

$$u = u_h + u_e$$

Thus

$$\sigma_v = \sigma'_v + u_h + u_e$$

Differentiating with respect to time t

$$\frac{\partial \sigma'_v}{\partial t} + \frac{\partial u_e}{\partial t} = 0$$

whence

$$\frac{\partial \sigma'_v}{\partial t} = -\frac{\partial u_e}{\partial t} \tag{4.7}$$

Now

$$\frac{\partial e}{\partial t} = \frac{\partial e}{\partial \sigma'_v} \frac{\partial \sigma'_v}{\partial t}$$

Therefore substituting Eqs (4.6) and (4.7)

$$\frac{\partial e}{\partial t} = a_v \frac{\partial u_e}{\partial t} \tag{4.8}$$

Substituting Eq. (4.8) in Eq. (4.5) then gives

$$\frac{k_v(1 + e)}{\rho_w g a_v} \frac{\partial^2 u_e}{\partial z^2} = \frac{\partial u_e}{\partial t} \tag{4.9}$$

This equation is more conveniently expressed in the form

$$c_v \frac{\partial^2 u_e}{\partial z^2} = \frac{\partial u_e}{\partial t} \tag{4.10}$$

where

$$c_v = \frac{k_v(1 + e)}{\rho_w g a_v} \tag{4.11}$$

is referred to as the *coefficient of vertical consolidation*. We also define

$$m_v = \frac{a_v}{1 + e} \tag{4.12}$$

where m_v is referred to as the *coefficient of volume compressibility*.

Equation (4.10) is the governing one-dimensional consolidation equation and was derived by Terzaghi in 1923. Figure 4.4 shows the equivalent rheological model and is a useful aid to visualizing the consolidation process.

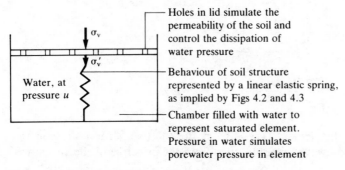

Figure 4.4 Rheological model of vertical consolidation process.

Solution of Governing Equation

For an infinitely wide loaded area, as herein, the applied pressure q is constant with depth and is initially carried by the porewater as an excess pressure u_{oe}. We thus have

Initial condition at $t = 0$: $u_e = u_{oe} = q$ for $0 \leq z \leq H$

Boundary condition at all t: $\frac{\partial u_e}{\partial z} = 0$ at $z = 0$, $u_e = 0$ at $z = H$

Final condition at $t = \infty$: $u_e = 0$ for $0 \leq z \leq H$

The solution of Eq. (4.10) is then given by

$$\frac{u_e}{u_{oe}} = \sum_{m=0}^{m=\infty} \frac{2}{M} \sin\left[M\left(1 - \frac{z}{H}\right)\right] \exp\left(-M^2 T_v\right) \tag{4.13}$$

where $M = \frac{\pi}{2}(2m + 1)$ with $m = 0, 1, 2, \ldots, \infty$

H = the maximum length of drainage path

and T_v = a dimensionless *vertical time factor* defined by

$$T_v = \frac{c_v t}{H^2} \tag{4.14}$$

Now the *degree of consolidation* of a soil element U_v is defined by

$$U_v = \frac{e_o - e}{e_o - e_f} \tag{4.15}$$

where e_o and e_f denote respectively the initial and final values of the void ratio.

With reference to Fig. 4.3.

$$\frac{e_o - e}{e_o - e_f} = \frac{\sigma'_v - \sigma'_{vo}}{\sigma'_{vf} - \sigma'_{vo}}$$

Thus

$$U_v = \frac{\sigma'_v - \sigma'_{vo}}{\sigma'_{vf} - \sigma'_{vo}} \tag{4.16}$$

From the principle of effective stress we have

At $t = 0$, just prior to the application of the surface pressure q

$$\rho_s g(H - z) = \sigma'_{vo} + u_h$$

and on application of the surface pressure

$$q + \rho_s g(H - z) = \sigma'_{vo} + u_h + u_{oe}$$

At $t = t$, $\qquad\qquad q + \rho_s g(H - z) = \sigma'_v + u_h + u_e$

At $t = \infty$, $\qquad\qquad q + \rho_s g(H - z) = \sigma'_{vf} + u_h$

Thus substituting in Eq. (4.16) gives

$$U_v = 1 - \frac{u_e}{u_{oe}} \tag{4.17}$$

The degree of consolidation is therefore equal to the degree of dissipation of excess porewater pressure. Substituting for u_e/u_{oe} from Eq. (4.13) gives

$$U_v = 1 - \sum_{m=0}^{m=\infty} \frac{2}{M} \sin\left[M\left(1 - \frac{z}{H}\right)\right] \exp\left(-M^2 T_v\right) \tag{4.18}$$

Equation (4.18) can be solved for values of U_v for given values of z/H and T_v. For the case considered of a soil layer resting on an impermeable boundary and draining from the top face, referred to as *single drainage*, the distribution of degree of consolidation with depth for various values of time factor is represented by the upper half of Fig. 4.5. For a soil layer resting on a permeable boundary with drainage consequently taking place from the bottom face as well as the top face, referred to as *double drainage*, the consolidation of the lower half of the soil layer is a mirror image of the upper half and thus the complete consolidation behaviour is represented by the whole of Fig. 4.5. This figure is therefore particularly informative as it gives a complete picture of the process of consolidation. It is seen that consolidation proceeds most rapidly at the drainage boundary(s) and least rapidly at the impermeable boundary of a single drained layer or the mid-plane of a doubly drained layer. Consider, for example, the curve for $T_v = 0.15$. This represents the conditions after a certain time as defined by Eq. (4.14). Assuming the soil layer to be single drained we see that at a depth of one-fifth the thickness of the layer, consolidation is 72 per cent complete, whereas at the base of the layer only 14 per cent consolidation has occurred. With increasing time, the percentage consolidation at every point increases until finally consolidation is 100 per cent complete at all depths, the excess porewater pressure everywhere is zero, and all the applied pressure is carried as effective pressure within the soil skeleton.

In addition to the point values of the degree of consolidation U_v, we also require to compute

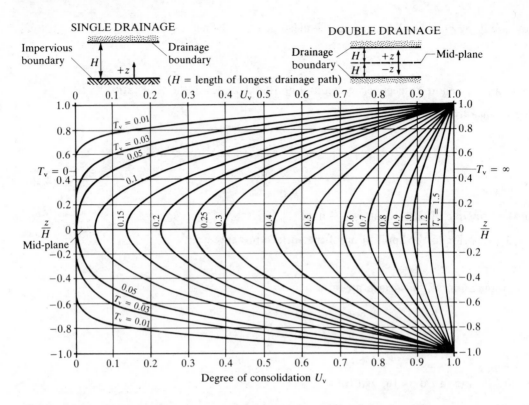

Figure 4.5 Degree of consolidation U_v as a function of depth factor z/H and time factor T_v.

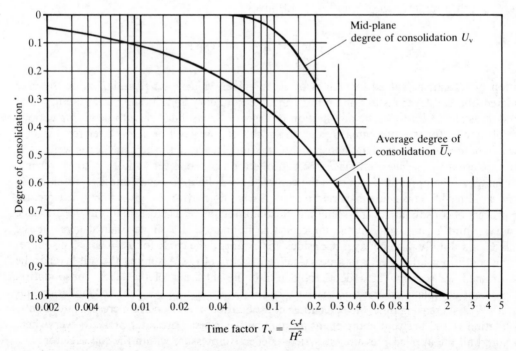

Figure 4.6 Average degree of consolidation $\bar{U}_v$ and mid-plane degree of consolidation U_v versus time factor T_v.

the *average degree of consolidation* $\bar{U}_v$. This reflects the surface settlement of the layer and hence the settlement of an engineering structure. By analogy with Eq. (4.17) we have then

$$\bar{U}_v = 1 - \frac{\bar{u}_e}{u_{oe}} = 1 - \frac{1}{H} \int_0^H \frac{u_e}{u_{oe}} \, dz$$

Substituting for u_e/u_{oe} from Eq. (4.13)

$$\bar{U}_v = 1 - \frac{1}{H} \int_0^H \sum_{m=0}^{m=\infty} \frac{2}{M} \sin\left[M\left(1 - \frac{z}{H}\right)\right] \exp\left(- M^2 T_v\right) dz$$

$$= 1 - \sum_{m=0}^{m=\infty} \frac{2}{M^2} \exp\left(- M^2 T_v\right) \tag{4.19}$$

Thus, for given values of the time factor T_v we may compute the corresponding values of the average degree of consolidation $\bar{U}_v$. The theoretical relationship between $\bar{U}_v$ and T_v is shown in Fig. 4.6 to a semi-logarithmic scale. Also shown plotted is the mid-plane degree of consolidation. This corresponds to the degree of consolidation at the centre of a soil layer drained from both faces, or the impermeable boundary for a soil layer undergoing single drainage.

4.3 VERTICAL CONSOLIDATION TEST

Apparatus and Procedure

The consolidation parameters c_v and m_v are obtained from a laboratory consolidation test which simulates the main Terzaghi assumptions of vertical strain and vertical flow of porewater.

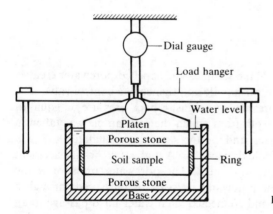

Figure 4.7 Conventional dead load consolidation cell.

Figure 4.7 shows the laboratory consolidation cell developed by Terzaghi, Casagrande, *et al.* in the thirties. In this apparatus a soil sample 75 mm diameter by 20 mm thick is contained inside a brass ring and sandwiched between two saturated porous stones. A load is applied to the soil through the top platen by means of a hanger, lever arm and dead weights. To perform a consolidation test, a load is applied to the soil (generally a load increment ratio of unity is adopted) and readings of settlement are taken at suitable intervals of time. The test is described fully in BS 1377: 1975, Test 17, and ASTM D–2435–70.

Figure 4.8 shows an alternative consolidation cell which was developed by Rowe *et al.* in the sixties (Rowe and Barden, 1966). In this apparatus a consolidation pressure is applied hydraulically to the sample through a convoluted rubber jack. Drainage of the sample is

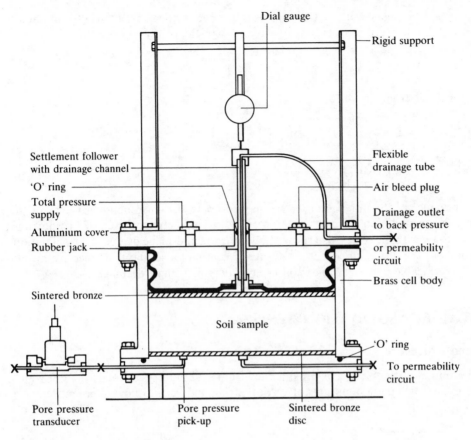

Figure 4.8 Rowe hydraulic consolidation cell.

vertically upwards to a porous disc placed on top of the sample. The expelled porewater escapes by way of a drilled vertical drainage hole in the central spindle and thence to a control valve. The sample may be allowed to drain to atmospheric pressure or against a back pressure set equal to the *in situ* hydrostatic pressure obtaining at the depth from which the soil sample was taken in the field. The spindle is fastened to the rubber jack and, as the sample consolidates, the jack extends to follow the movement and pulls the spindle downwards. A dial gauge or displacement transducer on top of the spindle then records the settlement. The porewater pressure at the bottom of the sample, representing the mid-plane porewater pressure, is measured through a saturated porous disc sealed flush in the cell base and connected via a water-filled passage to an electrical pressure transducer. With the drainage valve closed, a consolidation pressure is applied to the sample. When the build-up in excess porewater pressure is complete, the test is started by opening the drainage valve. Readings of settlement are then taken at suitable intervals of time.

Rowe consolidation cells are available for testing soil samples up to 500 mm diameter by 200 mm in thickness.

Analysis of Test Results

Coefficient of vertical consolidation c_v The value of c_v is determined by fitting the experimental and theoretical time curves. Two methods have been devised for this purpose, one involving the square root of time (after D. W. Taylor) and the other the logarithm of time (after Casagrande).

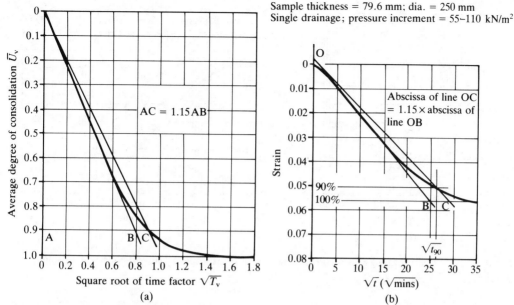

Figure 4.9 Square root of time fitting method: (a) theoretical curve, (b) experimental curve for remoulded kaolinite: test conducted in the Rowe cell.

Figure 4.9a illustrates the theoretical basis of the square root of time fitting method where we see that $\bar{U}_v$ is linear with $\sqrt{T_v}$ for a large part of the consolidation. It may readily be verified that the line OC drawn from the origin and passing through the 90 per cent consolidation point has abscissa values of 1.15 times those of the initial straight line. Thus considering an actual strain–$\sqrt{\text{time}}$ plot (Fig. 4.9b), a straight line is drawn through the initial points and a second line constructed having an abscissa 1.15 times that of the first. The intersection of this line with the consolidation curve defines the 90 per cent consolidation point and the vertical ordinate the square root of the time for 90 per cent consolidation, $\sqrt{t_{90}}$. The value of c_v is then determined from Eq. (4.14) in the form

$$T_{v90} = \frac{c_v t_{90}}{H^2}$$

In Fig. 4.9b, $\sqrt{t_{90}} = 26.25$ whence $t_{90} = 689$ minutes. The average thickness of the soil sample over the pressure increment is equal to 77.4 mm. As the test is conducted with single drainage, then H is also equal to 77.4 mm. From Fig. 4.6, $T_{v90} = 0.848$. Thus

$$c_v = \frac{0.848 \times (77.4)^2}{689} = 7.4 \text{ mm}^2/\text{min} = \underline{3.9 \text{ m}^2/\text{yr}}$$

In Fig. 4.9b, the intersection of the line OB with the vertical at zero time is a little above the zero of the vertical strain scale. This is due to the effects of viscous resistance to compression of the soil structure. In some soils the intersection point may be a little below the zero of the vertical strain scale because of the immediate compression of a small amount of air in the voids of the soil sample.

Figure 4.10a illustrates the theoretical basis of the logarithm of time fitting method where we see that the intersection of the tangent and asymptote to the consolidation curve coincides with the 100 per cent consolidation point. Use is made of this characteristic to establish the 100 per

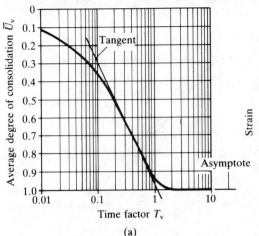
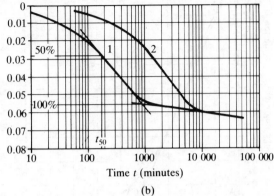

Sample thickness test 1 = 79.6 mm; dia. = 250 mm
Sample thickness test 2 = 238.8 mm; dia. = 500 mm
Single drainage; pressure increment = 55–110 kN/m²

Figure 4.10 Logarithm of time fitting method: (a) theoretical curve, (b) experimental curves for remoulded kaolinite: tests conducted in the Rowe cell.

cent consolidation point for experimental results. To demonstrate this the test data in Fig. 4.9b has been replotted as strain against logarithm of time and is represented by curve 1 in Fig. 4.10b. The intersection of the two corresponding tangents is at a vertical strain of 0.056 and defines the 100 per cent (primary) consolidation point for the sample. The value for c_v is based on fitting at the 50 per cent point and is calculated from Eq. (4.14) in the form

$$T_{v50} = \frac{c_v t_{50}}{H^2}$$

In Fig. 4.10b, $t_{50} = 170$ minutes and, as previously, $H = 77.4$ mm. From Fig. 4.6, $T_{v50} = 0.197$. Thus

$$c_v = \frac{0.197 \times (77.4)^2}{170} = 6.9 \text{ mm}^2/\text{min} = \underline{3.7 \text{ m}^2/\text{yr}}$$

The difference between the two computed values for c_v is unimportant; generally the agreement is within 10 per cent.

Values for c_v obtained from tests on undisturbed samples of conventional size (i.e., 75 mm diameter by 20 mm thick) tend to range between 1 and 10 m²/yr. Values for c_v obtained from tests on larger-sized undisturbed samples tend to exceed this upper limit, but there is not a great deal of information available at the present time.

Coefficient of volume compressibility m_v From Eq. (4.12)

$$m_v = \frac{a_v}{1 + e}$$

In practice, the void ratio–vertical effective stress relationship is mildly non-linear. The coefficient of compressibility a_v is then interpreted as the slope of the chord over the particular effective stress range. That is $a_v = \Delta e/\Delta\sigma_v'$. The void ratio e is taken to be the initial value e_o at the state of the increment. Thus m_v is given by

$$m_v = \frac{\Delta e}{1 + e_o} \frac{1}{\Delta\sigma_v'} \tag{4.20}$$

Now the soil element under test may be represented before and after consolidation by the diagrams shown in Fig. 4.11. Thus

$$\frac{\Delta e}{1 + e_o} = \frac{e_o - e_f}{1 + e_o} = \frac{\dfrac{\Delta D_{wo}}{\Delta D_s} - \dfrac{\Delta D_{wf}}{\Delta D_s}}{1 + \dfrac{\Delta D_{wo}}{\Delta D_s}} = \frac{\Delta D_{wo} - \Delta D_{wf}}{\Delta D_s + \Delta D_{wo}} = \frac{\Delta S}{\Delta D} \tag{4.21}$$

where ΔS is the ultimate consolidation settlement of the element and $\Delta S/\Delta D$ is the ultimate vertical strain of the element. Substituting Eq. (4.21) in Eq. (4.20)

$$m_v = \frac{\Delta S}{\Delta D} \frac{1}{\Delta \sigma_v'} \tag{4.22}$$

and hence m_v is readily calculated for any particular pressure increment. For the data given in Fig. 4.10b, the final (primary) strain for test sample 1 is 0.056 and the increment of effective stress is equal to 55 kN/m², whence

$$m_v = \frac{0.056}{55} = \underline{0.00102 \text{ m}^2/\text{kN}}$$

The coefficient of volume compressibility decreases as the effective pressure increases. For the effective stress range normally encountered in engineering practice, the values of m_v for clay soils tend to range between 0.001 and 0.0001 m²/kN.

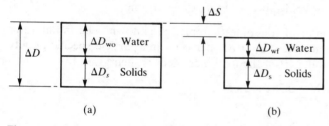

(a)   (b)

Figure 4.11 Representation of soil element: (a) before consolidation, (b) after consolidation.

Coefficient of vertical permeability k_v The value of k_v may be determined from Eqs (4.11) and (4.12) whence we have

$$k_v = c_v \rho_w g m_v \tag{4.23}$$

For the consolidation increment in Fig. 4.10b, the average value of k_v for the effective stress range 55 to 110 kN/m² is given by

$$k_v = 3.7 \times 1 \times 9.81 \times 0.00102 = \underline{0.037 \text{ m/yr}}$$

Values of vertical permeability deduced in this manner are generally considered accurate enough for most engineering purposes. For a more precise determination of the value of k_v at a particular effective stress, it is necessary to carry out a direct permeability test on the soil sample. For this purpose it is necessary during the setting-up stage to place a porous disc at the bottom of the sample in order to be able to apply a differential head across the soil at the end of a consolidation increment. During a consolidation stage, the drainage valve in the cell base is kept closed. The bottom disc then acts as a large pick-up and reflects the mid-plane porewater pressure. At the end of a consolidation stage the bottom drainage valve is opened and a constant differential head applied across the sample. This is accomplished by setting the bottom pressure equal to the value of the back pressure applied at the top of the sample and then lowering the top pressure a small amount, sufficient to cause a measurable flow rate, but not to result in a change in effective stress greater than 0.1 times the effective consolidation pressure. The amount of water flowing into and out of the sample is recorded and steady state conditions may be taken to be when the inflow and outflow agree to within 10 per cent. The vertical permeability is then determined from the direct application of Darcy's Law. Thus

$$k_v = \frac{Q \, \Delta D}{A \, \Delta h} \tag{4.24}$$

where Q is the flow rate, A is the plan area of the sample, ΔD is the thickness of the sample and Δh is the total head lost across the soil.

Coefficient of secondary consolidation C_α According to the Terzaghi theory, when the excess porewater pressure is fully dissipated, consolidation is complete and the settlement of the soil ceases. It is seen from Fig. 4.10b, however, that following the dissipation of excess porewater pressure the settlement continues at a rate which is linear with the logarithm of time. This continuing settlement is due to creep of the soil structure under constant effective stress and is referred to as *secondary consolidation*. Settlement resulting from the dissipation of the excess porewater pressure is then referred to as *primary consolidation*.

The observed linear relationship between the secondary consolidation and the logarithm of time is a characteristic feature of many clays and peats. The *coefficient of secondary consolidation*, designated C_α, is defined as

$$C_\alpha = \text{the change in void ratio per } \log_{10} \text{ cycle of time} \tag{4.25}$$

With reference to Fig. 4.10b, the relevant properties of test sample 1 are known to be: initial water content $w = 56.2$ per cent, degree of saturation $S_r = 100$ per cent and particle specific gravity $G_s = 2.65$. The initial void ratio e_o at the start of the load increment is then given by

$$e_o = \frac{wG_s}{S_r} = \frac{0.562 \times 2.65}{1} = 1.489$$

From Eq. (4.21), the void ratio e at a particular strain ε is given by

$$e = e_o - (1 + e_o)\varepsilon \tag{4.26}$$

Thus at a time of 1400 minutes, corresponding to the end of the primary consolidation, the strain is equal to 0.056 and therefore

$$e = 1.489 - 2.489 \times 0.056 = 1.350$$

At a time of 14 000 minutes, corresponding to an increase of one log cycle, the strain is equal to 0.061 and hence

$$e = 1.489 - 2.489 \times 0.061 = 1.337$$

Thus from Eq. (4.25), the coefficient of secondary consolidation is given by

$$C_\alpha = 1.350 - 1.337 = \underline{0.013}$$

Values of C_α obtained for normally consolidated clays tend to range between 0.005 and 0.05. For overconsolidated clays, C_α is generally less than 0.002. For peat soils, a typical value for C_α is 0.4.

The rate of secondary compression is controlled by the physical/chemical properties of the soil and is therefore independent of the sample thickness. The secondary compression line thus represents a basic *creep line*. The primary consolidation curve joins the creep line at a time dependent on H^2 [Eq. (4.14)]. To illustrate this, a consolidation test was carried out on a second sample with the same initial conditions as sample 1 in Fig. 4.10b but having a thickness three times as great (i.e., 238.8 mm). The result obtained is represented by curve 2 in Fig. 4.10b. From Eq. (4.14) it follows then that

$$\frac{T_{v1}}{T_{v2}} = \frac{c_{v1}t_1}{H_1^2} \cdot \frac{H_2^2}{c_{v2}t_2} = \frac{t_1 H_2^2}{t_2 H_1^2}$$

For the same average degree of consolidation $T_{v1} = T_{v2}$. Thus

$$\frac{t_2}{t_1} = \left[\frac{H_2}{H_1}\right]^2 \tag{4.27}$$

In this case $H_2 = 3H_1$ and therefore the time to reach the same degree of consolidation for the thicker sample is nine times that for the thinner sample. It is seen from Fig. 4.10b that this is so. It follows then that a prediction of the field consolidation curve may be made by extrapolating the laboratory secondary compression line and scaling the primary consolidation curve according to H^2 [Eq. (4.27)].

Void ratio–vertical effective stress relation We have shown for the consolidation test on sample 1 in Fig. 4.10b that at the initial effective pressure of 55 kN/m² the value of the void ratio is equal to 1.489, and at the end of the consolidation stage corresponding to an effective pressure of 110 kN/m² the value of the void ratio is equal to 1.350. These values are represented by points A and B respectively in Fig. 4.12a. On subjecting the sample to a series of further increments, the value of the void ratio at the end of each consolidation stage may be readily determined in the manner described using Eq. (4.26). For the tested sample of remoulded kaolinite, this gives the curve ABCD. This is a typical void ratio–vertical effective stress relationship for a remoulded soil.

If the void ratio is plotted against the logarithm of vertical effective pressure a linear relationship is obtained, as shown in Fig. 4.12b. This is referred to as the *virgin consolidation line* and the slope as the *compression index*, designated C_c. Thus

$$C_c = \text{the slope of the virgin consolidation line}$$
$$\quad = \text{the change in void ratio per } \log_{10} \text{ cycle of effective pressure} \tag{4.28}$$

Thus, for the remoulded sample of kaolinite we obtain $C_c = 0.50$. In general, values of C_c for clays tend to range between 0.2 and 0.8, and for peats between 5 and 10.

If a soil element is subjected to a decrease in load then the change in total stress causes an initial decrease in porewater pressure. This decrease in porewater pressure represents a 'negative excess' which then dissipates with time by drawing water into the soil. Consequently the soil *swells*. The rate of swell is controlled by the same factors as govern the rate of consolidation.

To illustrate the swelling characteristics of a soil, the sample of kaolinite referred to in Fig. 4.12 was consolidated to an effective pressure of 275 kN/m² and then unloaded back to an effective pressure of 55 kN/m². This produced the typical swell line represented by curve CEF in Fig. 4.12. It is seen that the swell line is much flatter than the initial consolidation line. The reason for this is that the deformations which take place on first loading result predominantly from slip between the soil particles and clearly these are not wholly recoverable on unloading. On subsequent reloading the sample initially reconsolidates along a *recompression* line FGC until the vertical effective pressure reaches the previous maximum value of 275 kN/m², which is referred to as the *preconsolidation pressure* or *maximum past pressure* to which the sample has been consolidated, after which consolidation continues along the initial deformation path which the sample would have followed had there been no unloading.

Consider now the likely laboratory behaviour of an undisturbed sample of natural soil recovered from the field. The void ratio–vertical effective stress relationship obtained for such a

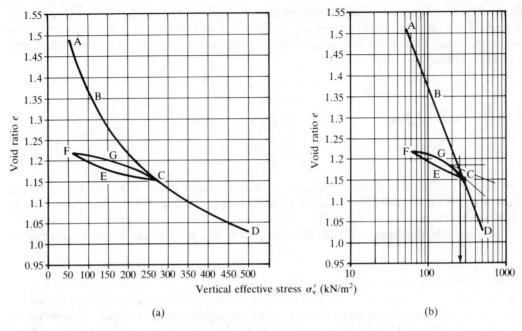

Figure 4.12 Void ratio versus vertical effective stress relationships for remoulded kaolinite.

sample would be expected to exhibit an initial recompression curve, if for no other reason than simply that on removal from the ground the sample would undergo unloading as a result of the relief of the overburden pressure. Knowing the depth from which the sample was taken, the *in situ* density of the soil deposit and the position of the water table, it is possible to estimate the effective overburden pressure acting on the sample in its *in situ* condition. It is of interest to superimpose this value on the e–log σ'_v plot. With some natural samples this coincides approximately with the point of transition from the recompression curve to the virgin consolidation line, as shown in Fig. 4.13a. This characteristic clearly indicates that the sample has never previously been loaded beyond its *in situ* effective overburden pressure and that the recompression is due entirely to the effects of stress relief on sampling. This then implies that the soil deposit in the field has never previously been subjected to effective stresses in excess of the present effective overburden pressures. Such a soil deposit is said to be *normally consolidated*, and it follows that for a normally consolidated soil deposit the preconsolidation pressure is equal to the present effective overburden pressure. Furthermore, if a normally consolidated soil deposit is loaded in the field, consolidation will occur down the virgin consolidation line.

For other natural samples the point of transition from the recompression curve to the virgin consolidation line occurs at an effective stress higher than the value of *in situ* effective overburden pressure, as shown in Fig. 4.13b. This indicates that the sample has previously been loaded to an effective stress in excess of the *in situ* effective overburden pressure and that recompression observed in the laboratory test is due to more than just the effects of stress relief on sampling. This implies that at some time in its past geological history the soil deposit has been consolidated to effective stresses in excess of the present effective overburden pressures. Such a soil deposit is said to be *overconsolidated* and is generally the result of either large fluctuations in natural groundwater level, the erosion of overlying strata or glaciation. It therefore follows that for an overconsolidated soil deposit, the preconsolidation pressure is greater than the present effective overburden pressure. Furthermore, if an overconsolidated soil deposit is loaded in the field, consolidation will occur initially at least along a recompression curve.

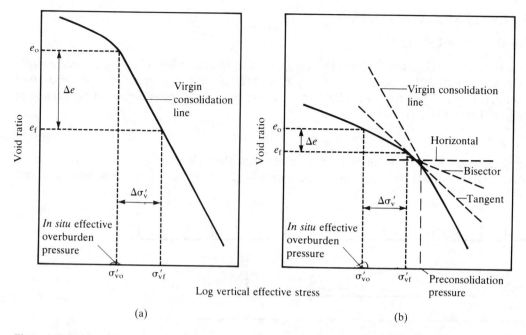

Figure 4.13 Void ratio versus log vertical effective stress for undisturbed samples of (a) normally consolidated clay, (b) overconsolidated clay.

The amount of overconsolidation of a soil deposit is expressed in terms of its *overconsolidation ratio* which is defined as

$$\text{Overconsolidation ratio} = \frac{\text{Preconsolidation pressure}}{\text{Present effective overburden pressure}}$$

From the considerations of the relationship between void ratio and vertical effective stress for natural soil deposits it follows that for the same increment of applied load, producing consolidation from an initial vertical effective stress σ'_{vo} to a final vertical effective stress σ'_{vf}, the settlement to be expected in a normally consolidated soil deposit, where field consolidation will occur entirely down the virgin consolidation line, will be greater than that to be expected in a heavily overconsolidated soil deposit, where field consolidation may well occur entirely along a much flatter recompression curve (compare the values of Δe in parts a and b respectively of Fig. 4.13). With a lightly overconsolidated soil deposit, the amount of settlement to be expected will depend to a great extent on whether or not the increment of applied load increases the effective stress in the soil beyond the preconsolidation pressure. The accurate determination of the preconsolidation pressure is therefore of prime importance. It has already been established that this is indicated approximately by the transition from the recompression curve to the virgin consolidation line. A more precise evaluation may be made using a method proposed by Casagrande. This utilizes a graphical construction technique applied to the e–log σ'_v plot and is illustrated in Fig. 4.13b. The method involves selecting the point of minimum radius of curvature on the recompression line, drawing horizontal and tangent lines at this point and bisecting the angle between them. The straight line portion of the laboratory plot, which represents the virgin consolidation line, is then projected backwards and the point of intersection with the bisector is taken as defining the preconsolidation pressure. For purposes of illustration, this technique has been applied to the test results shown in Fig. 4.12b and yields a preconsolidation pressure for the sample of 265 kN/m², which agrees closely with the known value of 275 kN/m².

4.4 SETTLEMENT ANALYSIS

Loaded Area of Infinite Size

This is the theoretical case considered by Terzaghi. The strains and flow of porewater occur solely in the vertical direction and the soil layer behaves as a soil element in the laboratory consolidation test. Thus, from Eq. (4.22) the ultimate consolidation settlement of an element in the layer (Fig. 4.14) is given by

$$\Delta S = m_v \, \Delta D \, \Delta \sigma_v' \qquad (4.29)$$

where $\Delta \sigma_v'$ is the increase in vertical effective stress in the element, ΔD is the thickness of the element and m_v is the coefficient of volume compressibility for the effective stress range involved.

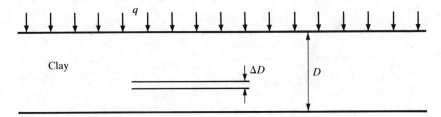

Figure 4.14 Loaded area of infinite size.

Initially we have that

$$\sigma_{vo} = \sigma_{vo}' + u_h$$

and at the end of consolidation

$$\sigma_{vf} = \sigma_{vf}' + u_h$$

Thus

$$\Delta \sigma_v = \Delta \sigma_v'$$

Hence

$$\Delta S = m_v \, \Delta D \, \Delta \sigma_v' = m_v \, \Delta D \, \Delta \sigma_v \qquad (4.30)$$

The ultimate consolidation settlement of the layer is then given by

$$S = \sum \Delta S = \sum m_v \, \Delta D \, \Delta \sigma_v' = \sum m_v \, \Delta D \, \Delta \sigma_v$$

Now the increase in total vertical stress $\Delta \sigma_v$ is constant with depth and equal to the applied surface pressure q. It is therefore not necessary to divide the clay deposit into a number of sublayers and we may take $\Delta D = D$, whence we obtain

$$S = m_v D \, \Delta \sigma_v' = m_v D \, \Delta \sigma_v = m_v D q \qquad (4.31)$$

Here m_v is the average value of the coefficient of volume compressibility over the depth of the clay layer for the applied stress range.

The *rate of settlement* of the clay layer is calculated using Eq. (4.14):

$$T_v = \frac{c_v t}{H^2}$$

If the clay layer has single drainage, then $H = D$. If the clay layer has double drainage, $H = D/2$. Thus, knowing the value of H and having obtained c_v from a consolidation test, then for a specified time t we can calculate the value of time factor T_v and hence from Fig. 4.6 obtain the average degree of consolidation $\bar{U}_v$ for the clay layer.

The theoretical conditions of vertical strain and vertical flow of porewater are closely approximated to in the field when the width of the loaded area is very much greater than the depth of the clay layer. This is generally the case for motorway embankments and land reclamation schemes.

Example 4.1 A motor embankment 5 m high and 30 m wide is to be founded on a 4-m thick deposit of boulder clay overlying sandstone. The fill material for the embankment is to be placed at a density of 2 Mg/m^3 and construction is to take 8 months. Calculate the ultimate settlement of the embankment and the settlement that will have occurred by the end of construction, given that the properties of the boulder clay are $m_v = 0.00012$ m^2/kN and $c_v = 1.5$ m^2/yr.

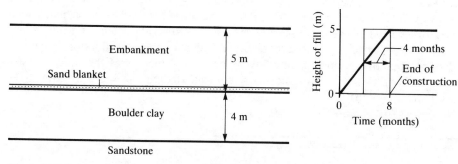

Figure 4.15 Example 4.1.

SOLUTION The problem is illustrated in Fig. 4.15. The width of the embankment is large compared with the thickness of the boulder clay and therefore the consolidation of the clay will be essentially vertical. Thus, from Eq. (4.31) the ultimate consolidation settlement of the clay deposit is given by

$$S = m_v Dq$$

The surface pressure q applied from the weight of the embankment is given by

$$q = 2 \times 9.81 \times 5 = 98.1 \text{ kN/m}^2$$

As boulder clay is an overconsolidated soil, m_v will remain sensibly constant over the depth of the layer and the value given can be assumed to represent the average value for the applied stress range. Thus with $D = 4$ m we obtain

$$S = 0.00012 \times 4 \times 98.1 = 0.047 \text{ m} = \underline{47 \text{ mm}}$$

From Eq. (4.14) $T_v = \dfrac{c_v t}{H^2}$

When constructing embankments over clay, the normal practice is to place a thin sand blanket on the surface of the clay to act as a top drainage boundary. As the boulder clay rests on sandstone, the layer will also drain from its lower face. We thus have double drainage, whence $H = D/2 = 2$ m. Now the Terzaghi theory assumes the foundation load to be applied instantaneously, whereas herein the pressure is only fully applied after a period of 8 months (Fig. 4.15). The actual consolidation by the end of construction will, however, be closely approximated by that which would obtain if the full embankment pressure were to be applied instantaneously after a period of 4 months. With a time then of 4 months to the end of construction we obtain

$$T_v = \frac{1.5 \times \frac{4}{12}}{2^2} = 0.125$$

whence from Fig. 4.6, $\bar{U}_v = 0.40$.

Thus the consolidation settlement at the end of construction $= 0.40 \times 47 = \underline{19 \text{ mm}}$.

The post-construction settlement $= 47 - 19 = 28$ mm and should not cause any long-term problems.

Example 4.2 A layer of sand 9 m thick is underlain by a 4-m thick deposit of normally consolidated clay resting on an impermeable shale. The groundwater level is initially 1 m below ground level. In order to facilitate the construction of an engineering works on an adjoining site, the groundwater level is to be lowered by 7 m over a very wide area and is to be maintained at this new level for a period of 1 year until the construction is complete, when the groundwater level will be allowed to rise back up to its original level. Calculate the consolidation settlement of the clay deposit after this period of time, given that the properties of the sand are $\rho = 1.90$ Mg/m^3, $\rho_s = 2.0$ Mg/m^3 and for the normally consolidated clay $\rho_s = 1.96$ Mg/m^3, $e_o = 0.825$, $C_c = 0.60$ and $c_v = 4$ m^2/yr.

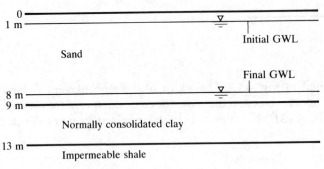

Figure 4.16 Example 4.2.

SOLUTION The problem is illustrated in Fig. 4.16.

The ultimate change in vertical effective stress at any point below the lowered water table is given by

$$\Delta\sigma'_v = \Delta\sigma_v - \Delta u$$

The total vertical stress decreases by an amount determined by the difference between the saturated and partially saturated density of the sand and the depth over which the water table is lowered. It is obvious that the porewater pressure also decreases. We thus obtain

$$\Delta\sigma'_v = (1.90 - 2.0) \times 9.81 \times 7 - (-1 \times 9.81 \times 7) = 61.80 \text{ kN/m}^2$$

As $\Delta\sigma'_v$ is positive, the vertical effective stress increases and the clay consolidates. The consolidation will be vertical since the groundwater level is lowered over a very wide area.

With $\Delta\sigma'_v$ the same for all points, the ultimate consolidation settlement of the clay deposit is given by Eq. (4.31):

$$S = m_v D \, \Delta\sigma'_v$$

where m_v represents the average compressibility of the layer.

Since the clay is normally consolidated, the compressibility of an element will decrease with increase in vertical effective stress through the layer. The decrease, however, is only mildly non-linear and consequently the compressibility of a soil element at the centre of the layer will closely approximate to the average compressibility of the deposit. Thus, if σ'_{vo} is the initial value of vertical effective stress at the centre of the clay and σ'_{vf} is the final value (wherein $\sigma'_{vf} - \sigma'_{vo} = \Delta\sigma'_v$), we obtain

$$m_v = \frac{\Delta e}{1 + e_o} \cdot \frac{1}{\Delta\sigma'_v} = \frac{C_c \log \dfrac{\sigma'_{vf}}{\sigma'_{vo}}}{(1 + e_o)\,\Delta\sigma'_v}$$

and hence

$$S = m_v D\,\Delta\sigma'_v = \frac{C_c D \log \dfrac{\sigma'_{vf}}{\sigma'_{vo}}}{1 + e_o} \qquad (4.32)$$

We have here

$$\sigma'_{vo} = (1.9 \times 9.81 \times 1 + 2.0 \times 9.81 \times 8 + 1.96 \times 9.81 \times 2) - 1 \times 9.81 \times 10$$
$$= 115.96 \text{ kN/m}^2$$

and

$$\sigma'_{vf} = (1.9 \times 9.81 \times 8 + 2.0 \times 9.81 \times 1 + 1.96 \times 9.81 \times 2) - 1 \times 9.81 \times 3$$
$$= 177.76 \text{ kN/m}^2$$

Alternatively

$$\sigma'_{vf} = \sigma'_{vo} + \Delta\sigma'_v = 115.96 + 61.80 = 177.76 \text{ kN/m}^2$$

Thus substituting in Eq. (4.32)

$$S = \frac{0.6 \times 4 \times \log \dfrac{177.76}{115.96}}{1.825} = \underline{0.244 \text{ m}}$$

Since $\Delta\sigma'_v$ is constant with depth, the theoretical solution for the rate of consolidation is as given earlier in Fig. 4.6. To determine the average degree of consolidation after a specified time, we need to calculate the corresponding value of the vertical time factor T_v defined by

$$T_v = \frac{c_v t}{H^2}$$

The clay deposit rests on impermeable shale and is overlain by sand, and so will consolidate under conditions of single drainage with $H = D = 4$ m. The groundwater level in the sand may be lowered rapidly so that the clay can be considered to be loaded instantaneously. Thus for $t = 1$ year we obtain

$$T_v = \frac{4 \times 1}{4^2} = 0.25$$

and therefore from Fig. 4.6, $\bar{U}_v = 0.57$.

Thus, the settlement of the clay layer after 1 year $= 0.57 \times 0.244 = \underline{0.139 \text{ m}}$.

Loaded Areas of Finite Size

Where the dimensions of the loaded area are small in relation to the depth of the soil layer, as for example in the case of footings, the resulting consolidation of the soil mass beneath the founda-

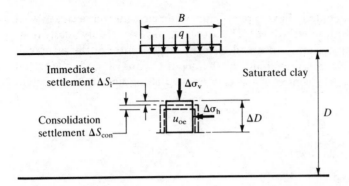

Figure 4.17 Loaded area of finite size.

tion will be three-dimensional. No attempt will be made here to predict the rate of settlement of the foundation; we confine our attention solely to predicting the ultimate settlement. For this purpose consider a soil element at some depth below the loaded area, as shown in Fig. 4.17. Because of the applied foundation pressure q, the element will be subjected to an increase in the total vertical stress $\Delta\sigma_v$ and a corresponding increase in the total horizontal stress $\Delta\sigma_h$. For compatibility with the imposed boundary conditions, the initial excess porewater pressure u_{oe} set up in the element will be less than $\Delta\sigma_v$ and greater than $\Delta\sigma_h$. That is

$$\Delta\sigma_h < u_{oe} < \Delta\sigma_v$$

The corresponding changes in the vertical and horizontal effective stresses are given by

$$\Delta\sigma_v' = \Delta\sigma_v - u_{oe}$$

and

$$\Delta\sigma_h' = \Delta\sigma_h - u_{oe}$$

The vertical effective stress therefore increases and the horizontal effective stress decreases, and the element undergoes an immediate settlement ΔS_i. Consolidation settlement of the element then takes place as the excess porewater pressure dissipates. As u_e decreases, the horizontal effective stress σ_h' increases and approaches the initial value σ_{ho}' which existed prior to loading. The element therefore initially undergoes recompression in the horizontal direction, the strains associated with this being very small. In the final stages of consolidation σ_h' exceeds σ_{ho}' and the element is subject to a nett increase in horizontal effective stress. Analyses carried out by Skempton and Bjerrum (1957) indicate that the lateral strains during consolidation are about 15 per cent of the vertical strains. It is therefore a reasonable assumption to consider that during consolidation the element only undergoes vertical compression. We may therefore use the consolidation test as a basis for predicting the ultimate consolidation settlement of the element, ΔS_{con}. Since the initial excess porewater pressure u_{oe} set up in the element is less than the increase in the total vertical stress $\Delta\sigma_v$, then clearly the ultimate consolidation settlement of the element will be less than that predicted by the consolidation test wherein for the saturated element u_{oe} would equal $\Delta\sigma_v$ with ΔS_{con} then given by $\Delta S_{con} = m_v\,\Delta D\,\Delta\sigma_v$ [Eq. (4.30)]. Thus, for the field case where $u_{oe} < \Delta\sigma_v$ we may write

$$\Delta S_{con} = \mu m_v\,\Delta D\,\Delta\sigma_v \qquad (4.33)$$

where μ is a factor which depends on the shape of the loaded area, the depth of the clay layer and the pore pressure characteristics of the soil as reflected by Skempton's pore pressure parameter A, a discussion of which is deferred until Chapter 5 on shear strength theory. Values of μ have been calculated by Skempton and Bjerrum and by Scott (1963) and are obtained from Fig. 4.18.

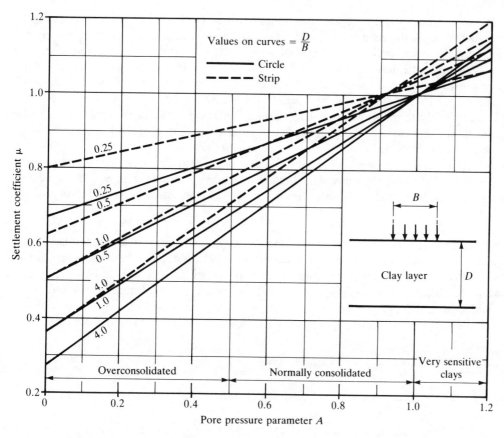

Figure 4.18 Values of settlement coefficient μ. (From Scott, 1963. Copyright Addison-Wesley Inc. Reprinted with permission.)

The total settlement of the element is therefore given by

$$\Delta S = \Delta S_i + \Delta S_{con}$$

Hence the total settlement of the clay beneath the foundation is given by

$$S = \sum \Delta S = \sum \Delta S_i + \sum \Delta S_{con}$$

Thus

$$S = S_i + \mu \sum m_v \,\Delta D \,\Delta\sigma_v \qquad (4.34)$$

For a square foundation, the depth of clay that is stressed is approximately equal to 3 times the width of the foundation. For a strip foundation, the corresponding depth is approximately 8 times the foundation width. To calculate the consolidation settlement we therefore divide the stressed zone into a number of sublayers and compute the increase in total vertical stress at the mid-depth of each sublayer; this is assumed constant over the thickness of the sublayer. We then compute the consolidation settlement of each sublayer and hence by summation obtain the consolidation settlement of the foundation. From Eq. (4.34), addition of the immediate surface settlement S_i then gives the total settlement S of the foundation.

In computing the consolidation settlement it is generally sufficient to take 6 to 8 sublayers. That is, take $\Delta D = \frac{1}{2}B$ for a square or circular foundation and $\Delta D = B$ for a strip foundation.

For a *flexible foundation*, the increase in total vertical stress $\Delta\sigma_v$ on any horizontal plane in the clay layer is a maximum under the centre of the foundation and a minimum under a corner point if the foundation is rectangular or edge if the foundation is circular. Consequently, the maximum settlement occurs under the centre and the minimum under a corner or edge. The *maximum differential settlement* is the difference between the maximum and minimum settlements. For a *rigid foundation* the development of differential settlements is severely restricted and where the rigidity is high the settlement profile can be assumed to be uniform. In consequence, a rigid foundation must result in a different distribution of $\Delta\sigma_v$ on any horizontal plane to that which applies under a flexible foundation. More precisely, the effect must be to decrease the value of $\Delta\sigma_v$ under the centre of the foundation and correspondingly increase the value under the corners and edges. Calculations indicate that the value of $\Delta\sigma_v$ under the centre of a rigid foundation is on average about 0.8 times the value of $\Delta\sigma_v$ that would exist if the foundation were flexible. Thus the approach generally adopted in estimating the *uniform total settlement of a rigid foundation* is to calculate the total central settlement which would result under the centre of the equivalent flexible foundation and then multiply this value by 0.8 to account for the effects of rigidity of the foundation.

Example 4.3 An oil tank 15 m in diameter and having a flexible base is to be founded on the surface of a soft deposit of normally consolidated estuarine clay and will impose a pressure of 60 kN/m² on the soil. The clay is 20 m thick and overlies bedrock. The water table is 1 m below ground level. Calculate the maximum settlement and maximum differential settlement of the tank given that the properties of the clay are $\rho_s = 1.90$ Mg/m³, $E = 2500$ kN/m², $A = 0.7$ and $C_c = 0.2$. Typical e–σ_v' results obtained from laboratory consolidation tests were as follows:

Depth of sample = 3.5 m

σ_v', kN/m²	25	50	100	200	400
e	1.06	1.03	0.97	0.91	0.85

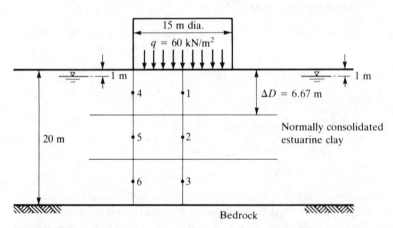

Figure 4.19 Example 4.3.

SOLUTION The problem is illustrated in Fig. 4.19.
Immediate settlement. The immediate surface settlement S_i of a circular foundation is given by

$$S = \frac{qR}{E} I_s \qquad (2.23 \text{ bis})$$

Here $q = 60$ kN/m², $R = 7.5$ m and $E = 2500$ kN/m². The value of the influence factor I_s is determined from Fig. 2.20. Thus, with $D/R = 20/7.5 = 2.67$ and $v = 0.5$ we obtain by linear interpolation: for the centre of the tank $I_s = 0.69$

whence
$$S_i = \frac{60 \times 7.5 \times 0.69}{2500} = \underline{0.124 \text{ m}}$$

and for the edge of the tank $I_s = 0.365$

whence
$$S_i = \frac{60 \times 7.5 \times 0.365}{2500} = \underline{0.066 \text{ m}}$$

Consolidation settlement. The consolidation settlement of a soil element is given by Eq. (4.33)

$$\Delta S_{con} = \mu m_v \, \Delta D \, \Delta \sigma_v$$

From Fig. 4.18, for $D/B = 20/15 = 1.33$ and $A = 0.7$ we obtain $\mu = 0.8$.

For a circular foundation the required thickness of sublayer is of the order of one-half the diameter, which in this case $= \frac{1}{2} \times 15 = 7.5$ m. As the clay layer is 20 m thick, we need to consider a maximum of 3 sublayers which we take to be of equal thickness of 6.67 m, as shown in Fig. 4.19. The increase in vertical stress $\Delta \sigma_v$ at the mid-depth of each sublayer is determined by the use of Newark's influence chart (Fig. 2.14).

As the clay is normally consolidated the average value of m_v over the depth of a sublayer is represented by the compressibility of an element at the mid-depth. Thus, if the vertical effective stress at the mid-depth of the sublayer increases by $\Delta \sigma'_v$ from an initial value σ'_{vo} to a final value σ'_{vf} then

$$m_v = \frac{\Delta e}{1 + e_o} \cdot \frac{1}{\Delta \sigma'_v} = \frac{C_c \log \dfrac{\sigma'_{vf}}{\sigma'_{vo}}}{(1 + e_o)\, \Delta \sigma'_v}$$

With $\Delta \sigma'_v = \Delta \sigma_v$ we then obtain

$$\Delta S_{con} = \mu m_v \, \Delta D \, \Delta \sigma_v = \frac{\mu C_c \, \Delta D \log \dfrac{\sigma'_{vf}}{\sigma'_{vo}}}{1 + e_o} \tag{4.35}$$

and
$$S_{con} = \sum \Delta S_{con}$$

We thus obtain the following results:

Point	Depth (m)	σ_{vo} (kN/m^2)	u_h (kN/m^2)	σ'_{vo} (kN/m^2)	e_o	n	$\Delta\sigma_v$ (kN/m^2)	σ_{vf} (kN/m^2)	σ'_{vf} (kN/m^2)	ΔS_{con} (m)
1	3.34	62.25	22.96	39.29	1.05	188	56.40	118.65	95.69	0.201
2	10.00	186.39	88.29	98.10	0.97	100	30.00	216.39	128.10	0.063
3	16.67	310.71	153.72	156.99	0.93	48	14.40	325.11	171.39	0.021
4	3.34	62.25	22.96	39.29	1.05	84	25.20	87.45	64.49	0.112
5	10.00	186.39	88.29	98.10	0.97	55	16.50	202.89	114.60	0.037
6	16.67	310.71	153.72	156.99	0.93	35	10.50	321.21	167.49	0.016

Figure 2.14

Hence consolidation settlement under centre of tank

$$= 0.201 + 0.063 + 0.021 = \underline{0.285 \text{ m}}$$

and consolidation settlement under edge of tank

$$= 0.112 + 0.037 + 0.016 = \underline{0.165 \text{ m}}$$

Thus   total settlement at centre of tank   = 0.124 + 0.285 = 0.409 m
total settlement at edge of tank   = 0.066 + 0.165 = 0.231 m
and   maximum differential settlement of tank = 0.409 − 0.231 = 0.178 m

Example 4.4 A vertical concrete column is to carry a total load of 520 kN, inclusive of self-weight above ground level. The column is to be supported by a square concrete footing 2 m × 2 m founded at a depth of 1.5 m in a 14-m thick deposit of firm boulder clay. The clay is fully saturated and overlies Bunter sandstone. Calculate the total settlement of the footing, given that the properties of the clay are $E = 10\,500$ kN/m², $A = 0.4$ and $m_v = 0.00012$ m²/kN. Neglect the difference in density between the concrete and the clay.

SOLUTION The problem is illustrated in Fig. 4.20.
As a concrete footing is a rigid foundation, there can be no differential settlement. As discussed earlier, we proceed by calculating the central settlement for the equivalent flexible foundation and then multiply by 0.8 to account for the actual rigidity of the base.

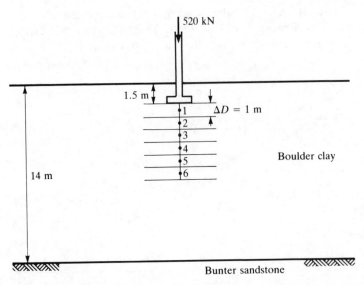

Figure 4.20 Example 4.4.

Immediate settlement at centre of footing. The immediate surface settlement S_i at the *corner* of a rectangular foundation is given by

$$S_i = \frac{qB(1 - v^2)}{E} I_s \qquad (2.21\ bis)$$

Here $q = 520/(2 \times 2) = 130$ kN/m², $B = 2/2 = 1$ m, $v = 0.5$ and $E = 10\,500$ kN/m². The value of I_s is given by Eq. (2.22) which for $v = 0.5$ reduces to $I_s = F_1$. The parameter F_1 is obtained from Fig. 2.19 where for $D/B = 12.5$ and $L/B = 1$ we find $F_1 = 0.49$. Hence, $I_s = 0.49$ and thus

$$S_i = \frac{130 \times 1 \times 0.75 \times 0.49}{10\,500} = 0.0046\ m$$

Therefore, the immediate surface settlement at the centre of the footing

$$= 0.0046 \times 4 = 0.018\ m = \underline{18\ mm}$$

Consolidation settlement at centre of footing. The consolidation settlement of a soil element is given by Eq. (4.33)

$$\Delta S_{con} = \mu m_v \, \Delta D \, \Delta \sigma_v$$

The value of μ is determined from Fig. 4.18. Thus, for $D/B = 12.5/2 = 6.25$ and $A = 0.4$ we have $\mu = 0.60$ for a strip and $\mu = 0.53$ for a circle. For a square foundation the value for μ will lie closer to the value for the circle than for the strip. Therefore take $\mu = 0.53$.

From the soil description and data given, the clay is overconsolidated. Thus, m_v ($= 0.00012 \text{ m}^2/\text{kN}$) is sensibly constant for the deposit.

As the foundation is square, take $\Delta D = \frac{1}{2}B = 1$ m and consider 6 sublayers, as shown in Fig. 4.20. The value of $\Delta \sigma_v$ at the mid-depth of each sublayer is determined by the use of Fadum's influence chart (Fig. 2.10). We thus obtain the following results:

Point	z (m)	B (m)	L (m)	$m = B/z$	$n = L/z$	I_σ	$\Delta\sigma_v$ (kN/m^2)	ΔS_{con} (m)
				Figure 2.10				
1	0.5	1	1	2.0	2.0	0.229	119.08	0.0076
2	1.5	1	1	0.67	0.67	0.123	63.96	0.0041
3	2.5	1	1	0.40	0.40	0.060	31.20	0.0020
4	3.5	1	1	0.29	0.29	0.037	19.24	0.0012
5	4.5	1	1	0.22	0.22	0.024	12.48	0.0008
6	5.5	1	1	0.18	0.18	0.016	8.32	0.0005

$$\sum = 0.0162 \text{ m}$$
$$= 16 \text{ mm}$$

Hence central settlement of equivalent flexible footing $= 18 + 16 = 34$ mm.

Therefore settlement of actual footing $= 0.8 \times 34 = \underline{27 \text{ mm}}$.

This should be satisfactory.

4.5 RADIAL CONSOLIDATION THEORY

Figure 4.21a again shows a homogeneous deposit of saturated clay of infinite lateral extent subject to a uniform pressure q applied over the whole of the surface area. The clay rests on an impermeable base and is free to drain from its upper face. If the clay is soft, it is often necessary to accelerate the rate of consolidation to limit the long-term settlement to an acceptable value. This may be achieved by installing a system of vertical sand drains as shown. The excess porewater pressures then dissipate by both vertical and radial flow. The resulting strains, however, will still only be in the vertical direction.

If the foundation through which the pressure applied to the clay deposit is *flexible*, the surface settles *differentially* during consolidation as the clay adjacent to the vertical sand drains consolidates faster than the soil in the outer zones of influence. This is referred to as the *free vertical strain* case. If on the other hand the foundation is perfectly *rigid*, the soil surface settles *uniformly* during consolidation. This is referred to as the *equal strain* case.

Considering the vertical and radial flow of porewater through an element of soil at a height z above the impermeable base and radial distance r from the vertical axis of a sand drain (Fig. 4.21) then in a similar manner to the development of the Terzaghi consolidation theory in Sec. 4.2, we

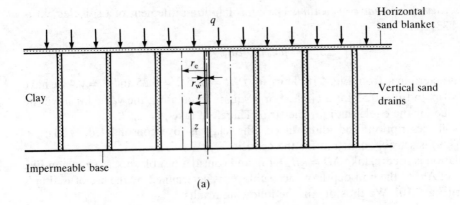

(a)

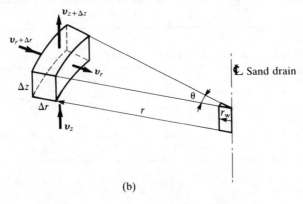

(b)

Figure 4.21 Combined vertical and radial consolidation of a soil layer.

obtain the following governing consolidation equation for conditions of *free vertical strain*:

$$c_v \frac{\partial^2 u_e}{\partial z^2} + c_h \left[\frac{\partial^2 u_e}{\partial r^2} + \frac{1}{r} \frac{\partial u_e}{\partial r} \right] = \frac{\partial u_e}{\partial t} \qquad (4.36)$$

where

$$c_v = \frac{k_v(1 + e)}{\rho_w g a_v} \qquad (4.11 \text{ bis})$$

is the coefficient of vertical consolidation, as previously defined,

and

$$c_h = \frac{k_h(1 + e)}{\rho_w g a_v} \qquad (4.37)$$

is the corresponding *coefficient of horizontal consolidation*.

It has been shown by Carrillo (1942) that Eq. (4.36) can be resolved into the linear vertical consolidation equation

$$c_v \frac{\partial^2 u_e}{\partial z^2} = \frac{\partial u_e}{\partial t} \qquad (4.10 \text{ bis})$$

and into the plane radial consolidation equation

$$c_h \left[\frac{\partial^2 u_e}{\partial r^2} + \frac{1}{r} \frac{\partial u_e}{\partial r} \right] = \frac{\partial u_e}{\partial t} \qquad (4.38)$$

If $\bar{U}_v$ is the average degree of consolidation due to vertical flow at a particular time and $\bar{U}_r$ is the *average degree of consolidation due to radial flow* at the same time, the *average degree of consolidation due to the combined vertical and radial flow*, $\bar{U}_{vr}$, is determined by the equation

$$(1 - \bar{U}_{vr}) = (1 - \bar{U}_v)(1 - \bar{U}_r) \tag{4.39}$$

As we have the solution of Eq. (4.10) for the average degree of vertical consolidation [Eq. (4.19)], then to define $\bar{U}_{vr}$ we simply require the solution of Eq. (4.38) for the average degree of radial consolidation. This has been given by Barron (1948) as

$$\bar{U}_r = 1 - \sum_{\alpha_1 \alpha_2 \dots}^{\alpha = \infty} \frac{4U_1^2(\alpha)}{\alpha^2(n^2 - 1)[n^2 U_0^2(\alpha n) - U_1^2(\alpha)]} \exp\left(-\alpha^2 n^2 T_r\right) \tag{4.40}$$

where $U_1(\alpha) = J_1(\alpha)Y_0(\alpha) - Y_1(\alpha)J_0(\alpha)$

$U_0(\alpha n) = J_0(\alpha n)Y_0(\alpha) - Y_0(\alpha n)J_0(\alpha)$

J_0, J_1 = Bessel functions of first kind, of zero order and first order respectively

Y_0, Y_1 = Bessel functions of second kind, of zero order and first order respectively

$\alpha_1, \alpha_2 \dots$ = roots of the Bessel functions which satisfy $J_1(\alpha n)Y_0(\alpha) - Y_1(\alpha n)J_0(\alpha) = 0$

$n = r_e/r_w$ where r_w is the *radius of the drain* and r_e the *radius of influence*

and T_r is a dimensionless *radial time factor* defined by

$$T_r = \frac{c_h t}{r_e^2} \tag{4.41}$$

Thus, for a specified value of n and given values of the time factor T_r, we may compute the corresponding values of the average degree of consolidation, $\bar{U}_r$. We therefore obtain the family of curves shown in Fig. 4.22. As the value of n decreases the rate of consolidation increases, as expected.

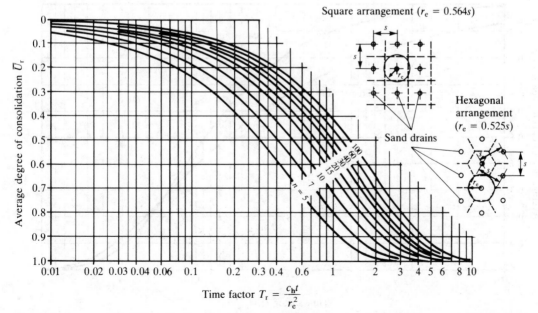

Figure 4.22 Inward radial consolidation. Average degree of consolidation $\bar{U}_r$ as a function of time factor T_r and sand drain parameter $n = r_e/r_w$.

For *equal vertical strain*, the governing consolidation equation is given by

$$c_v \frac{\partial^2 u_e}{\partial z^2} + c_h \left[\frac{\partial^2 u_e}{\partial r^2} + \frac{1}{r} \frac{\partial u_e}{\partial r} \right] = \frac{\partial \bar{u}_e}{\partial t} \tag{4.42}$$

where $\bar{u}_e$ is the average value of excess porewater pressure at any depth.

For radial flow only, Eq. (4.42) becomes

$$c_h \left[\frac{\partial^2 u_e}{\partial r^2} + \frac{1}{r} \frac{\partial u_e}{\partial r} \right] = \frac{\partial \bar{u}_e}{\partial t} \tag{4.43}$$

The solution of this equation for the average degree of radial consolidation $\bar{U}_r$ has been given by Barron (1948) as

$$\bar{U}_r = 1 - \exp \left[-\frac{2T_r}{F(n)} \right] \tag{4.44}$$

where
$$F(n) = \frac{n^2}{n^2 - 1} \ln (n) - \frac{3n^2 - 1}{4n^2}$$

For values of $n > 5$, the solution of Eq. (4.44) closely approximates that of Eq. (4.40). Therefore for all practical purposes Fig. 4.22 may be used, regardless of the imposed boundary strain condition.

In a laboratory consolidation test to measure c_h, the flow may be radially inwards to a central sand drain (Fig. 4.24a) or radially outwards to a peripheral drain (Fig. 4.24b). In the latter case we will require the corresponding theoretical solutions. Thus, for outward radial flow to a peripheral drain under conditions of free vertical strain McKinlay (1961) has obtained

$$\bar{U}_r = 1 - 4 \sum_{\alpha_1 \alpha_2 \ldots}^{\alpha = \infty} \frac{1}{\alpha^2} \exp (- \alpha^2 T_r) \tag{4.45}$$

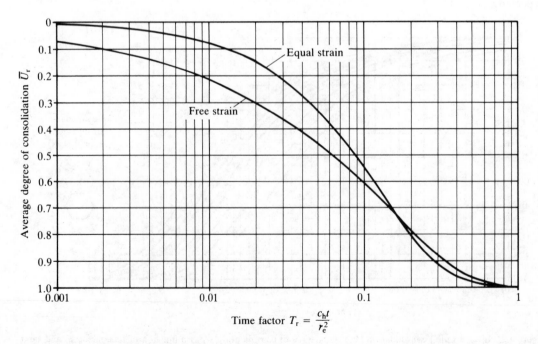

Figure 4.23 Outward radial consolidation. Average degree of consolidation $\bar{U}_r$ versus time factor T_r.

where α_1, α_2... are the roots of the Bessel function $J_0(\alpha) = 0$, and for outward radial flow to a peripheral drain under conditions of equal vertical strain Scott (1963) gives

$$\bar{U}_r = 1 - \exp(-8T_r) \tag{4.46}$$

The theoretical solutions are shown in Fig. 4.23.

4.6 RADIAL CONSOLIDATION TEST

The radial consolidation test is conveniently conducted in the Rowe cell. The flow may be radially inwards to a central sand drain (Fig. 4.24a) or radially outwards to a peripheral drain (Fig. 4.24b). The sample may be subjected to free strain or equal strain conditions. Figure 4.24 shows the arrangement for a free strain condition where the rubber jack rests directly on top of the sample. For an equal strain condition, a rigid platen is placed on top of the sample.

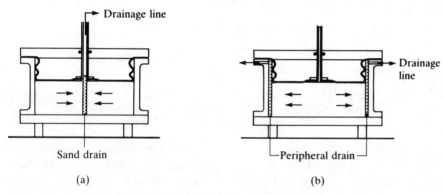

Figure 4.24 Radial consolidation tests in the Rowe cell.

The radial consolidation test is performed in much the same way as the vertical consolidation test. For free strain conditions, however, the volume change of the sample is recorded by measuring the outflow of water from the drainage line; the measurement of the central settlement is of no particular relevance here.

In a similar manner to Taylor's square root of time fitting method for determining c_v, square root of time fitting methods have also been developed for determining c_h. The relevant scaling factors are summarized in Table 4.1.

As the sample only undergoes vertical strain, the coefficient of volume compressibility m_v is determined in the same manner as for vertical consolidation tests (see Sec. 4.3).

Table 4.1 Scaling factors for 90 per cent radial consolidation

Flow direction	Strain condition	Time base	Scaling factor	T_{r90}
Inward	Free	$\sqrt{t}$	1.17	Varies with
	Equal	$\sqrt{t}$	1.17	n value— see Fig. 4.22
Outward	Free	$t^{0.465}$	1.22	0.335
	Equal	$\sqrt{t}$	1.17	0.288

The coefficient of horizontal permeability k_h may be deduced from Eq. (4.37) which on rearranging gives

$$k_h = c_h \rho_w g m_v \qquad (4.47)$$

The coefficient of horizontal permeability may also be measured directly. For this purpose the sample is set up with both a peripheral drain and and a central sand drain in order to be able to apply a differential total head radially across the sample at the end of a consolidation increment. For steady state conditions the problem is one of steady state, radially symmetrical, confined flow to a central well, the solution for which is given by Eq. (3.40):

$$Q = \frac{2\pi k D (h_e - h_w)}{\ln \dfrac{r_e}{r_w}}$$

Here $k = k_h$, $D = \Delta D$ (the thickness of the sample) and $h_e - h_w = \Delta h$ (the differential total head across the sample). $Q =$ the steady state flow rate. Thus

$$Q = \frac{2\pi k_h \, \Delta D \, \Delta h}{\ln \dfrac{r_e}{r_w}}$$

and therefore

$$k_h = \frac{Q \ln \dfrac{r_e}{r_w}}{2\pi \, \Delta D \, \Delta h} \qquad (4.48)$$

Figure 4.25 shows a comparison of results obtained from inward and outward radial consolidation tests on remoulded kaolinite under free strain conditions in the 150 mm diameter and 250 mm diameter Rowe cells. We see that the primary consolidation curves join the basic creep line at a time dependent on the boundary conditions and r_e^2 [Eq. (4.41)]. For an n value of 27 (as used herein) and the same value of r_e, an inward radial test is approximately 10 times slower than an outward radial test (compare Figs 4.22 and 4.23) and therefore the primary con-

Curves 1 and 2: outward radial consolidation in 150 mm dia. and 250 mm dia. Rowe cells
Curves 3 and 4: inward radial consolidation in 150 mm dia. and 250 mm dia. Rowe cells. $n = 27$

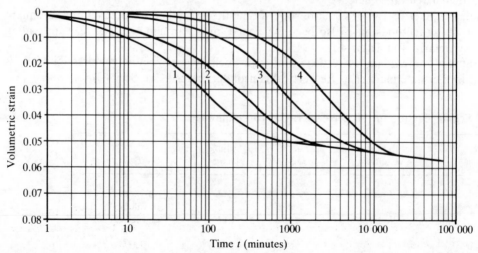

Figure 4.25 Typical radial consolidation test results.

solidation curves should be separated by approximately one cycle of time. This is seen to be so. It may also be verified that the primary consolidation curves for the inward and outward radial consolidation tests scale according to r_e^2, as defined by Eq. (4.41). In this particular case the scaling factor is

$$\frac{t_2}{t_1} = \left[\frac{r_{e2}}{r_{e1}}\right]^2 = \left[\frac{125}{75}\right]^2 = 2.78$$

4.7 DESIGN OF VERTICAL SAND DRAINS

The principal application of the radial consolidation theory is in the design of vertical sand drains to accelerate the rate of consolidation of soft clay deposits. This is illustrated in the following examples.

Example 4.5 A motorway embankment 5 m high and 30 m wide is to be constructed on a 7 m thick deposit of normally consolidated alluvial clay which overlies 4 m of sand resting on bedrock. The water table is at a depth of 1 m.

The embankment is to be constructed in 6 months and surfacing is to be carried out 1 year after completion. If a maximum settlement of 40 mm can be tolerated after surfacing, design a system of vertical sand drains which would enable this condition to be complied with. For the fill $\rho = 2.10$ Mg/m³ and for the clay $\rho_s = 1.80$ Mg/m³, $e_o = 1.06$, $C_c = 0.30$, $c_v = 1.5$ m²/yr and $c_h = 7$ m²/yr.

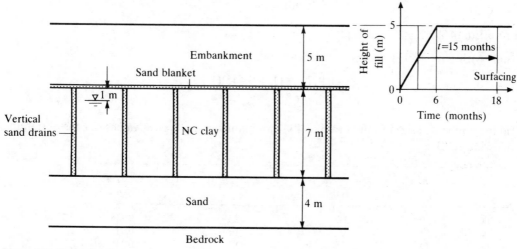

Figure 4.26 Example 4.5.

SOLUTION The problem is illustrated in Fig. 4.26.

The surface pressure q applied from the weight of the embankment is given by

$$q = 2.1 \times 9.81 \times 5 = 103.01 \text{ kN/m}^2$$

The width of the embankment is large compared with the thickness of the clay, and therefore the increase in total vertical stress $\Delta\sigma_v$ in the clay is constant with depth and equal to the applied surface pressure q. Thus

$$\Delta\sigma_v = 103.01 \text{ kN/m}^2$$

The initial vertical effective stress at the mid-depth of the clay layer is given by

$$\sigma'_{vo} = 1.8 \times 9.81 \times 3.5 - 1 \times 9.81 \times 2.5 = 37.28 \text{ kN/m}^2$$

The final vertical effective stress is then

$$\sigma'_{vf} = \sigma'_{vo} + \Delta\sigma_v = 37.28 + 103.01 = 140.29 \text{ kN/m}^2$$

whence the ultimate consolidation settlement of the clay is given by [Eq. (4.32)]

$$S = \frac{C_c D \log \dfrac{\sigma'_{vf}}{\sigma'_{vo}}}{1 + e_o} = \frac{0.3 \times 7 \times \log \dfrac{140.29}{37.28}}{2.06} = 0.587 \text{ m}$$

Thus settlement required prior to surfacing = $587 - 40 = \underline{547 \text{ mm}}$.

Now the average time to commencement of surfacing = 15 months = 1.25 years. $H = 3.5$ m, since the clay is double drained, and therefore

$$T_v = \frac{c_v t}{H^2} = \frac{1.5 \times 1.25}{3.5^2} = 0.153$$

Thus, from Fig. 4.6 $\bar{U}_v = 0.445$

Hence settlement of clay due to vertical consolidation only = $0.445 \times 587 = 261$ mm. As we require to achieve a settlement of 547 mm, we will need to install vertical sand drains to accelerate the rate of consolidation. The required value of $\bar{U}_{vr}$ is given by

$$\bar{U}_{vr} = \frac{547}{587} = 0.932$$

From Eq. (4.39) $(1 - \bar{U}_{vr}) = (1 - \bar{U}_v)(1 - \bar{U}_r)$

Thus, with $\bar{U}_{vr} = 0.932$ and $\bar{U}_v = 0.445$ we obtain

$$(1 - 0.932) = (1 - 0.445)(1 - \bar{U}_r)$$

giving $\bar{U}_r = 0.877$

Taking a practical size of sand drain of 400 mm diameter and typical values of n we obtain the following results:

r_w (mm)	n	$r_e = r_w n$ (m)	$T_r = \dfrac{c_h t}{r_e^2}$	$\bar{U}_r$ (Fig. 4.22)
200	10	2.0	2.19	0.935
200	11	2.20	1.81	0.88
200	12	2.40	1.52	0.82

We see then that 400-mm diameter sand drains at an effective radius of 2.20 m will give the required degree of consolidation. In a similar manner other suitable combinations of r_w and r_e may be determined. For example, 300 mm drains at $r_e = 2.10$ m will achieve the same effect.

4.8 PRELOADING

Preloading is a technique used to reduce to an acceptable level the post-construction settlements of soft clays and peats. The principle is illustrated in Fig. 4.27 with particular reference to the

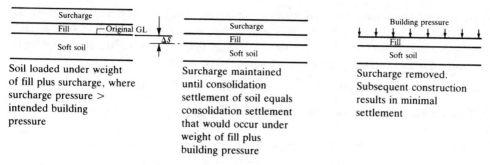

Figure 4.27 Principle of preloading.

construction of housing and industrial estates. Considering the normal practice of constructing on a specified height of compacted fill, the height is initially increased a predetermined amount above this level. This additional height of fill is referred to as the *surcharge* and is maintained in place until the consolidation settlement of the deposit equals that which would result under the direct application of the fill and the building pressure. The surcharge is then removed and subsequent construction results in minimal settlement. The greater the surcharge applied, the shorter the period it needs to be maintained to achieve the required consolidation settlement.

Preloading may also be used in conjunction with vertical sand drains, as illustrated in the following example.

Example 4.6 An investigation at a particular site for a new Industrial Estate showed 6 m of soft normally consolidated clay overlying a thick deposit of sand. The water table was at a depth of 1 m.

It is proposed to support the various buildings and access roads on 2 m of compacted fill material spread over the whole area. The fill is to be placed at a rate of 0.5 m per month and construction of the buildings is to commence 1 year after the start of placement of the fill. It is estimated that the buildings will impose an additional uniform pressure of 25 kN/m². If the post-construction settlement is not to exceed 60 mm and if a temporary surcharge of 1 m of fill is to be applied, design a suitable system of vertical sand drains to enable this requirement to be met. For the fill $\rho = 2 \, \text{Mg/m}^3$ and for the clay $\rho_s = 1.87 \, \text{Mg/m}^3$, $e_o = 0.95$, $C_c = 0.40$, $c_v = 3 \, \text{m}^2/\text{yr}$ and $c_h = 5.5 \, \text{m}^2/\text{yr}$.

SOLUTION The problem is illustrated in Fig. 4.28.

The initial vertical effective stress at the mid-depth of the clay layer is

$$\sigma'_{vo} = 1.87 \times 9.81 \times 3 - 1 \times 9.81 \times 2 = 35.41 \, \text{kN/m}^2$$

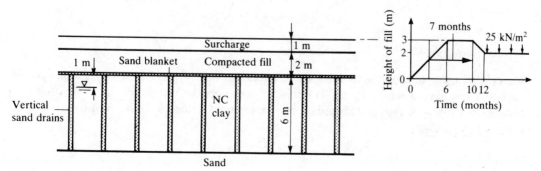

Figure 4.28 Example 4.6.

The loaded area will be wide compared with the thickness of the clay layer, and therefore the increase in total vertical stress in the clay will be constant with depth and equal to the applied surface pressure. Hence, the final vertical effective stress at the mid-depth of the clay layer under the 2 m of fill and the building pressure of 25 kN/m² is given by

$$\sigma'_{vf} = 35.41 + 2 \times 9.81 \times 2 + 25 = 99.65 \text{ kN/m}^2$$

whence the ultimate consolidation settlement of the clay is [Eq. (4.32)]

$$S = \frac{0.4 \times 6 \times \log \dfrac{99.65}{35.41}}{1.95} = 0.533 \text{ m} = \underline{553 \text{ mm}}$$

The final vertical effective stress at the mid-depth of the clay layer under 2 m of fill only is

$$\sigma'_{vf} = 35.41 + 2 \times 9.81 \times 2 = 74.65 \text{ kN/m}^2$$

whence
$$S = \frac{0.4 \times 6 \times \log \dfrac{74.65}{35.41}}{1.95} = 0.399 \text{ m} = \underline{399 \text{ mm}}$$

If all of this settlement were to be achieved prior to the construction of the buildings, the post-construction settlement would equal $553 - 399 = 154$ mm, which is considerably in excess of the specified maximum value of 60 mm. We thus need to incorporate a temporary surcharge, as stipulated in the problem.

The required settlement of the clay layer prior to the commencement of the building construction $= 553 - 60 = 493$ mm. The 2 m of fill plus the surcharge must be capable of producing an ultimate consolidation settlement greater than this. Thus, for the stipulated surcharge height of 1 m we obtain

$$\sigma'_{vf} = 35.41 + 2 \times 9.81 \times 3 = 94.27 \text{ kN/m}^2$$

and
$$S = \frac{0.4 \times 6 \times \log \dfrac{94.27}{35.41}}{1.95} = 0.523 \text{ m} = \underline{523 \text{ mm}}$$

The surcharge height of 1 m is therefore satisfactory.

The required settlement of 493 mm must in fact be achieved after a period of 10 months (see Fig. 4.28), since the settlement of the clay layer will be arrested during the removal of the surcharge. The 3 m of fill will then have been acting for an average time of 7 months. Thus

$$T_v = \frac{c_v t}{H^2} = \frac{3 \times \dfrac{7}{12}}{3^2} = 0.194$$

whence from Fig. 4.6
$$\bar{U}_v = 0.495$$

Hence settlement of clay due to vertical consolidation only $= 0.495 \times 523 = 259$ mm. As we require to achieve a settlement of 493 mm, we will need to install vertical sand drains to accelerate further the rate of consolidation. The required value of $\bar{U}_{vr}$ is given by

$$\bar{U}_{vr} = \frac{493}{523} = 0.943$$

From Eq. (4.39)
$$(1 - \bar{U}_{vr}) = (1 - \bar{U}_v)(1 - \bar{U}_r)$$

Thus with $\bar{U}_{vr} = 0.943$ and $\bar{U}_v = 0.495$ we obtain

$$(1 - 0.943) = (1 - 0.495)(1 - \bar{U}_r)$$

giving $\qquad\qquad \bar{U}_r = 0.887$

Considering 300 mm diameter sand drains we obtain the following results:

r_w	n	$r_e = r_w n$	$T_r = \dfrac{c_h t}{r_e^2}$	$\bar{U}_r$
(mm)		(m)		(Fig. 4.22)
150	10	1.50	1.43	0.83
150	9	1.35	1.76	0.905

Thus, 300 mm diameter sand drains at an effective radius of 1.35 m will give the required degree of consolidation. Alternatively, 250 mm drains at $r_e = 1.31$ m would also suffice.

4.9 INFLUENCE OF MACROSTRUCTURE OF CLAY DEPOSITS ON THE MEASURED VALUE OF c_h

If a clay deposit is uniform, a conventional small-sized sample (i.e., 75 mm diameter by 20 mm thick) will be representative of the mass, and the value of c_h obtained will be applicable to the mass. In practice, however, clay deposits often contain a more permeable macrostructure, as for example layered and varved clays, and silt-filled fissured clays, and unless one tests a sample which is large enough to encompass the natural fabric of the clay, the value of c_h obtained will not reflect the mass value.

To demonstrate the influence of macrostructure on the measured value of c_h, consider the three test situations shown in Fig. 4.29. The tests may be envisaged as being conducted in the 75 mm, 150 mm and 250 mm diameter Rowe cells. In test 1 on the conventional sized sample, the same is

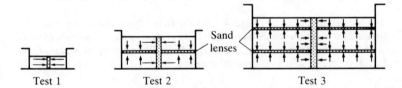

Test 1   Test 2   Sand lenses   Test 3

Figure 4.29 Radial consolidation tests on samples of a layered clay.

not large enough to encompass any of the sand lenses. As a result, the flow is purely radial to the sand drain and the value of c_h obtained reflects that of a uniform clay. In test 2 the sample is sufficiently large to encompass a single sand lens. The flow of water in elements furthest away from the sand drain will now take the shorter vertical route to the sand lens which drains rapidly in the radial direction. As a result, the time for consolidation of the sample is shorter than it would be if the sand lens had not been present and consequently the measured value of c_h will be greater than that measured in test 1. In test 3, on an even larger sample, we see that the internal geometry is such that the flow pattern will be predominantly vertical to the sand lenses. The measured value of c_h will now be greater than that in test 2.

Thus for laminated, layered or varved clays, the measured value of the coefficient of horizontal consolidation increases as the size of the sample increases, ultimately approaching the field value. The form of the relationship is illustrated in Fig. 4.30. The shape of the curve depends on the

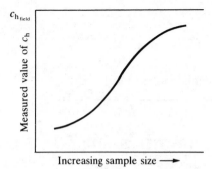

Figure 4.30 Influence of sample size on measured value of c_h.

internal geometry of the sand and clay layers and their relative permeability values. If the maximum value of c_h is not reached in the range tested, then it may be estimated by extrapolation. In some cases it may be necessary to deduce the field value of c_h from *in situ* measurements of k_h coupled with laboratory measurements of m_v using $c_h = k_h/\rho_w g m_v$.

It has been found by Rowe (1968b) that the value of c_h obtained from tests on 250-mm diameter samples may be as much as 100–1000 times the value obtained from tests on conventional sized samples. In a number of cases this indicated that the natural rate of consolidation of the soil mass would be sufficient without the use of sand drains.

Because the installation of sand drains is expensive, it is important that only the minimum number necessary are used in any project. An essential prerequisite for this is that the field value of c_h is accurately assessed for use in the design.

PROBLEMS

4.1 The soil conditions at a small private airfield consist of, in succession, 5 m of sand, 8 m of normally consolidated estuarine clay, 1 m of gravel and 7 m of boulder clay overlying impermeable bedrock. The water table is 0.5 m below ground level.

An adjacent site is scheduled for extensive development, the first stage of which will be to install a dewatering system. It is estimated that the effect of this on the airfield will be to lower the water table to an average depth of 3 m below ground level. If the water table is maintained at this new level for a period of two years, calculate the resulting settlement of the ground surface at the airfield given that the properties of the various soil strata are

Sand: $\rho = 1.84$ Mg/m^3, $\rho_s = 2.07$ Mg/m^3
Estuarine clay: $\rho_s = 1.88$ Mg/m^3, $e_o = 0.94$, $C_c = 0.46$, $c_v = 1.05$ m^2/yr
Gravel: $\rho_s = 1.95$ Mg/m^3
Boulder clay: $\rho_s = 1.96$ Mg/m^3, $m_v = 0.00026$ m^2/kN, $c_v = 2.34$ m^2/yr
[Ans. 76 mm (64 mm from the estuarine clay, 12 mm from the boulder clay)]

4.2 A surface deposit of sand 10 m thick overlies a 6-m thick layer of normally consolidated clay which rests on a layer of dense gravel. The groundwater level in the sand is 2 m below ground level. If this is lowered to a depth of 8 m, calculate the vertical total stress, porewater pressure and vertical effective stress at the mid-depth of the clay layer

(a) before lowering the water table,
(b) immediately after lowering the water table,
(c) an infinitely long time after lowering the water table, and
(d) one year after lowering the water table.

The properties of the sand are $\rho = 1.67$ Mg/m^3, $\rho_s = 2.0$ Mg/m^3, and of the clay $\rho_s = 1.80$ Mg/m^3, $c_v = 2.7$ m^2/yr.

Ans. (a) 242.70 kN/m^2, 107.91 kN/m^2, 134.79 kN/m^2
(b) 223.28 kN/m^2, 88.49 kN/m^2, 134.79 kN/m^2
(c) 223.28 kN/m^2, 49.05 kN/m^2, 174.23 kN/m^2
(d) 223.28 kN/m^2, 72.71 kN/m^2, 150.57 kN/m^2

4.3 The soil profile at a particular site consists of 10 m of firm brown overconsolidated clay, 3 m of dense sand and 12 m of stiff grey overconsolidated clay resting on a thick deposit of gravel. The natural groundwater level and the piezometric level for the gravel are both at the ground surface, while the piezometric level for the dense sand is 4 m above the ground surface.

It is proposed to install a number of wells in the sand and abstract water to supplement a local water supply scheme. The effect of this will be to reduce the piezometric level for the sand by 3 m over a wide area. Calculate the long-term effect of this reduction in piezometric level on the ground surface level over the site, given that for the brown clay $m_v = 0.0003$ m^2/kN and for the grey clay $m_v = 0.0002$ m^2/kN.

[Ans.   79 mm settlement (44 mm from the brown clay, 35 mm from the grey clay)]

4.4 An oil tank 18 m diameter and having a flexible base is to be founded on the surface of a soft deposit of normally consolidated estuarine clay and will impose a pressure of 50 kN/m^2 on the soil. The clay is 6 m thick and overlies bedrock. The water table is at the ground surface. Calculate the maximum differential settlement of the tank given that the properties of the clay are $\rho_s = 1.85$ Mg/m^3, $E = 1800$ kN/m^2, $v = 0.5$, $e_o = 0.95$, $C_c = 0.40$ and $A = 0.8$.

[Ans.   262 mm (central settlement = 612 mm, edge settlement = 350 mm)]

4.5 A vertical concrete column is to carry a total load of 648 kN, inclusive of self-weight above ground level. The column is to be supported by a concrete footing 1.5 m × 2.5 m founded at a depth of 1.5 m in an 8-m thick deposit of firm boulder clay. The clay is fully saturated and overlies a thick deposit of dense gravel. Calculate the total settlement of the footing given that the properties of the clay are $E = 6300$ kN/m^2, $v = 0.5$, $A = 0.2$ and $m_v = 0.0002$ m^2/kN. Neglect the difference in density between the concrete and the clay.

[Ans.   50 mm]

4.6 An investigation at a particular site for a housing development revealed a 5-m thick deposit of clay ($m_v = 0.0006$ m^2/kN, $c_v = 3.12$ m^2/yr, $c_h = 9.50$ m^2/yr) overlying a thick deposit of dense sand. The land area is low lying and prone to flooding, and therefore it is decided to raise the ground level by 2.5 m. This is to be done by spreading a thin drainage blanket of sand on the surface of the clay followed by the rapid placement of compacted fill at a density of 1.90 Mg/m^3.

(a) Calculate the total settlement of the clay deposit which would result from this loading, and the time required for 90 per cent consolidation.

(b) In order that construction of the houses can commence on schedule, it is necessary to achieve this 90 per cent degree of consolidation within one year of placing the fill. The contractor considers that this can be achieved either by the installation of vertical sand drains or by the application of a surcharge load in the form of an increased height of fill material, the excess of which would be removed after one year. For these proposals

 (i) design a suitable system of vertical sand drains, and
(ii) calculate the required surcharge height of fill material.

⎡Ans.   (a) 140 mm; 1.70 yr
⎢   (b) (i) 300 mm diameter sand drains at $r_e = 3.15$ m.   (ii) 0.433 m⎤

4.7 An investigation carried out at the site of a proposed motorway embankment revealed the following soil profile.

Depth	Soil type	Properties
0–6 m	Grey CLAY containing frequent thin layers of silt and sand	$m_v = 0.00035$ m^2/kN $c_v = 0.7$ m^2/yr $c_h = 40.7$ m^2/yr
6–8 m	Dense sandy GRAVEL	
8–12 m	Brown silty CLAY	$m_v = 0.00025$ m^2/kN $c_v = 5.0$ m^2/yr $c_h = 7.9$ m^2/yr
Below 12 m	SANDSTONE	

The fill material for the embankment has a bulk density of 1.9 Mg/m^3, and it is anticipated that construction of the embankment to its completed height of 15 m will take 6 months. Thereafter, surfacing has to commence a further 6 months after construction is complete. If the maximum permissible settlement after surfacing is 50 mm, design a sand drain installation which would enable this condition to be complied with.

[Ans.   400 mm diameter sand drains at $r_e = 3.30$ m installed in the grey clay only]

FIVE

SHEAR STRENGTH THEORY

The *shear strength* of a soil is its maximum resistance to shear. Its value determines such factors as the stability of a slope, the allowable bearing capacity of a foundation and the thrust of a soil against a retaining wall. A knowledge of the shear strength is thus an essential prerequisite to any analysis concerned with the stability of a soil mass.

5.1 COULOMB FAILURE EQUATION

In 1776 Coulomb observed that if the thrust of a soil against a retaining wall caused the wall to move forward slightly, an essentially straight slip plane formed in the retained soil. He postulated that the *maximum resistance to shear*, τ_f, on the failure plane is given by

$$\tau_f = c + \sigma \tan \phi \qquad (5.1)$$

where σ is the total stress normal to the failure plane

ϕ is the *angle of friction* of the soil

and c is the *cohesion* of the soil.

Coulomb's equation is purely an empirical relationship and is based on Amonton's law of friction for sliding between two plane surfaces, with the inclusion of a cohesion term c to account for the inherent 'stiction' of clay soils. For granular materials $c = 0$ and hence $\tau_f = \sigma \tan \phi$.

The use of Coulomb's equation did not always result in the successful design of soil structures. The reason for this did not become apparent until 1925 when Terzaghi published the principle of effective stress, $\sigma = \sigma' + u$ [Eq. (2.2)]. It was then readily appreciated that, since water cannot sustain shear stress, the shear resistance of a soil must result solely from the frictional resistance arising at the particle contact points, the magnitude of which depends solely on the magnitude of the effective stress carried by the soil skeleton. Thus, the greater the effective stress normal to a potential failure plane, the greater the resistance to shear on the plane. Hence, expressing Coulomb's equation in terms of effective stress:

$$\tau_f = c' + \sigma' \tan \phi' \qquad (5.2)$$

in which the parameters c' and ϕ' are properties of the *soil skeleton*, referred to respectively as the *effective cohesion* and the *effective angle of friction*.

Since the shear strength is controlled by the effective stresses in the soil, then fundamentally a stability analysis should be carried out in terms of effective stress. In certain circumstances, however, the analysis may be in terms of total stress and therefore in general we require to determine both the effective stress and total stress shear strength parameters of the soil. That is, the values of c', ϕ' and c, ϕ. These are usually obtained from laboratory tests on representative samples of the soil mass using either the direct shear test (ASTM D–3080–72) or the triaxial compression test (ASTM D–2850–70).

5.2 DIRECT SHEAR TEST

Figure 5.1a shows the essential details of the direct shear apparatus in which a soil sample is contained in a box split horizontally into two halves. A normal force N is applied to the sample through the top loading platen and, by constraining the upper half of the box, the sample is sheared on a horizontal plane by the application of a shear force S. The vertical movement of the sample during shear is measured by means of a dial gauge resting on the top platen.

The design of the shear box does not allow control of drainage of the sample. This is not a limitation in the case of sands and gravels which are free-draining materials and as such will generally shear under fully drained conditions. For clay deposits, however, depending on the rate at which the mass is stressed, a soil element in the field may fail either completely undrained (no dissipation of excess porewater pressure), partially drained (some dissipation of excess porewater pressure) or fully drained (complete dissipation of excess porewater pressure). Although an attempt could be made to measure the *undrained* strength by shearing a sample rapidly in a few minutes, because there is no control over the drainage there would obviously be a degree of uncertainty as to whether this represented the true value of the undrained strength. For this reason the undrained shear strength of a clay soil is usually measured in the triaxial cell which permits full control over drainage of the sample. The direct shear test may, however, be used to measure the *drained* strength of clay soils by first consolidating the sample fully under the applied normal load and then shearing the sample at a sufficiently slow rate to ensure that excess porewater pressures set up by the shear force dissipate as fast as they are generated, so that u remains equal to zero throughout the shearing process. Thus, for drained clays and sands the effective stress normal to the shear plane is given by $\sigma' = N/A$ and the associated shear stress $\tau = S/A$ where A is the plan area of the shear box.

Figure 5.1b shows typical stress–strain–volume change relationships obtained for drained tests on loose and dense sands. For a *loose* sand the volume decreases during shear as the soil particles in the failure zone move into a denser packing. At large shear strains of the order of 20 per cent, the sample shears at a *constant volume* under a *constant value of shear stress*. At these large strains the tendency for a volume increase as some particles move up and over each other is nullified by adjacent particles moving down into the void spaces created, with the result that the *nett volume change is zero*. At this condition the sample is said to be in the *critical void ratio state* or *constant void ratio state*. For a *dense* sand, the interlocking grains have to move apart (i.e., move up and over each other) in order to allow relative movement or shear between the grains to occur. Thus the sample expands during shear, a phenomenon known as *dilatancy*, and consequently does work against the confining pressure. The *peak shear stress* therefore occurs at that particular value of shear strain where the *dilatancy rate is a maximum*. With increasing shear strain, the dilatancy rate decreases as the sample approaches the constant void ratio state and the shear stress decreases to a *residual value*. For the same confining pressure, the residual shear stress of a dense sample is

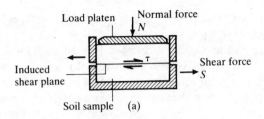

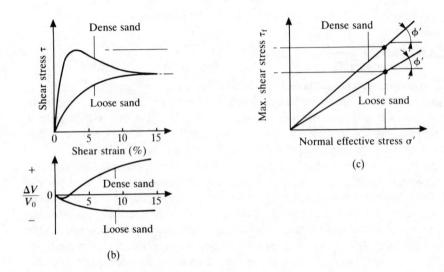

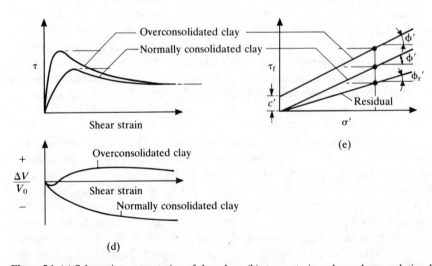

Figure 5.1 (a) Schematic representation of shear box, (b) stress–strain–volume change relationships for drained tests on sands, (c) failure envelopes for drained tests on sands, (d) stress–strain–volume change relationships for drained tests on clays, (e) failure envelopes for drained tests on clays.

Table 5.1 Values of ϕ' for granular soils (after Terzaghi and Peck, 1967)

Soil type	ϕ' (degrees)	
	Loose	Dense
Silt	27–30	30–34
Silty sand	27–33	30–35
Uniform sand	28	34
Well graded sand	33	45
Sandy gravel	35	50

equal to the maximum shear stress of a loose sample. Typical failure strains for loose sands are around 12–16 per cent; for dense sands around 2–4 per cent.

The effective angle of friction for a particular density state is obtained by plotting the maximum value of shear stress τ_f against the effective normal stress σ' (Fig. 5.1c). A number of tests are carried out at different values of confining pressure and a straight line drawn from the origin (since $c' = 0$ for granular soils) and passing through the respective points defines the *failure envelope*, the slope of the line denoting the value of ϕ'. Typical values for granular soils are given in Table 5.1.

It is clear from parts b and c of Fig. 5.1 that volume changes have a fundamental influence on the shear strength of a soil. Such effects are reflected empirically in the Coulomb ϕ' value. A detailed consideration, however, requires a study of the particulate behaviour of a soil to separate the strength component due to particle structure from that of interparticle friction (see, for example, Rowe, 1962, 1972a; Horne, 1965, 1969).

Figure 5.1d shows the form of stress–strain–volume change relationships obtained for drained tests on normally consolidated and overconsolidated clays. For *normally consolidated clays*, the decrease in shear stress from the peak to the residual is associated with a gradual orientation of the clay particles in the shear zone with their flat surfaces aligning parallel to the failure plane, thus presenting the minimum resistance to shear. The fall-off in post-peak shear stress increases with increase in plasticity index. For *overconsolidated clays* there is a marked decrease in shear stress from the peak to the residual as a result partly of dilatancy within the plane of failure and partly of horizontal alignment of the clay particles. The difference between the peak and residual shear stresses increases with increase in overconsolidation ratio and plasticity index. Typical failure strains in normally consolidated clays are around 20 per cent; in overconsolidated clays around 6 per cent.

Very large shear strains are necessary to establish the residual state and cannot be reached by a single displacement in the shear box. Repeated reversals of shear direction are sometimes used to build-up the required displacements but this disturbs the particle alignment and does not achieve the true minimum state. The problem is overcome by using the ring shear apparatus (Bishop *et al.*, 1971) which tests an annulus of soil in a ring split horizontally at its mid-section, allowing the lower half of the sample to be sheared continuously in one direction over a stationary-held upper half with no change in contact area between the two faces.

Figure 5.1e shows the form of the failure envelopes obtained from direct shear tests on drained samples of normally consolidated and overconsolidated clays. Overconsolidated clays are characterized by an intercept on the vertical τ_f axis defining a value of c' for the soil. This usually ranges from 5 to 30 kN/m². For fissured clays there is some evidence that c' measured in a laboratory test tends to zero with time in the field. For normally consolidated clays $c' = 0$, the failure envelope passing through the origin. The value of ϕ' is not influenced appreciably by overconsolidation and generally ranges from about 30° to 20°, decreasing with increasing plasticity index. The *residual* effective angle of friction ϕ'_r may be as low as 9° or so for clays of high plasticity index and determines the stability of embankments and cuttings formed on ground which has suffered previous shear failure at some past geological time. For clay deposits which have randomly oriented fissures, the mass behaves with an average value of ϕ' intermediate between that of the peak value of the intact clay and that of the residual value on a fissure plane (Skempton, 1964).

5.3 TRIAXIAL COMPRESSION TEST

The measurement of soil properties in the triaxial test has been considered in detail by Bishop and Henkel (1962) and is the standard reference work on this subject.

Apparatus and Procedure

Figure 5.2 shows the essential details of the triaxial cell in which a soil sample is sealed within a water-tight rubber membrane and enclosed in a cell filled with water through which a confining pressure is applied to the sample. Drainage facility is provided by strips of filter paper placed vertically around the sample. These connect with a porous disc in the top platen, the take-off being through a nylon tube which passes out of the cell through its base. The porewater pressure in the sample is measured through a saturated porous disc sealed flush in the base pedestal and connected via a water-filled duct to an electrical pressure transducer. The sample is sheared by a vertical piston load applied through the top platen. To minimize the friction forces at the top and bottom of the sample and allow an unrestricted lateral deformation during shear, greased rubber discs are placed between the sample and the end caps. The form of the test may either be *strain*

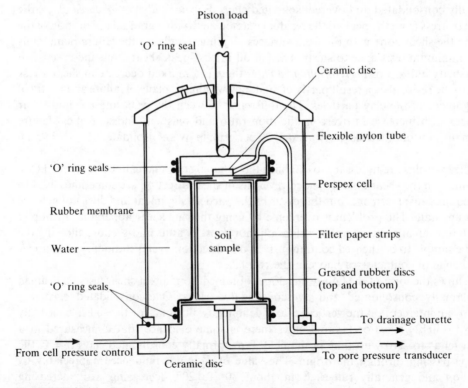

Figure 5.2 Triaxial cell.

controlled, in which case the vertical piston load is applied by a motorized loading frame geared to deform the sample vertically at a constant rate of strain, or *stress controlled*, in which case the sample is allowed to strain freely under a vertical piston load applied by dead weights.

By eliminating the shear stresses on the top and bottom boundaries of the sample, and since no shear stress can act between the cell water and the vertical surface of the sample, it follows that the axial stress and the ambient cell pressure are both principal stresses. Under the conditions of the triaxial test, the major principal stress σ_1 is the axial stress and the intermediate and minor principal stresses, σ_2 and σ_3, are both equal to the all-round cell pressure. This of course acts not only on the vertical surface of the sample but also on the end faces. Thus, if at some stage of the shear test the vertical piston load is P and the current cross-sectional area of the sample is A then

$$\sigma_1 = \frac{P}{A} + \sigma_3$$

whence

$$\frac{P}{A} = \sigma_1 - \sigma_3 \tag{5.3}$$

The applied piston stress P/A is therefore in actual fact equal to the difference between the major and minor principal total stresses, $\sigma_1 - \sigma_3$, which is termed the *deviator stress* and denoted as D.

The application of the all-round cell pressure and application of the deviator stress form two separate stages of the test. Whether drainage of the sample is permitted during each stage depends upon the soil type and nature of the field problem being investigated. As noted in Sec. 5.2, a soil element in the field (notably an element of clay soil) may fail either undrained, partially drained or drained. We thus have three basic types of test: undrained, consolidated–undrained and drained.

Undrained Test

This test is applicable to the short-term stability analysis of works formed on or in clay deposits where it is considered that insufficient time has elapsed for any dissipation of excess porewater pressure to have occurred by the end of construction. Such works generally include small embankments, cuttings, retaining walls and foundations for buildings.

The undrained strength of a clay is obtained by testing a soil sample throughout under undrained conditions, no drainage being permitted during the application of the cell pressure nor during the application of the deviator stress. Figure 5.3 shows the typical form of the stress–strain curves obtained for undisturbed samples of normally consolidated and overconsolidated clays. The failure strains are usually in the range 2–5 per cent but may be as high as 30 per cent in the case of boulder clays and remoulded soils.

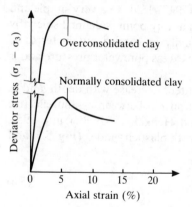

Figure 5.3 Stress–strain relationships for undrained tests on undisturbed samples of clay.

If the clay sample is saturated the increase in cell pressure is carried entirely by the porewater as an excess porewater pressure with no change in effective stress in the sample and therefore no change in shear strength. Thus, the deviator stress required to fail the sample is independent of the cell pressure at which the test is run. Figure 5.4 shows the corresponding Mohr stress circles, the common tangent to which defines the failure envelope for the soil, which in this case is horizontal giving $\phi_u = 0$; the intercept on the vertical shear stress axis defines the *undrained cohesion* c_u. The undrained shear strength, τ_{fu}, in terms of total stress is thus

$$\tau_{fu} = c_u + \sigma \tan \phi_u$$

Since $\phi_u = 0$ then

$$\tau_{fu} = c_u \tag{5.4}$$

The undrained cohesion thus defines the undrained shear strength. As such, c_u is more generally referred to as the *undrained shear strength*. And as the failure envelope is horizontal

$$c_u = \tfrac{1}{2}(\sigma_1 - \sigma_3)_f = \tfrac{1}{2}D_f \tag{5.5}$$

where the deviator stress at failure, D_f, defines the *compression strength of the sample.*

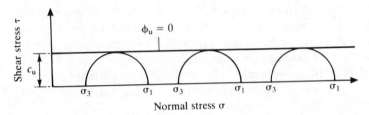

Figure 5.4 Failure envelope for undrained tests on saturated clay.

In Fig. 5.4 the samples are failed in the conventional manner by holding σ_3 constant and increasing σ_1. Since the deviator stress at failure is independent of the cell pressure, the same result is obtained no matter what stress path is followed. The undrained total stress parameters are thus unique and independent of the test procedure used to measure them. This is a particularly important result for it means that soil elements in the field where the stress path conditions to failure are more complex with σ_1 and σ_3 both varying, will all have the same value of c_u and $\phi_u = 0$. This would suggest that where the stress change likely to cause failure occurs under undrained conditions, the stability analysis may be carried out in terms of total stress. The reasonableness of this assumption is borne out by the close agreement that has been obtained between observed and predicted short-term failures of works formed on and in clay deposits (Cooling and Golder, 1942; Skempton and Golder, 1948; Bjerrum and Eide, 1956). This particular form of analysis, known as the $\phi_u = 0$ *analysis* after Skempton (1948), leads to a very simple and rapid assessment of stability since the undrained shear strength at any point is defined solely by the undrained cohesion c_u (Eq. 5.4). Such analyses could equally be carried out in terms of effective stress, but this requires the explicit determination of the excess porewater pressure and is therefore more involved than a total stress analysis.

In a normally consolidated clay the void ratio and water content decrease with depth, and in consequence the undrained shear strength increases. The relationship between c_u and effective overburden pressure σ'_{vo} is found to be linear (Skempton and Henkel, 1953; Bjerrum, 1954; Milligan et al., 1962), The ratio c_u/σ'_{vo} is also found to increase with plasticity index (Fig. 5.5) and is closely approximated by the equation (Skempton, 1957)

$$\frac{c_u}{\sigma'_{vo}} = 0.11 + 0.0037 \, I_p \tag{5.6}$$

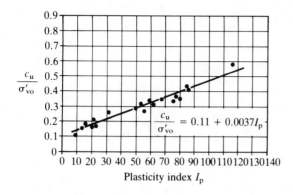

$$\frac{c_u}{\sigma'_{vo}} = 0.11 + 0.0037 I_p$$

Plasticity index I_p

Figure 5.5 (From Skempton, 1957.)

Overconsolidated clays do not, in general, show a marked reduction in water content or increase in shear strength with depth. c_u cannot be related to the index properties of the soil, partly because these cannot reflect adequately the stress history of a deposit and partly because the measured value of undrained shear strength is strongly influenced by the macrostructure (i.e., whether the clay is fissured or intact).

The value of the undrained shear strength of a clay may be used to indicate its consistency state. Table 5.2 shows the definitions given in BS 5930: 1981 and those employed by Terzaghi and Peck (1967).

If the porewater pressure is measured in a series of undrained tests on saturated samples it is found that the same effective stress failure circle is obtained in each case, and hence the effective stress parameters c' and ϕ' cannot be determined from such tests. Recourse is made to consolidated–undrained or drained tests for this purpose.

Undrained tests may also be carried out on partially saturated soils, for example, samples of a rolled clay fill or laboratory-compacted samples of earth fill. In this case the increase in cell pressure is carried partly by the porewater and partly by the soil skeleton. Thus, the greater the cell pressure the greater the increase in the effective confining pressure, and therefore the greater the increase in shear strength and consequently the greater the increase in deviator stress required to cause failure. The increase in the deviator stress becomes progressively smaller and finally ceases when the applied stresses are large enough to force all the air in the voids into solution in the porewater, when the sample behaves as a saturated soil with $\phi_u = 0$. The failure envelope with respect to total stresses is thus curved (Fig. 5.6a) and values of c_u and ϕ_u vary with the magnitude of the normal stress on the failure plane. If the porewater pressure is measured during each test, Mohr circles of effective stress can be drawn and it is found that the failure envelope in terms of effective stress is linear over a wide range of σ', as illustrated in Fig. 5.6b.

Table 5.2 Consistency of clays

	Undrained shear strength c_u (kN/m^2)	
Consistency	BS 5930: 1981	Terzaghi and Peck
Very soft	<20	<12
Soft	20–40	12–25
Firm }	40–75	
Medium }		25–50
Stiff	75–150	50–100
Very stiff	>150	100–200
Hard		>200

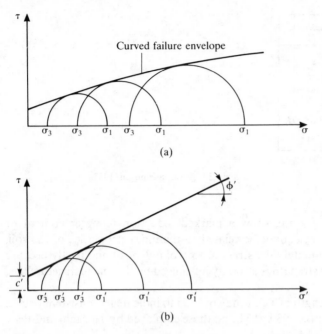

Figure 5.6 Failure envelopes for undrained tests on partially saturated clay with respect to (a) total stress, (b) effective stress.

Consolidated–Undrained Test

In the previous section we have considered the relevance of the undrained test to model a field situation where a clay deposit is subject to a stress change which is rapid in relation to the time for the dissipation of excess porewater pressure so that a potential failure would occur under undrained conditions. If, however, the construction period extends over several seasons (as, for example, in the case of an earth dam) it is reasonable to assume that some consolidation of the soil mass will have occurred by the end of construction. If at this stage the shear stresses induced in the soil are of sufficient magnitude to cause failure, this would occur quickly under conditions of no further drainage. This behaviour is modelled in the consolidated–undrained test in which a soil sample is fully consolidated under the cell pressure and then sheared by the deviator stress under undrained conditions. Figure 5.7 shows typical deviator stress–axial strain and porewater pressure–axial strain curves obtained for normally consolidated and overconsolidated clays. For a normally consolidated soil the porewater pressure rises to failure, reflecting the volume decrease that would occur if drainage were to be allowed. For a heavily overconsolidated clay the porewater pressure decreases during shear, reflecting the dilatancy that would occur if the sample were free to undergo volume change.

The greater the pressure to which a sample is consolidated, the greater the deviator stress required to cause failure. Figure 5.8a shows typical Mohr circles of total stress. The intercept and slope of the failure envelope define the total stress shear strength parameters for the soil, which for a consolidated–undrained test are denoted by c_{cu} and ϕ_{cu} respectively. If the porewater pressure is measured during the test, as is the usual practice, then the corresponding Mohr circles of effective stress may be drawn (Fig. 5.8b), the failure envelope now defining the effective stress shear strength parameters c' and ϕ'. The effective stress circles may lie either to the left or right of their respective total stress circles, depending on whether the porewater pressure at failure is positive or negative.

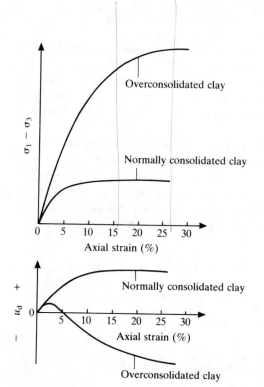

Figure 5.7 Stress–strain–porepressure relationships for consolidated–undrained tests on clay.

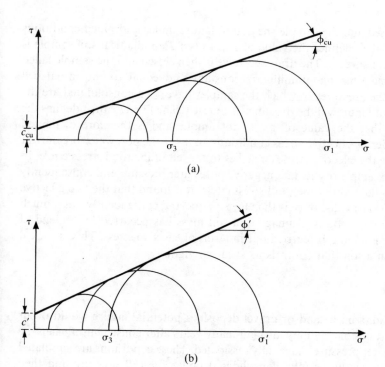

Figure 5.8 Failure envelopes for consolidated–undrained tests on clay with respect to (a) total stress, (b) effective stress.

For normally consolidated clays, the failure envelopes with respect to total and effective stress pass through the origin giving c_{cu} and c' equal to zero; for overconsolidated clays c_{cu} and c' usually range between 5 and $30\,kN/m^2$. The value of ϕ' is not influenced appreciably by overconsolidation and, as noted in Sec. 5.2, ranges from about 30° to 20°, decreasing with increasing plasticity index. The value of ϕ_{cu} varies similarly and its relation to ϕ' is determined by the magnitude of the porewater pressure at failure.

In the standard triaxial test the sample is failed in a conventional manner by holding σ_3 constant and increasing σ_1. In a field situation the stress changes leading to potential failure of an element are more complex than this and in general range from σ_3 constant and σ_1 increasing to σ_1 constant and σ_3 decreasing. It is important to consider the possible influence of this on the measured values of the shear strength parameters. This is illustrated in Fig. 5.9 for the case of a normally consolidated clay. In test 1 a soil sample is fully consolidated under a cell pressure σ_3.

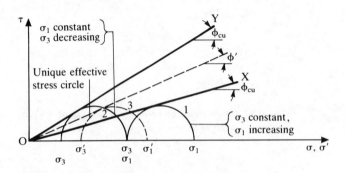

Figure 5.9 Influence of test procedure on ϕ_{cu} and ϕ'.

The drainage valve is then closed and the sample sheared to failure under undrained conditions by increasing σ_1. The line OX then defines the value of ϕ_{cu}. In test 2 an identical soil sample is consolidated to the same cell pressure σ_3. The drainage valve is then closed and the sample failed by decreasing σ_3, at the same time maintaining σ_1 constant and equal to the initial cell consolidation pressure. Since the pressures to which the samples have been consolidated are the same, then the deviator stress at failure will be the same as in test 1. The line OY then defines the value of ϕ_{cu}. It is thus seen that the value of ϕ_{cu} is not unique and is therefore of limited application in practice. Considering effective stress conditions, in test 1 the porewater pressure at failure is positive and therefore the effective stress circle lies to the left of the total stress circle. In test 2, failure by unloading the sample results in a negative porewater pressure and consequently the effective stress circle lies to the right of the total stress circle. It is found that the two effective stress circles coincide (circle 3). The value of ϕ' is therefore unique and consequently has a much wider application in practice. Thus, if any drainage of a soil mass has occurred by the end of construction, a stability analysis should be carried out in terms of effective stress. This is logical since it is the effective stress in a soil that controls its shear strength.

Drained Test

Where construction in the field is on a sand or gravel deposit, a potential failure would occur under drained conditions. Cuttings in clay may also fail many years after construction when the initial (negative) excess porewater pressures have fully dissipated. These conditions are simulated by the drained test in which a sample is fully consolidated under the cell pressure and then sheared under drained conditions at a rate compatible with no build-up in excess porewater pressure, so that u remains equal to zero throughout the shearing stage. The form of the stress–strain–volume change relationship for sands and clays is similar to those obtained from direct shear tests (Figs 5.1b and 5.1d, Sec. 5.2).

Since $u = 0$ throughout the shearing process, $\sigma_3' = \sigma_3$, $\sigma_1' = \sigma_1$ and the Mohr circles of effective stress and total stress coincide (Fig. 5.10). The failure envelope defines the effective stress parameters c' and ϕ'. These are often denoted c_d and ϕ_d respectively. As before, sands and normally consolidated clays show zero intercept ($c_d = 0$).

Generally there is little difference between the effective stress parameters obtained from drained and consolidated–undrained tests. However, for sands and heavily overconsolidated clays ϕ_d is slightly higher than ϕ', because of the work done by the sample as it expands against the confining pressure during shear.

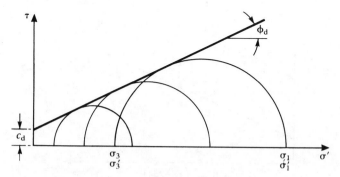

Figure 5.10 Failure envelope for drained tests on clay.

5.4 DIRECTION OF FAILURE PLANE AND RELATIONSHIP BETWEEN PRINCIPAL STRESSES AND SHEAR STRENGTH PARAMETERS

Figure 5.11a shows the effective stress conditions acting on a soil element at failure in the triaxial test. These are represented by the Mohr circle of effective stress in Fig. 5.11b where the circle is tangent to the effective stress failure envelope. For the conditions of the triaxial test the pole point is at C and hence the line CF is parallel to the failure plane, inclined at angle α to the major principal plane. Now angle $FAO = \phi'$ and therefore angle $FOA = 90 - \phi'$. But angle $FOA = 180 - 2\alpha$. Hence

$$90 - \phi' = 180 - 2\alpha$$

whence
$$\alpha = 45 + \frac{\phi'}{2} \tag{5.7}$$

Thus *the failure plane is inclined at an angle of $45 + \phi'/2$ to the major principal plane.*

Considering Fig. 5.11b further, we also have

$$OF = OA \sin \phi'$$

$\therefore$
$$\tfrac{1}{2}(\sigma_1' - \sigma_3') = [c' \cot \phi' + \tfrac{1}{2}(\sigma_1' + \sigma_3')] \sin \phi' \tag{5.8}$$

from which
$$\sigma_3' = \sigma_1' \left[\frac{1 - \sin \phi'}{1 + \sin \phi'}\right] - 2c'\left[\frac{\cos \phi'}{1 + \sin \phi'}\right]$$

whence
$$\phi_3' = \sigma_1' \tan^2\left(45 - \frac{\phi'}{2}\right) - 2c' \tan\left(45 - \frac{\phi'}{2}\right) \tag{5.9}$$

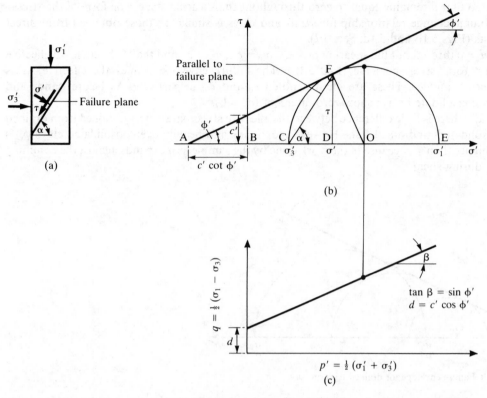

Figure 5.11 (a) Effective stresses on triaxial sample at failure, (b) Mohr failure circle in terms of effective stress, (c) $p' - q$ plot.

and on rearranging
$$\sigma_1' = \sigma_3' \tan^2\left(45 + \frac{\phi'}{2}\right) + 2c' \tan\left(45 + \frac{\phi'}{2}\right) \tag{5.10}$$

In terms of total stress we obtain in a similar manner

$$\sigma_3 = \sigma_1 \tan^2\left(45 - \frac{\phi}{2}\right) - 2c \tan\left(45 - \frac{\phi}{2}\right) \tag{5.11}$$

and
$$\sigma_1 = \sigma_3 \tan^2\left(45 + \frac{\phi}{2}\right) + 2c \tan\left(45 + \frac{\phi}{2}\right) \tag{5.12}$$

Equations (5.9), (5.10), (5.11) and (5.12) are used later in Chapter 6 in the analysis of the limiting values of horizontal stress that may be developed at a point in a soil mass.

In Eq. (5.8) the effective deviator stress is equal to the total deviator stress since

$$\sigma_1' - \sigma_3' = (\sigma_1 - u) - (\sigma_3 - u) = \sigma_1 - \sigma_3$$

Thus if
$$q = \tfrac{1}{2}(\sigma_1' - \sigma_3') = \tfrac{1}{2}(\sigma_1 - \sigma_3) \tag{5.13}$$

and
$$p' = \tfrac{1}{2}(\sigma_1' + \sigma_3') \tag{5.14}$$

then Eq. (5.8) may be written as

$$q = c' \cos \phi' + p' \sin \phi' \tag{5.15}$$

which plots as a straight line as q against p' (Fig. 5.11c), the slope of the line defining $\sin \phi'$ and the intercept $c' \cos \phi'$, and thus provides an alternative method for determining the effective stress shear strength parameters from the results of triaxial tests. In a similar manner a p–q plot allows the determination of the total stress parameters.

5.5 PORE PRESSURE PARAMETERS

In addition to determining the shear strength parameters of a soil, the triaxial test is also used to furnish data for predicting the initial excess porewater pressure set up at a point in a soil mass by a change in the total stress conditions. Such predictions are required in conjunction with an effective stress stability analysis and are made by means of experimentally determined *pore pressure parameters*.

To introduce the idea of pore pressure parameters, consider the soil element shown in Fig. 5.12 wherein the element is subject to a triaxial loading in which $\Delta\sigma_2$ is equal to $\Delta\sigma_3$. We may consider

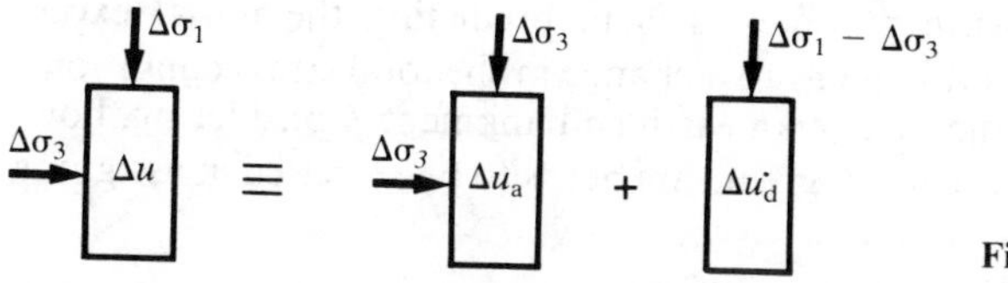

Figure 5.12

this stress system to be composed of an isotropic change of stress $\Delta\sigma_3$ plus a uniaxial change of deviator stress $\Delta\sigma_1 - \Delta\sigma_3$. This, of course, is the stress system imposed in the triaxial test and it is clear that the excess porewater pressure generated within the element will result firstly from the change in the all-round stress and secondly from the change in the deviator stress. If Δu_a denotes the excess porewater pressure induced in the element by the application of $\Delta\sigma_3$ and Δu_d that by $\Delta\sigma_1 - \Delta\sigma_3$, then assuming these pore pressures to be a simple proportion of the applied stresses, we may write

$$\Delta u_a = B \, \Delta\sigma_3 \tag{5.16}$$

and
$$\Delta u_d = \bar{A}(\Delta\sigma_1 - \Delta\sigma_3) \tag{5.17}$$

where B and $\bar{A}$ are experimentally determined pore pressure parameters. If Δu denotes the total excess porewater pressure in the element, then assuming the principle of superposition

$$\Delta u = \Delta u_a + \Delta u_d$$

and hence
$$\Delta u = B \, \Delta\sigma_3 + \bar{A}(\Delta\sigma_1 - \Delta\sigma_3) \tag{5.18}$$

This problem was considered by Skempton (1954) who gives

$$\Delta u = B[\Delta\sigma_3 + A(\Delta\sigma_1 - \Delta\sigma_3)] \tag{5.19}$$

This is of the same form as Eq. (5.18) where AB replaces $\bar{A}$.

The pore pressure parameters are obtained from a triaxial compression test. The parameter B is determined by measuring the increase in porewater pressure resulting from the increase in cell pressure and varies from 1 for a fully saturated soil to 0 for a dry soil. The parameter $\bar{A}$, and hence A, is determined by measuring the porewater pressure induced in the sample by the application of the deviator stress. The value of A depends upon the initial consolidation stress system (whether isotropic or anisotropic), the stress history (as reflected by the overconsolidation ratio), the proportion of the failure stress applied (i.e., on the strain of the sample) and the type of stress change (whether loading or unloading). Typical failure values (A_f) are given in Table 5.3.

Table 5.3 Values of the pore pressure parameter A at failure (A_f)

Soil type	A_f
Sensitive clay	1.5–2.5
Normally consolidated clay	0.7–1.3
Lightly overconsolidated clay	0.3–0.7
Heavily overconsolidated clay	−0.5–0.0

With $B = 1$ for a saturated soil, $\bar{A} = A$ and Eqs (5.18) and (5.19) reduce to

$$\Delta u = \Delta\sigma_3 + A(\Delta\sigma_1 - \Delta\sigma_3)$$

(5.20)

or

$$\Delta u = \Delta\sigma_3 + A\,\Delta D$$

The main application of the pore pressure parameters is in predicting the initial excess porewater pressure at a point in a soil mass subsequent to a change in the total stress conditions. This is considered in Chapter 7 for the specific case of an earth embankment. Considering, however, the many factors that influence the parameter A, great care needs to be exercised in assigning particular values to a soil deposit.

5.6 USE OF TOTAL STRESS AND EFFECTIVE STRESS SHEAR STRENGTH PARAMETERS

The shear strength of a soil results from the frictional resistance arising at the particle contact points and, as such, its value is determined solely by the magnitude of the effective stress carried by the soil skeleton; the greater the pressure between the grains, the greater the resistance to shear. Fundamentally, therefore, one would expect all stability analyses to be done in terms of effective stress using the effective stress parameters c' and ϕ'. Being unique for any soil, these parameters have a wide application in practice and lead to relatively straightforward stability analyses.

However, for the special case of a saturated clay in which the stress change likely to cause a potential shear failure occurs under undrained conditions, the soil exhibits equally unique values of total stress parameters c_u and $\phi_u = 0$, which suggests the alternative use of a total stress approach to analyse a potential undrained shear failure. The reasonableness of this is supported by the close agreement that has been obtained between observed and predicted short-term failures of engineering works formed on and in clay deposits. The $\phi_u = 0$ analysis leads to a very simple and rapid assessment of stability since the undrained shear strength at any point is defined solely by the undrained cohesion c_u. Such analyses could be carried out in terms of effective stress but this would require the explicit determination of the excess porewater pressures and would therefore be significantly more involved than a total stress analysis.

We may summarize the practical application of the shear strength parameters thus: in general, soil stability analyses should be carried out in terms of effective stress since it is the effective stress in the soil that controls its shear strength. However, for the special case of a potential undrained shear failure in a saturated soil mass, the analysis may be carried out in terms of total stress.

Example 5.1 A series of conventional consolidated–undrained triaxial compression tests carried out on undisturbed samples of a saturated clay gave the following results:

Test No.	Cell consolidation pressure (kN/m²)	Deviator stress at failure (kN/m²)	Pore pressure at failure (kN/m²)
1	200	227.0	68.1
2	400	421.4	126.4
3	600	615.7	184.7

Calculate the effective stress shear strength parameters for the soil:

(a) by plotting Mohr circles of effective stress and
(b) by plotting q against p'.

SOLUTION Analysis of the test data gives the following results:

Test No.	σ_3 (kN/m²)	$\sigma_1 - \sigma_3$ (kN/m²)	u_f (kN/m²)	σ_3' (kN/m²)	σ_1' (kN/m²)	$q = \frac{1}{2}(\sigma_1 - \sigma_3)$ (kN/m²)	$p' = \frac{1}{2}(\sigma_1' + \sigma_3')$ (kN/m²)
1	200	227.0	68.1	131.9	358.9	113.5	245.4
2	400	421.4	126.4	273.6	695.0	210.7	484.3
3	600	615.7	184.7	415.3	1031.0	307.9	723.2

(a) Figure 5.13a shows the Mohr circles of effective stress and the associated failure envelope. The slope of the line gives $\phi' = 24°$ and the intercept $c' = 15 \text{ kN/m}^2$.
(b) Figure 5.13b shows the plot of q against p'. The slope of the line defines $\sin \phi'$. We thus obtain $\sin \phi' = \tan 22.1$, giving $\phi' = 24°$. The intercept of the line defines $c' \cos \phi'$. We thus have $c' \cos \phi' = 13.7$, from which $c' = 15 \text{ kN/m}^2$.

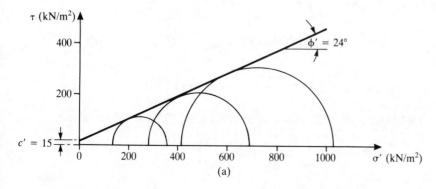

(a)

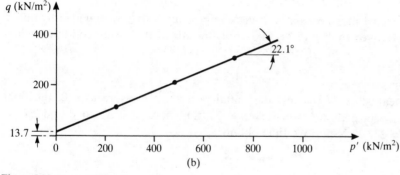

(b)

Figure 5.13 Example 5.1.

Example 5.2 A saturated sample of normally consolidated clay was consolidated in the triaxial cell under an all-round cell pressure of 400 kN/m^2. When consolidation was complete, the drainage valve was closed and with the cell pressure maintained constant a gradually increasing deviator stress was applied to the sample under undrained conditions until failure occurred. Calculate:

(a) the compression strength of the sample,
(b) the magnitude of the porewater pressure at failure and
(c) the value of the pore pressure parameter A at failure,

given that the shear strength parameters of the clay are $c_{cu} = 0$, $\phi_{cu} = 13°$ and $c' = 0$, $\phi' = 22°$.

SOLUTION (a) For a total stress analysis, Eq. (5.12) gives

$$\sigma_1 = \sigma_3 \tan^2\left(45 + \frac{\phi_{cu}}{2}\right) + 2c_{cu} \tan\left(45 + \frac{\phi_{cu}}{2}\right)$$

$$\therefore \qquad \sigma_1 - \sigma_3 = \sigma_3\left[\tan^2\left(45 + \frac{\phi_{cu}}{2}\right) - 1\right] + 2c_{cu} \tan\left(45 + \frac{\phi_{cu}}{2}\right)$$

Thus with $\sigma_3 = 400 \text{ kN/m}^2$, $\phi_{cu} = 13°$ and $c_{cu} = 0$ we obtain

$$D_f = 400\left[\tan^2\left(45 + \frac{13}{2}\right) - 1\right] = \underline{232.2 \text{ kN/m}^2}$$

(b) For an effective stress analysis, Eq. (5.10) gives

$$\sigma_1' = \sigma_3' \tan^2\left(45 + \frac{\phi'}{2}\right) + 2c' \tan\left(45 + \frac{\phi'}{2}\right)$$

$$\therefore \qquad \sigma_1' - \sigma_3' = \sigma_3'\left[\tan^2\left(45 + \frac{\phi'}{2}\right) - 1\right] + 2c' \tan\left(45 + \frac{\phi'}{2}\right)$$

$$\therefore \qquad D_f = (\sigma_3 - u_f)\left[\tan^2\left(45 + \frac{\phi'}{2}\right) - 1\right] + 2c' \tan\left(45 + \frac{\phi'}{2}\right)$$

We have here $\sigma_3 = 400 \text{ kN/m}^2$, $\phi' = 22°$, $c' = 0$ and with $D_f = 232.2 \text{ kN/m}^2$ we obtain

$$232.2 = (400 - u_f)\left[\tan^2\left(45 + \frac{22}{2}\right) - 1\right]$$

from which $\qquad\qquad u_f = \underline{206.2 \text{ kN/m}^2}$

(c) The change in porewater pressure in a *saturated* sample subject to a triaxial loading under undrained conditions is given by Eq. (5.20) and applying this to the failure condition when $A = A_f$ we obtain

$$\Delta u = \Delta\sigma_3 + A_f \Delta D$$

For the undrained shear stage of the test the initial porewater pressure $u_0 = 0$, the final porewater pressure $u_f = 206.2 \text{ kN/m}^2$, whence $\Delta u = 206.2 \text{ kN/m}^2$. Also $\Delta\sigma_3 = 0$ and $\Delta D = D_f - D_0 = 232.2 - 0 = 232.2 \text{ kN/m}^2$. We thus obtain

$$206.2 = 232.2 A_f$$

from which $\qquad\qquad A_f = \underline{0.89}$

PROBLEMS

5.1 A saturated sample of normally consolidated clay was consolidated in the triaxial cell under a cell pressure of $200 \, \text{kN/m}^2$. The drainage valve was then closed and the sample failed by the gradual application of a deviator stress. Calculate the value of:

(a) the compression strength of the sample,
(b) the porewater pressure at failure, and
(c) the pore pressure parameter A at failure,

given that the shear strength parameters of the clay are $c_{cu} = 0$, $\phi_{cu} = 14°$ and $c' = 0$, $\phi' = 25°$.

[Ans. (a) $127.7 \, \text{kN/m}^2$, (b) $112.8 \, \text{kN/m}^2$, (c) 0.88]

5.2 A saturated sample of clay was consolidated in the triaxial cell under a cell pressure of $200 \, \text{kN/m}^2$ and a deviator stress of $50 \, \text{kN/m}^2$. The drainage valve was then closed and the deviator stress gradually increased to record a compression strength of $200 \, \text{kN/m}^2$. Calculate the value of the pore pressure parameter A at failure given that $c' = 15 \, \text{kN/m}^2$ and $\phi' = 20°$.

[Ans. 0.33]

5.3 A saturated sample of clay was consolidated in the triaxial cell under a cell pressure of $220 \, \text{kN/m}^2$. The drainage valve was then closed, the cell pressure raised to $300 \, \text{kN/m}^2$ and the sample failed under undrained conditions by the gradual application of a deviator stress. Calculate:

(a) the compression strength of the sample,
(b) the porewater pressure at failure, and
(c) the pore pressure parameter A at failure,

given that the shear strength parameters of the clay are $c_{cu} = 25 \, \text{kN/m}^2$, $\phi_{cu} = 19°$ and $c' = 15 \, \text{kN/m}^2$, $\phi' = 25°$.

[Ans. (a) $282.5 \, \text{kN/m}^2$, (b) $139.2 \, \text{kN/m}^2$, (c) 0.21]

5.4 A series of conventional consolidated–undrained triaxial tests carried out on undisturbed samples of a saturated normally consolidated clay gave the following results:

Test No.	Cell consolidation pressure (kN/m²)	Deviator stress at failure (kN/m²)	Pore pressure at failure (kN/m²)
1	150	88	77
2	280	163	145
3	400	233	207

A fourth sample of the same clay was fully consolidated in the triaxial cell under a cell pressure of $250 \, \text{kN/m}^2$. The drainage valve was then closed and the sample sheared to failure under undrained conditions by gradually decreasing the cell pressure while maintaining the axial stress constant at $250 \, \text{kN/m}^2$. Calculate the value of cell pressure at failure. Calculate also the porewater pressure in the sample at failure, assuming A_f to have the same value on unloading.

[Ans. $104.9 \, \text{kN/m}^2$; $-16.0 \, \text{kN/m}^2$]

5.5 A sample of clay was placed in the triaxial cell and under zero cell pressure the pore pressure transducer recorded an initial suction in the sample of $-40 \, \text{kN/m}^2$. On applying a cell pressure of $200 \, \text{kN/m}^2$, the pore pressure was observed to rise rapidly and stabilize at a value of $160 \, \text{kN/m}^2$. The drainage valve was then opened in order to permit consolidation of the sample under this cell pressure.

Although not detected until later, a fault developed in the pore pressure transducer circuit during the consolidation stage and, owing to the observed pore pressure dissipation rate being incorrect, the drainage valve was closed before consolidation under the applied cell pressure was complete. The cell pressure was then raised to $250 \, \text{kN/m}^2$ and maintained at this higher value while the sample was sheared to failure under a gradually increasing deviator stress. This gave a compression strength for the sample of $214 \, \text{kN/m}^2$. Calculate the residual porewater pressure in the sample at the end of the consolidation stage given that $c' = 25 \, \text{kN/m}^2$, $\phi' = 28°$ and $A_f = 0.4$.

[Ans. $40.5 \, \text{kN/m}^2$]

5.6 A sample of normally consolidated saturated clay was consolidated in the triaxial cell under an all-round cell pressure σ_3. When consolidation was complete the drainage valve was closed and with the cell pressure maintained constant a gradually increasing deviator stress was applied to the sample under undrained conditions until failure occurred, when the following results were obtained:

$$\tfrac{1}{2}(\sigma_1 - \sigma_3) = \tfrac{1}{3}\sigma_3 \quad \text{and} \quad \tfrac{1}{2}(\sigma_1' + \sigma_3') = \tfrac{2}{3}\sigma_3$$

Show that (a) $\phi' = 30°$, (b) $u_f = \tfrac{2}{3}\sigma_3$, (c) $A_f = 1$. Show also that if the sample had been sheared under drained conditions then at failure the following results would have obtained:

$$\tfrac{1}{2}(\sigma_1 - \sigma_3) = \sigma_3 \quad \text{and} \quad \tfrac{1}{2}(\sigma_1' + \sigma_3') = 2\sigma_3$$

LATERAL EARTH PRESSURE AND RETAINING WALLS

6.1 INTRODUCTION

A *retaining wall* is a structure that is used to provide lateral support for a vertical or near-vertical slope of soil. Figure 6.1a shows a traditional type of wall employed for this purpose. The rear of the wall, AB, is referred to as the *back*, and the front of the wall, CD, as the *face*. Point B is called the *heel* and point C the *toe*. The soil placed against the back after construction of the wall is referred to as the *backfill* and this should preferably be a free-draining granular material.

Various types of retaining wall are shown in Figs 6.1 to 6.5 and are widely employed in civil engineering works ranging from their use in road and rail construction to support cuts and fills where space is limited to prevent the formation of appropriate side slopes, to the construction of marine structures such as docks, harbours and jetties.

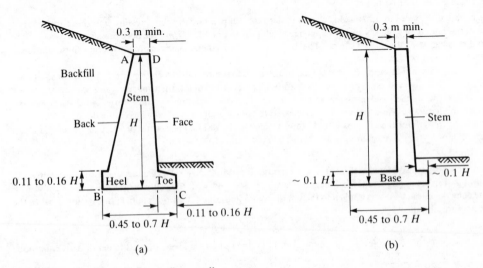

Figure 6.1 (a) Gravity wall, (b) cantilever wall.

The walls shown in Fig. 6.1 are essentially *stiff* structures. The *gravity* wall is built of plain concrete or stone masonry, being proportioned of considerable thickness so that no tensile stresses are produced in any part of the structure, the wall depending solely on its large mass and compression strength to resist the forces acting on it. Such walls are expensive in materials and current practice favours the *cantilever* wall (Fig. 6.1b) where the weight of backfill on the heel slab serves the same purpose as the large mass of wall material and provides the necessary stability. The structural elements are subject to bending moments and are reinforced. For high walls (>8 m), thin vertical slabs, known as *counterforts*, may be used at regular intervals along the back of the wall to tie the stem and base slab together, thus reducing the shear and bending moments. Alternatively, the vertical slabs may be placed against the face to form a *buttress* wall.

A *crib* wall (Fig. 6.2a) consists of interlocking short precast reinforced concrete beams, of two types, known as *stringers* and *ties*, which form a structural framework encasing a granular soil in-fill. The whole unit acts as a gravity wall and has the advantages that it allows some economy in concrete, it is quickly erected, and can tolerate appreciable differential settlement along its face. A *gabion* wall system (Fig. 6.2b) consists of a stacked arrangement of rock or aggregate filled metal cages, commonly 1 m × 1 m in section by 2 m in length.

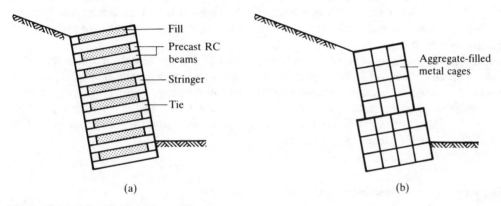

Figure 6.2 (a) Crib wall, (b) gabion wall.

Figure 6.3 shows a modern development in earth retention methods in which horizontal reinforcing strips are embedded in a granular soil, thereby stabilizing the mass by the frictional resistance developed with the surrounding soil, a technique devised (and patented) by Vidal (1969) and referred to as *reinforced earth*.

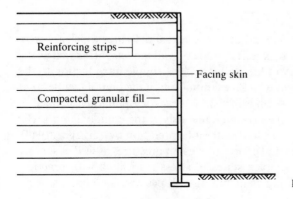

Figure 6.3 Reinforced earth wall.

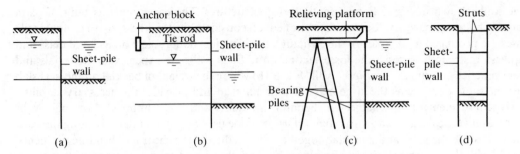

Figure 6.4 Sheet-pile walls: (a) cantilever, (b) anchored, (c) pinned or *encastré*, (d) strutted.

Sheet-pile walls (Fig. 6.4) consist of a continuous line of interlocking piles driven into the soil. They are *flexible* structures which derive their stability from fixity developed over their embedded length and, with the exception of the *cantilever* wall (Fig. 6.4a), from horizontal support provided either by a system of *tie rods* and *anchor blocks* (Fig. 6.4b), or by directly fixing (pinned or *encastré*) to a rigid structure such as a *relieving platform* (Fig. 6.4c), or in the case of a *sheeted* excavation (Fig. 6.4d) by *struts* at different levels. Early walls were built in timber and later in precast reinforced concrete, but steel sheet piling is used mainly at the present time owing to its high strength to weight ratio.

Basement walls for buildings and other underground structures are also designed as retaining walls and a particular method is often used for their construction whereby the wall is cast in place *before* excavation of the basement material, thus minimizing ground movements and possible damage to adjacent buildings. These *diaphragm* walls are formed in a trench supported by bentonite clay slurry through which a reinforcing cage is lowered and the slurry then displaced by concrete placed with a tremie pipe (Fig. 6.5).

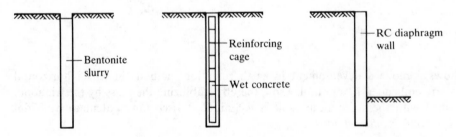

Figure 6.5 Stages in the construction of a diaphragm wall.

The design of a retaining wall requires the determination of the lateral pressures which act on it. These are influenced by the type of wall and the degree and mode of wall movement, as well as the soil type, drainage conditions and the geometry of the problem. As a simple introduction to the determination of lateral earth pressures, we begin with an examination of the limiting values that can be developed in a semi-infinite mass of soil which is in a state of *plastic equilibrium*, defined as a condition in which each element of soil in the mass is simultaneously at the point of failure. The analysis follows the initial work of Rankine (1857) and its later interpretation by Terzaghi (1943), and is a useful means of introducing the fundamental concepts of earth pressures as well as serving as a basis from which to consider the more complex states of stress associated with practical engineering problems involving not only retaining walls but also slopes and foundations.

6.2 RANKINE ACTIVE AND PASSIVE STATES

Sand

Consider a semi-infinite mass of sand having a horizontal surface and let the water table be at great depth so that the porewater pressure u is zero throughout the mass (Fig. 6.6a). The vertical and horizontal effective stresses, σ'_v and σ'_h, acting on a typical soil element at depth h on the vertical plane AB, are principal stresses. $\sigma'_v = \rho g h$ whereas σ'_h is not immediately definable, although it is less than σ'_v for a normally consolidated deposit. The element is not at failure and therefore the Mohr circle of stress is drawn wholly below the failure envelope, as shown in Fig. 6.6b.

For a state of plastic equilibrium to develop in the sand, and the element therefore to fail, the soil mass must be permitted to undergo lateral deformation. Thus, if the mass is *stretched* in the horizontal direction then σ'_h decreases (σ'_v remaining constant) and the element fails when the Mohr circle of stress becomes tangential to the failure envelope (Fig. 6.6d), the lateral strain to achieve this condition being unknown. The sand is then said to be in the *Rankine active state* and the minimum value for σ'_h, denoted by σ'_{ha}, is termed the *effective active earth pressure*. Failure occurs simultaneously at all points throughout the sand, and slip takes place along two sets of conjugate planes to form a *slip line field* (Fig. 6.6c), the planes being inclined at $(45 + \phi'/2)$ to the major principal plane and hence in this case at $(45 + \phi'/2)$ to the horizontal. Invoking the effective stress failure equation from shear strength theory in the form of Eq. (5.9) and noting that $c' = 0$ for a sand, we have

$$\sigma'_3 = \sigma'_1 \tan^2\left(45 - \frac{\phi'}{2}\right)$$

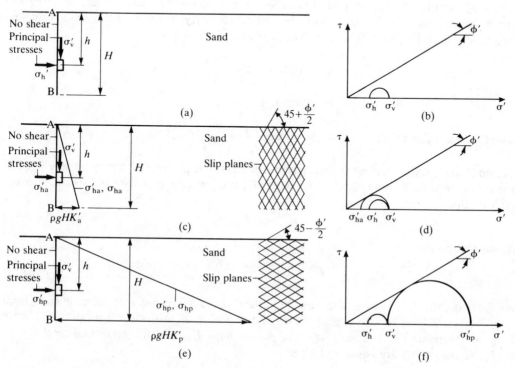

Figure 6.6 Rankine active and passive states of failure in sand.

In Fig. 6.6d, $\sigma'_3 = \sigma'_{ha}$ and $\sigma'_1 = \sigma'_v$ whence

$$\sigma'_{ha} = \sigma'_v \tan^2\left(45 - \frac{\phi'}{2}\right) \tag{6.1}$$

Equation (6.1) defines the *minimum* value of horizontal effective pressure that may be developed at any point in the sand. We also define $\sigma'_{ha}/\sigma'_v = K'_a$ where K'_a is termed the *effective active earth pressure coefficient*. Thus

$$\sigma'_{ha} = \sigma'_v K'_a \tag{6.2}$$

whence comparing Eqs (6.2) and (6.1), we have for this case

$$K'_a = \tan^2\left(45 - \frac{\phi'}{2}\right) = \left[\frac{\cos\phi'}{1 + \sin\phi'}\right]^2 \tag{6.3}$$

Since $\sigma'_v = \rho g h$ then $\sigma'_{ha} = \rho g h K'_a$, so that the distribution of effective active earth pressure on the vertical plane AB in Fig. 6.6c varies linearly from zero at point A to $\rho g H K'_a$ at point B at depth H. This is also the distribution of the *total active earth pressure* σ_{ha}, as $u = 0$ throughout the sand. The area of the active earth pressure diagram then defines both the *horizontal effective active force* P'_{ha} and the *horizontal total active force* P_{ha} acting on the vertical plane AB. That is

$$P_{ha} = P'_{ha} = \tfrac{1}{2}\rho g H^2 K'_a \tag{6.4}$$

For a loose sand with $\phi' = 30°$ we have that $K'_a = \tan^2(45 - 30/2) = 0.333$, whereas for a dense sand with $\phi' = 45°$, $K'_a = 0.172$. Therefore, the active thrust of a loose sand is approximately twice that of a dense sand.

Alternatively, if the mass of sand is *compressed* laterally then the horizontal effective stress increases and the element fails when, with $\sigma'_h > \sigma'_v$, the Mohr circle of stress touches the failure envelope (Fig. 6.6f). The sand is now said to be in the *Rankine passive state* and the maximum value for σ'_h, denoted by σ'_{hp}, is termed the *effective passive earth pressure*. The associated slip planes make an angle of $(45 + \phi'/2)$ with the vertical (the new direction of the major principal plane), as shown in Fig. 6.6e. With $c' = 0$ for a sand, Eq. (5.10) gives

$$\sigma'_1 = \sigma'_3 \tan^2\left(45 + \frac{\phi'}{2}\right)$$

In Fig. 6.6f, $\sigma'_1 = \sigma'_{hp}$ and $\sigma'_3 = \sigma'_v$,

and therefore it follows that $\sigma'_{hp} = \sigma'_v \tan^2\left(45 + \frac{\phi'}{2}\right) \tag{6.5}$

Equation (6.5) gives the *maximum* value of horizontal effective pressure that may be developed at any point in the sand. Writing $\sigma'_{hp}/\sigma'_v = K'_p$, where K'_p is termed the *effective passive earth pressure coefficient*, then

$$\sigma'_{hp} = \sigma'_v K'_p \tag{6.6}$$

and thus for this case

$$K'_p = \tan^2\left(45 + \frac{\phi'}{2}\right) \tag{6.7}$$

From Eq. (6.6), the distribution of σ'_{hp} on the vertical plane AB in Fig. 6.6e varies linearly from zero at A to $\rho g H K'_p$ at B. This is also the distribution of *total passive earth pressure* σ_{hp} (since $u = 0$), and therefore the *horizontal effective passive force* P'_{hp} and the *horizontal total passive force* P_{hp} acting on AB are equal and given by

$$P_{hp} = P'_{hp} = \tfrac{1}{2}\rho g H^2 K'_p \tag{6.8}$$

For typical values of $\phi' = 30°$ and $45°$ for loose and dense sands, Eq. (6.7) gives $K'_p = 3.0$ and 5.83 respectively. Therefore the passive resistance of a loose sand is approximately one-half that of a dense sand.

Comparing Eqs (6.8) and (6.4), the ratio of total passive resistance to total active thrust is given by

$$\frac{P_{hp}}{P_{ha}} = \frac{K'_p}{K'_a} = \frac{\tan^2 (45 + \phi'/2)}{\tan^2 (45 - \phi'/2)} \tag{6.9}$$

This gives for a loose sand with $\phi' = 30°$, $P_{hp}/P_{ha} = 9.0$, and for a dense sand with $\phi' = 45°$, $P_{hp}/P_{ha} = 34.0$. The passive resistance of a sand is therefore very much greater than the active thrust.

If a water table is present then this will influence the distribution of σ'_v and therefore the distributions of σ'_{ha} and σ'_{hp} and, ultimately, the distributions of σ_{ha} and σ_{hp}. This is illustrated in Fig. 6.7a for the active case and in Fig. 6.7b for the passive problem. The procedure for the determination of the lateral earth pressure at a particular depth is outlined with particular reference to the calculation of σ'_{ha} and σ_{ha} at point B in Fig. 6.7a. At this depth

$$\sigma'_v = \rho g h + \rho' g (H - h)$$

and therefore from Eq. (6.2)

$$\sigma'_{ha} = \rho g h K'_a + \rho' g (H - h) K'_a$$

From the principle of effective stress, the value of σ_{ha} is then given by

$$\sigma_{ha} = \sigma'_{ha} + u$$

Thus

$$\sigma_{ha} = \rho g h K'_a + \rho' g (H - h) K'_a + \rho_w g (H - h)$$

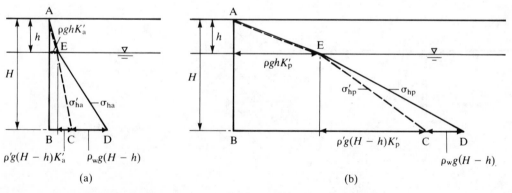

Figure 6.7 Rankine pressure distributions in sand with water table: (a) active, (b) passive.

The pressure diagrams in Fig. 6.7 are drawn essentially to scale to aid comparison of the relative magnitudes of σ_{ha} and σ_{hp}. The area ABCE defines the horizontal effective forces P'_{ha} and P'_{hp} on the vertical plane AB, and the area ECD the *horizontal water force* P_{hw}. The total horizontal forces on AB are given by $P_{ha} = P'_{ha} + P_{hw}$ and $P_{hp} = P'_{hp} + P_{hw}$, or calculated directly from the area ABDE.

Saturated Clay

For a semi-infinite mass of clay, the states of stress at failure will be greatly influenced by how much dissipation of excess porewater pressure (i.e., by how much drainage) has taken place within the soil prior to failure. The analysis is therefore carried out for two limiting conditions corresponding to the *undrained* and *fully drained* states. Thus, if the clay mass is stretched or compressed *instantaneously* then at failure no dissipation of the excess porewater pressures will have taken place. Hence the clay fails under *undrained* conditions and consequently the analysis may be carried out in terms of *total stress*. If, however, the clay mass is stretched or compressed *infinitely slowly*, then the excess porewater pressure will be completely dissipated throughout the deformation process and the clay will fail under *fully drained* conditions. Consequently the analysis must be carried out in terms of *effective stress*.

Undrained failure Figure 6.8a shows the total stress analysis for undrained active and passive failure of a saturated soil element. For *active* conditions (circle 1) we obtain the *total active earth pressure* σ_{ha} as

$$\sigma_{ha} = \sigma_v - 2c_u \qquad (6.10a)$$

$$= \rho_s gh - 2c_u \qquad (6.10b)$$

The distribution of σ_{ha} on the vertical plane AB in Fig. 6.8b thus varies linearly from $-2c_u$ at A to $(\rho_s gH - 2c_u)$ at B. Above the level of point C, σ_{ha} has a negative value and is consequently a tensile stress. Generally, soils cannot withstand tensile stresses and it is therefore likely that a

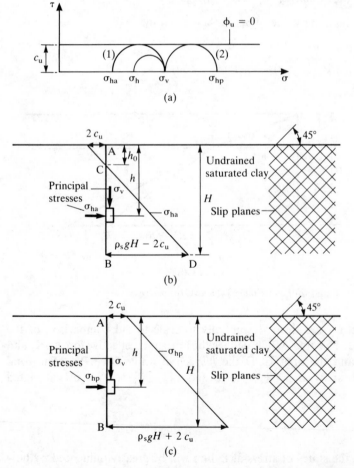

Figure 6.8 Rankine active and passive states of failure in undrained saturated clay.

series of tension cracks will develop over this depth. The depth h_0 of this tension zone can be calculated directly from Eq. (6.10b) by putting $h = h_0$ when $\sigma_{ha} = 0$. We thus obtain

$$h_0 = \frac{2c_u}{\rho_s g} \tag{6.11}$$

The *horizontal total active force* P_{ha} acting on the vertical plane AB is thus defined by the area CBD of the total active earth pressure diagram. That is

$$P_{ha} = \tfrac{1}{2}(\rho_s g H - 2c_u)(H - h_0) = \tfrac{1}{2}\rho_s g H^2\left(1 - \frac{2c_u}{\rho_s g H}\right)\left(1 - \frac{2c_u}{\rho_s g H}\right)$$

whence $\qquad P_{ha} = \tfrac{1}{2}\rho_s g H^2(1 - 2S)^2 \tag{6.12}$

where $\qquad S = \dfrac{c_u}{\rho_s g H} \tag{6.13}$

is a dimensionless parameter referred to as the *stability number*.

For *passive* failure (circle 2 in Fig. 6.8a) we obtain the *total passive earth pressure* σ_{hp} as

$$\sigma_{hp} = \sigma_v + 2c_u \tag{6.14a}$$

$$= \rho_s g h + 2c_u \tag{6.14b}$$

The distribution of σ_{hp} on the vertical plane AB in Fig. 6.8c is then as shown, from which the *horizontal total passive force* P_{hp} is given by

$$P_{hp} = \tfrac{1}{2}(2c_u + \rho_s g H + 2c_u)H = \tfrac{1}{2}\rho_s g H^2\left(1 + \frac{4c_u}{\rho_s g H}\right)$$

whence $\qquad P_{hp} = \tfrac{1}{2}\rho_s g H^2(1 + 4S) \tag{6.15}$

From Eqs (6.15) and (6.12), the ratio of total passive resistance to total active thrust for an undrained saturated clay is given by

$$\frac{P_{hp}}{P_{ha}} = \frac{1 + 4S}{(1 - 2S)^2} \tag{6.16}$$

For a very soft clay with $S = 0.05$ this gives $P_{hp}/P_{ha} = 1.5$ and for a stiff clay with $S = 0.35$, $P_{hp}/P_{ha} = 26.7$. These ratios may be compared with those generated by Eq. (6.9) for sand. We may also note that, comparing Eqs (6.12) and (6.4), the active thrust of a soft undrained clay is approximately three times that of loose sand.

Drained failure For active and passive failure under fully drained conditions, an effective stress analysis similar to that presented earlier for a sand gives the following governing earth pressure equations:

$$\sigma'_{ha} = \sigma'_v \tan^2\left(45 - \frac{\phi'}{2}\right) - 2c'\tan\left(45 - \frac{\phi'}{2}\right) \tag{6.17}$$

and

$$\sigma'_{hp} = \sigma'_v \tan^2\left(45 + \frac{\phi'}{2}\right) + 2c'\tan\left(45 + \frac{\phi'}{2}\right) \tag{6.18}$$

Adopting the subscripts u and d to denote the undrained and drained states, Table 6.1 shows various comparisons between the passive resistance and active thrust for a very soft, normally consolidated clay with $S = 0.05$, $S' = 0$, $\phi' = 20°$, and for a stiff overconsolidated clay with $S = 0.35$, $S' = 0.01$, $\phi' = 25°$. For the drained condition the water table is taken to be at depth, so that u is zero throughout the mass.

Table 6.1 Comparison of Rankine active and passive forces for a clay

Soil type	$\dfrac{P_{hpu}}{P_{hau}}$	$\dfrac{P_{had}}{P_{hau}}$	$\dfrac{P_{hpd}}{P_{hpu}}$	$\dfrac{P_{hpd}}{P_{had}}$
Soft clay	1.5	0.6	1.7	4.2
Stiff clay	26.7	4.2	1.1	6.6

We see from column 3 that the active thrust of a soft clay decreases from the undrained to the drained condition, whereas the active thrust of a stiff clay increases. From column 4, the passive resistance of a soft clay increases from the undrained to the drained state, whereas the passive resistance of a stiff clay tends to remain essentially constant.

6.3 THE AT-REST STATE

For a soil mass formed by horizontal deposition, consolidation will have occurred solely in the vertical direction with no lateral deformation across any vertical plane. The soil mass is then said to be in a *state of rest* or the *at-rest condition* and the ratio of the principal effective stresses σ_h' and σ_v' acting on an element is referred to as the *at-rest earth pressure coefficient*, denoted by K_0'. That is

$$K_0' = \frac{\sigma_h'}{\sigma_v'} \tag{6.19}$$

For normally consolidated clays and sands, $K_0' < 1$ and has been found to agree closely with the value predicted by an empirical equation proposed by Jaky (1944), namely

$$K_0' = 1 - \sin \phi' \tag{6.20}$$

If the soil mass is further consolidated vertically by a uniform loading $\Delta\sigma_v$ applied over the whole of the surface area, the vertical effective stress increases to $\sigma_v' + \Delta\sigma_v'$ and the horizontal effective stress increases a proportionate amount to $\sigma_h' + \Delta\sigma_h'$. The soil is still in the at-rest condition and normally consolidated, and therefore the ratio of horizontal to vertical effective stress remains unaltered.

If the surface loading is subsequently removed so that the soil becomes overconsolidated, the soil swells vertically and the vertical effective stress on the element reduces to its original value σ_v'. But as no deformation occurs in the horizontal direction, there is only a partial relaxation of the horizontal effective stress, with some of the increase $\Delta\sigma_h'$ remaining 'locked in'. Consequently, overconsolidation of a soil deposit results in an increase in the value of K_0'. Note, however, that the maximum value that K_0' can attain is that of K_p'. Typical values of K_0' for various soils are given in Table 6.2.

Table 6.2 Values of K_0'

Soil type	K_0'
Loose sand	0.5
Dense sand	0.35
Compacted sand	1.0–1.5
Normally consolidated clay	0.5–0.7
Overconsolidated clay	1.0–4.0
Compacted clay	1.0–2.0

6.4 GRAVITY AND CANTILEVER WALLS

Figure 6.9a shows the general arrangement of a gravity wall. Maximum foundation settlement occurs under the toe (where the bearing pressure is greatest) and consequently the wall tilts outwards. Some forward sliding also occurs so that the wall undergoes a degree of both rotation and translation. The effects of such movements on the distribution of pressure against the back of the wall were investigated experimentally by Terzaghi (1934), using a large-scale stiff retaining wall. For a very small outward yield, amounting to 0.1 per cent of the wall height for a dense sand and 0.4 per cent for a loose sand, the pressures dropped rapidly from the at-rest state to the active values, with the development of a *local* zone rupture behind the wall, as indicated by the boundary slip line BCD in Fig. 6.9a. Since this state is achieved without significant wall movement, it is only necessary for the wall to be able to withstand the active thrust.

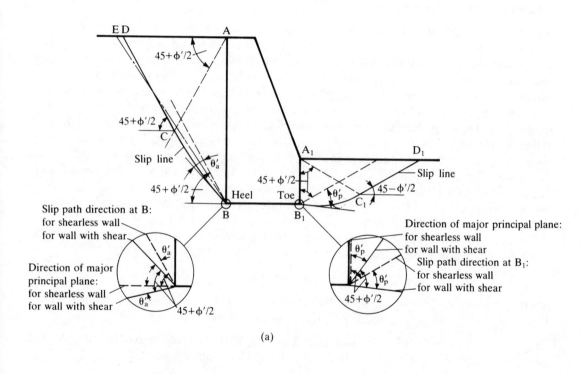

(a)

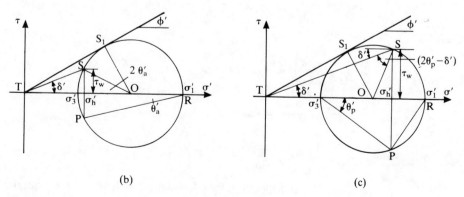

(b)   (c)

Figure 6.9 Influence of wall shear on slip path direction.

The rapid fall in pressures on the back of the wall to the active values is accompanied by a gradual increase in passive pressures against the buried part of the face (Fig. 6.9a), the maximum values being developed at lateral displacements of the order of 2 per cent of the soil height for a dense sand to 10 per cent for a loose sand.

As the wall yields, the retained soil mass settles vertically and imparts a downward shear force on the back of the wall. On the passive side, the soil is displaced upwards and thus imparts an upward shear force to the front face. The presence of these boundary shear forces influences the direction of the slip surface in the active and passive zones, and consequently the distributions of active and passive pressures on the wall, and hence the magnitude and direction of the active and passive forces.

Influence of Wall Shear on Slip Path Direction

Active zone Consider the retained soil in Fig. 6.9a to be a sand. If the back of the wall were shearless, the major principal plane at point B at the heel of the wall would be horizontal and the slip path would rise at an angle of $(45 + \phi'/2)$. In general, though, a shear stress acts on the soil–wall interface so that the major principal plane must lie in some direction other than the horizontal. As the shear reaction from the wall to the soil is upwards, then to fit the sign convention that anticlockwise shears are positive (see Sec. 2.2), the direction of the major principal plane and the direction of the slip path at the heel must be shifted anti-clockwise through some angle θ'_a, as shown by the detailed inset diagram in Fig. 6.9a. This may be verified from Fig. 6.9b, which shows the Mohr circle representing the effective stress conditions in an element of soil at point B. A line drawn from R parallel to the direction of the major principal plane locates the pole point P and a line from P parallel to the soil–wall interface cuts the circle at S, the ordinate of which then defines the positive shear stress τ_w on a vertical plane in the soil at B, and the abscissa the associated horizontal effective stress σ'_h.

Invoking the Mohr–Coulomb failure criterion, the vertical shear stress τ_w on the soil–wall interface at B can be expressed as

$$\tau_w = \sigma'_h \tan \delta'$$

where δ' = the *effective angle of friction between the soil and the wall* (or sometimes referred to as the *effective angle of wall friction*)

This equation is represented by the line TS in Fig. 6.9b. With reference then to the triangle OTS, angle TOS $= 2\theta'_a$ and angle OST $= 180 - (2\theta'_a + \delta')$. Thus from the sine rule

$$\frac{\text{OT}}{\text{OS}} = \frac{\sin \text{OST}}{\sin \text{OTS}} = \frac{\sin (2\theta'_a + \delta')}{\sin \delta'}$$

Also, since OS = OS_1

$$\frac{\text{OT}}{\text{OS}} = \frac{\text{OT}}{\text{OS}_1} = \operatorname{cosec} \phi'$$

Thus

$$\frac{\sin (2\theta'_a + \delta')}{\sin \delta'} = \operatorname{cosec} \phi'$$

whence

$$\theta'_a = \frac{1}{2}\left[\sin^{-1} \frac{\sin \delta'}{\sin \phi'} - \frac{\delta'}{\phi'} \phi' \right] \tag{6.21}$$

wherein $0 \leqslant \delta'/\phi' \leqslant 1$. Typically $\delta'/\phi' = \frac{3}{4}$, and therefore for a loose sand with $\phi' = 30°$ we obtain $\theta'_a = 13.7°$ and for a dense sand with $\phi' = 40°$, $\theta'_a = 10.5°$.

Thus θ'_a is in the order of $12° \pm 2°$. That is, the slip path at the heel of the wall is shifted anti-clockwise through approximately $12°$ (Fig. 6.9a) from the direction it would take if the wall were shearless. As the slip path passes further and further into the soil mass away from the back of the wall, the influence of wall shear diminishes and consequently the angular shift in the slip path direction becomes progressively less. It is generally assumed (Terzaghi, 1943) that the influence of wall shear is negligible at point C, the intersection of the slip path with the theoretical conjugate slip plane AC which just clears the top of the wall. The slip path is then a straight line rising at $(45 + \phi'/2)$ to the horizontal. The theoretical slip path is therefore curved over BC and linear over CD. However, since the typical degree of curvature is relatively slight, for all practical purposes the slip path BCD is closely approximated by a *straight* slip plane, represented by BE, inclined at some angle α to the horizontal. The inclination α is taken as that which gives the maximum value for the force on the back of the wall. This generally differs from that based on the actual slip path by less than 5 per cent.

It may also be shown that the assumption of a straight slip plane is equally valid for a clay backfill.

Passive zone Considering the sand in front of the wall (Fig. 6.9a), the shear reaction from the wall to the soil is downwards, and therefore the directions of the major principal plane and the slip path at the toe are shifted clockwise through some angle θ'_p from that associated with a shearless wall. This may be verified from the effective stress Mohr diagram in Fig. 6.9c.

The vertical shear stress τ_w on the soil–wall interface at point B_1 at the toe of the wall can be expressed as

$$\tau_w = \sigma'_h \tan \delta'$$

which is represented by the line TS in Fig. 6.9c. Thus with reference to the triangle OTS

$$\frac{OT}{OS} = \frac{\sin OST}{\sin OTS} = \frac{\sin (2\theta'_p - \delta')}{\sin \delta'}$$

Also

$$\frac{OT}{OS} = \frac{OT}{OS_1} = \operatorname{cosec} \phi'$$

Hence

$$\frac{\sin (2\theta'_p - \delta')}{\sin \delta'} = \operatorname{cosec} \phi'$$

whence

$$\theta'_p = \frac{1}{2}\left[\sin^{-1} \frac{\sin \delta'}{\sin \phi'} + \frac{\delta'}{\phi'} \phi' \right] \tag{6.22}$$

Taking $\delta'/\phi' = \frac{3}{4}$ with $\phi' = 30°$ (loose sand) and $40°$ (dense sand), $\theta'_p = 36.2°$ and $40.5°$ respectively. Thus, the slip path at the toe of the wall is shifted clockwise through approximately $38°$ (Fig. 6.9a) from the direction it would take if the wall were shearless. As in the active case, the influence of wall shear diminishes as the slip path passes into the soil mass away from the front of the wall, and as a result the angular shift in the slip path direction becomes progressively less. It is again assumed (after Terzaghi, 1943) that the influence of wall shear is negligible at point C_1, the intersection of the slip path with the conjugate slip plane A_1C_1. The slip plane is then a straight line rising at $(45 - \phi'/2)$ to the horizontal. It is seen from Fig. 6.9a that the theoretical slip path $B_1C_1D_1$ is distinctly curved over the length B_1C_1, which suggests that in this case the assumption of a straight slip plane would give an entirely erroneous solution. In fact, such an assumption leads to an overestimate of the available passive resistance and thus constitutes an error on the unsafe side. Therefore when determining the passive earth pressure of sands, it is necessary to take account of curvature of the slip path.

This is also generally the case for clay soils.

Active Earth Pressure

Sand Consider a gravity wall having a vertical back of height H retaining a sand level with the coping and sustaining a uniform surcharge pressure q (Fig. 6.10a). Let the water table be at or below the base of the wall so that $u = 0$ throughout the backfill. Assuming a straight slip plane, the forces acting on the wedge of sand are as shown, wherein α is the inclination of the failure plane, S_f and N are the shear resistance and normal reaction on the failure plane, X and P_h are the vertical and horizontal reactions between the soil and the wall, W is the weight of the soil wedge, and Q is the vertical force exerted by the surcharge.

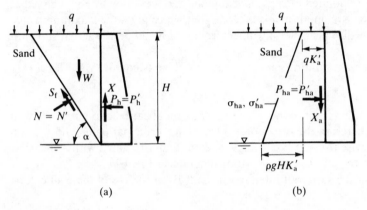

(a)   (b)

Figure 6.10 Gravity wall retaining sand: (a) forces on failure wedge, (b) active earth pressure distribution.

As $u = 0$ throughout the mass

$$N = N' \quad \text{and} \quad P_h = P'_h$$

We also have

$$S_f = N' \tan \phi', \quad X = P'_h \tan \delta', \quad W = \tfrac{1}{2}\rho g H^2 \cot \alpha \quad \text{and} \quad Q = qH \cot \alpha$$

Resolving horizontally

$$P'_h = N' \sin \alpha - S_f \cos \alpha = N' \sin \alpha - N' \tan \phi' \cos \alpha = N' \cos \alpha(\tan \alpha - \tan \phi') \quad (6.23)$$

and resolving vertically

$$Q + W - X = N' \cos \alpha + S_f \sin \alpha = N' \cos \alpha + N' \tan \phi' \sin \alpha = N' \cos \alpha(1 + \tan \alpha \tan \phi')$$
$$(6.24)$$

Dividing Eq. (6.23) by Eq. (6.24)

$$\frac{P'_h}{Q + W - X} = \tan(\alpha - \phi')$$

$$\therefore \quad P'_h = (Q + W - X) \tan(\alpha - \phi') = (Q + W - P'_h \tan \delta') \tan(\alpha - \phi')$$

$$\therefore \quad P'_h = \frac{(Q + W) \tan(\alpha - \phi')}{1 + \tan \delta' \tan(\alpha - \phi')} = (qH + \tfrac{1}{2}\rho g H^2) \frac{\cot \alpha \tan(\alpha - \phi')}{1 + \tan \delta' \tan(\alpha - \phi')}$$

P'_h increases initially with increase in α and passes through a maximum point. The critical value of α which makes the wall force a maximum, thus defining the active thrust P'_{ha}, is given by solving the equation $\partial P'_h / \partial \alpha = 0$. This leads to the result

$$P'_{ha} = (qH + \tfrac{1}{2}\rho g H^2)K'_a \tag{6.25}$$

where

$$K'_a = \left[\frac{\cos \phi'}{1 + \sin \phi'\sqrt{1 + \tan \delta'/\tan \phi'}}\right]^2 \qquad (6.26)$$

Comparing Eqs (6.26) and (6.3), we see that the influence of wall shear is to reduce the value of K'_a and hence the thrust on the wall.

Replacing H by h in Eq. (6.25) and differentiating with respect to h gives the effective active earth pressure at any depth h below the top of the wall as

$$\sigma'_{ha} = (q + \rho g h)K'_a \qquad (6.27)$$

This indicates a trapezoidal pressure distribution (Fig. 6.10b), becoming triangular when $q = 0$. The term $(q + \rho g h)$ denotes the vertical effective stress σ'_v at depth h, and therefore we may write Eq. (6.27) as

$$\sigma'_{ha} = \sigma'_v K'_a \qquad (6.28)$$

If the wall retains two different granular layers, the upper layer may be treated as a surcharge acting on the lower layer. There will be a discontinuity in the pressure diagram at the interface as a result of the different values of shear strength parameters. This is considered in Example 6.1.

The analysis may be extended for the case of a wall inclined away from the sand at angle θ to the vertical with the soil surface sloping upwards at angle i to the horizontal (Fig. 6.11). The expression for K'_a for use in Eq. (6.28) is now given by

$$K'_a = \left[\frac{\cos (\phi' - \theta)}{\cos \theta + \sin \phi' \sqrt{\dfrac{(1 + \tan \delta'/\tan \phi')(1 - \tan i/\tan \phi')}{(1 - \tan \theta \tan \delta')(1 + \tan \theta \tan i)}}}\right]^2 \qquad (6.29)$$

This problem was considered by Coulomb in 1776. For the particular case of $\theta = i = 0$, Eq. (6.29) reduces to Eq. (6.26).

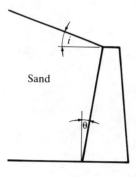

Figure 6.11

Undrained saturated clay Consider a gravity wall having a vertical back of height H retaining a saturated clay level with the coping (Fig. 6.12a). If the construction period is relatively short and it can reasonably be assumed that there has been no dissipation of excess porewater pressure by the end of construction, then the clay will be undrained and the short-term stability analysis may be carried out in terms of total stress.

Assuming a straight slip plane, the forces acting on the clay wedge are as shown. The clay is in tension towards the soil surface (see Sec. 6.2) and hence tension cracks will develop in the soil, the depth of the tension zone being denoted by h_0. The length of the slip plane $= (H - h_0)$ cosec α, whence

$$S_f = c_u(H - h_0) \text{ cosec } \alpha + N \tan \phi_u = c_u(H - h_0) \text{ cosec } \alpha$$

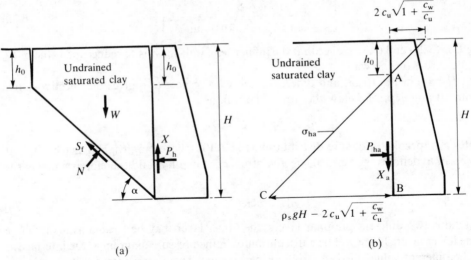

Figure 6.12 Gravity wall retaining undrained saturated clay: (a) forces on failure wedge, (b) distribution of total active earth pressure σ_{ha} (short-term condition).

as $\phi_u = 0$ for a saturated clay. In a similar manner

$$X = c_w(H - h_0)$$

where c_w = the adhesion between the wall and the clay

Also $\quad W = \frac{1}{2}\rho_s g(H + h_0)(H - h_0)\cot\alpha = \frac{1}{2}\rho_s g(H^2 - h_0^2)\cot\alpha$

Resolving horizontally

$$N\sin\alpha = P_h + S_f\cos\alpha = P_h + c_u(H - h_0)\cot\alpha \tag{6.30}$$

and resolving vertically

$$N\cos\alpha = W - X - S_f\sin\alpha = \frac{1}{2}\rho_s g(H^2 - h_0^2)\cot\alpha - c_u(H - h_0)\left(1 + \frac{c_w}{c_u}\right) \tag{6.31}$$

Dividing Eq. (6.30) by Eq. (6.31) and rearranging:

$$P_h = \frac{1}{2}\rho_s g(H^2 - h_0^2) - c_u(H - h_0)\left[\left(1 + \frac{c_w}{c_u}\right)\tan\alpha + \cot\alpha\right]$$

Thus $\quad \dfrac{\partial P_h}{\partial \alpha} = -c_u(H - h_0)\left[\left(1 + \dfrac{c_w}{c_u}\right)\sec^2\alpha - \operatorname{cosec}^2\alpha\right] = 0$

for a maximum, from which

$$\tan\alpha = \frac{1}{\sqrt{1 + c_w/c_u}}$$

Hence $\quad P_{ha} = \frac{1}{2}\rho_s g(H^2 - h_0^2) - 2c_u(H - h_0)\sqrt{1 + \dfrac{c_w}{c_u}} \tag{6.32}$

Replacing H by h and differentiating gives the total active earth pressure at any depth h below the top of the wall as

$$\sigma_{ha} = \rho_s g h - 2c_u\sqrt{1 + \frac{c_w}{c_u}} \tag{6.33}$$

The pressure distribution thus varies linearly from $-2c_u\sqrt{1 + c_w/c_u}$ at the coping to $\rho_s gH - 2c_u\sqrt{1 + c_w/c_u}$ at the heel (Fig. 6.12b). The depth of the tension crack is given by

$$h_0 = \frac{2c_u\sqrt{1 + c_w/c_u}}{\rho_s g} \tag{6.34}$$

If a uniform surcharge pressure q is applied to the soil surface then

$$\sigma_{ha} = q + \rho_s gh - 2c_u\sqrt{1 + \frac{c_w}{c_u}} \tag{6.35a}$$

whence

$$\sigma_{ha} = \sigma_v - 2c_u\sqrt{1 + \frac{c_w}{c_u}} \tag{6.35b}$$

If $q \geqslant 2c_u\sqrt{1 + c_w/c_u}$, a tension crack will not be formed.

Drained clay A long time after construction, the excess porewater pressures in a clay backfill will have dissipated completely and the soil will be fully drained. An analysis of the long-term active force on the wall must therefore be in terms of effective stress. The approach is similar to that demonstrated for a sand and, for the case of a wall having a vertical back with the clay soil level with the coping, the following effective active earth pressure equation is obtained:

$$\sigma'_{ha} = \sigma'_v K'_{a1} - c' K'_{a2} \tag{6.36}$$

where

$$K'_{a1} = \left[\frac{\cos \phi'}{1 + \sin \phi'\sqrt{1 + \tan \delta'/\tan \phi'}} \right]^2 \tag{6.37}$$

and

$$K'_{a2} = \frac{\cos \phi'[2\sqrt{1 + c'_w/c'} + (2 + c'_w/c') \sin \phi']}{[1 + \sin \phi'\sqrt{1 + \tan \delta'/\tan \phi'}]^2} \tag{6.38}$$

The analysis assumes that the same ratio of δ'/ϕ' as c'_w/c' is mobilized on the back of the wall.

Example 6.1 Figure 6.13 shows a gravity wall, 12 m high, having a vertical back retaining 8 m of dense gravel overlain by 4 m of loose sand. The surface of the sand is level with the top of the wall and supports a surcharge of 40 kN/m². The sand and gravel layers are both drained with the water table below the base of the wall. Calculate

(a) the horizontal component of the active force on the wall,
(b) the vertical shear force on the wall, and
(c) the overturning moment about the heel of the wall.

The properties of the sand are $\rho = 1.60$ Mg/m³, $\phi' = 32°$ and $\delta' = 24°$.
The properties of the gravel are $\rho = 1.80$ Mg/m³, $\phi' = 40°$ and $\delta' = 30°$.

SOLUTION For a gravity wall having a vertical back retaining granular soil level with the coping

$$\sigma'_{ha} = \sigma'_v K'_a \tag{6.28 bis}$$

wherein

$$K'_a = \left[\frac{\cos \phi'}{1 + \sin \phi'\sqrt{1 + \tan \delta'/\tan \phi'}} \right]^2 \tag{6.26 bis}$$

Thus for the loose sand with $\phi' = 32°$ and $\delta' = 24°$ we obtain $K'_a = 0.251$ and for the dense gravel with $\phi' = 40°$ and $\delta' = 30°$ we obtain $K'_a = 0.174$. $u = 0$ throughout and therefore

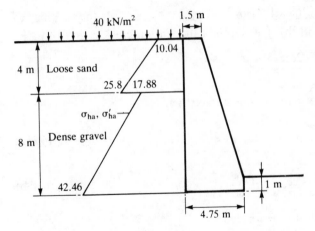

Figure 6.13 Example 6.1.

$\sigma_v' = \sigma_v$ at all points. Hence

At the top of the wall: $\quad \sigma_v' = 40\ \text{kN/m}^2 \Rightarrow \sigma_{ha}' = 40 \times 0.251 = 10.04\ \text{kN/m}^2$
At a depth of 4 m: $\quad\quad \sigma_v' = 40 + 1.6 \times 9.81 \times 4 = 102.78\ \text{kN/m}^2$
  Therefore for the sand $\quad \sigma_{ha}' = 102.78 \times 0.251 = 25.80\ \text{kN/m}^2$
  and for the gravel $\quad\quad \sigma_{ha}' = 102.78 \times 0.174 = 17.88\ \text{kN/m}^2$
At the base of the wall: $\quad\ \sigma_v' = 102.78 + 1.8 \times 9.81 \times 8 = 244.05\ \text{kN/m}^2$
$\quad\quad\quad\quad\quad\quad\quad\quad\ \ \sigma_{ha}' = 244.05 \times 0.174 = 42.46\ \text{kN/m}^2$

The distribution of σ_{ha}' on the back of the wall is then as shown in Fig. 6.13. This is also the distribution of σ_{ha} since $u = 0$ throughout the retained mass. We thus obtain:

For the loose sand

$$P_{ha} = P_{ha}' = \tfrac{1}{2}(10.04 + 25.80)4 = 71.68\ \text{kN/m}$$

$$X_a = 71.68 \times \tan 24° = 31.91\ \text{kN/m}$$

$$M_a = 10.04 \times 4 \times 10 + \tfrac{1}{2}(25.80 - 10.04) \times 4 \times 9.3 = 695.79\ \text{kN m/m}$$

and for the dense gravel

$$P_{ha} = P_{ha}' = \tfrac{1}{2}(17.88 + 42.46)8 = 241.36\ \text{kN/m}$$

$$X_a = 241.36\ \tan 30° = 139.35\ \text{kN/m}$$

$$M_a = 17.88 \times 8 \times 4 + \tfrac{1}{2}(42.46 - 17.88) \times 8 \times 2.6 = 834.35\ \text{kN m/m}$$

Thus total horizontal component of active force on the wall $= 71.68 + 241.36 = \underline{313.04\ \text{kN/m}}$, total vertical shear force on the back of the wall $= 31.91 + 139.35 = \underline{171.26\ \text{kN/m}}$, and total overturning moment about the heel $= 695.79 + 834.35 = \underline{1530.14\ \text{kN m/m}}$.
    The lever arm, l_a, for P_{ha} is given by

$$l_a = \frac{M_a}{P_{ha}} = \frac{1530.14}{313.04} = \underline{4.89\ \text{m}}$$

Example 6.2 Figure 6.14a shows the details of a gravity wall founded on an impermeable rock and provided with a vertical drain down the back face. The wall retains a fine sand fill which is subjected to continuous rainfall over a prolonged period with subsequent steady seepage

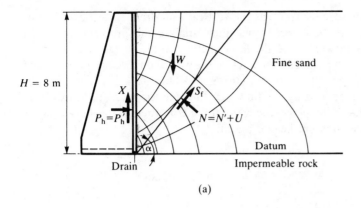

(a)

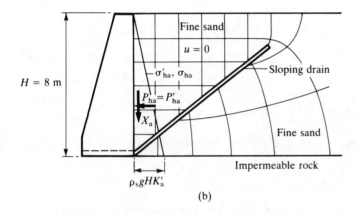

(b)

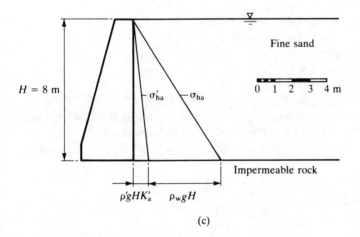

(c)

Figure 6.14 Example 6.2.

towards the drain. Calculate the active thrust on the wall given that the properties of the sand are $\rho_s = 1.90 \text{ Mg/m}^3$, $\phi' = 35°$ and $\delta' = 25°$.

Calculate also the active thrust on the wall (a) if instead of a vertical drain the wall had been built with a sloping drain (located below any potential failure surface) and (b) if no drainage system were to be provided with the water table subsequently rising to the ground surface.

SOLUTION The flow net for steady seepage towards the vertical wall drain is as shown in Fig. 6.14a. The presence of this seepage flow means we must analyse the problem from first principles. Thus, assuming a straight slip plane, the forces acting on the wedge of sand are as shown. We have here that $u = 0$ at all points on the back of the wall and therefore $P_h = P_h'$ and $X = P_h' \tan \delta' = P_h \tan \delta'$. On the potential failure plane $S_f = N' \tan \phi'$.

The pressure head at a point is defined by the flow net. Plotting the pressure head values along the slip plane at right angles to the plane, the water force U normal to the slip surface is equal to $\rho_w g$ times the area of the pressure head diagram.

Resolving horizontally

$$P_h = N \sin \alpha - S_f \cos \alpha = (N' + U) \sin \alpha - N' \tan \phi' \cos \alpha$$

$$\therefore \qquad P_h - U \sin \alpha = N' \cos \alpha (\tan \alpha - \tan \phi') \qquad (6.39)$$

Resolving vertically

$$W - X = N \cos \alpha + S_f \sin \alpha = (N' + U) \cos \alpha + N' \tan \phi' \sin \alpha$$

$$\therefore \qquad W - X - U \cos \alpha = N' \cos \alpha (1 + \tan \alpha \tan \phi') \qquad (6.40)$$

Dividing Eq. (6.39) by Eq. (6.40)

$$\frac{P_h - U \sin \alpha}{W - X - U \cos \alpha} = \tan (\alpha - \phi')$$

Substituting $W = \frac{1}{2} \rho_s g H^2 \cot \alpha$ and $X = P_h \tan \delta'$ gives, on rearranging

$$P_h = \frac{\frac{1}{2} \rho_s g H^2 \cot \alpha \tan (\alpha - \phi') + U[\sin \alpha - \cos \alpha \tan (\alpha - \phi')]}{1 + \tan \delta' \tan (\alpha - \phi')} \qquad (6.41)$$

We have here $\rho_s = 1.90 \text{ Mg/m}^3$, $\phi' = 35°$, $\delta' = 25°$ and $H = 8 \text{ m}$, whence we obtain for

$$\begin{aligned}
\alpha = 46°, \quad &U = 148.9 \text{ kN/m} \quad \text{and} \quad P_h = 182.4 \text{ kN/m} \\
\alpha = 48°, \quad &U = 136.5 \text{ kN/m} \quad \text{and} \quad P_h = 184.5 \text{ kN/m} \\
\alpha = 50°, \quad &U = 125.0 \text{ kN/m} \quad \text{and} \quad P_h = 185.2 \text{ kN/m} \\
\alpha = 52°, \quad &U = 113.9 \text{ kN/m} \quad \text{and} \quad P_h = 184.5 \text{ kN/m} \\
\alpha = 54°, \quad &U = 103.7 \text{ kN/m} \quad \text{and} \quad P_h = 182.8 \text{ kN/m}
\end{aligned}$$

Thus $\alpha_{\text{crit}} = 50°$ whence $P_h \Rightarrow P_{ha} = \underline{185.2 \text{ kN/m}}$ and $X_a = 185.2 \tan 25° = \underline{86.4 \text{ kN/m}}$.

If the wall had been built with a sloping drain, as illustrated in Fig. 6.14b, the flow lines and equipotential lines above the drain would be vertical and horizontal respectively. Thus, the porewater pressures within the active zone would be zero. With $U = 0$ on any potential failure plane, Eq. (6.41) then becomes

$$P_h = \frac{1}{2} \rho_s g H^2 \frac{\cot \alpha \tan (\alpha - \phi')}{1 + \tan \delta' \tan (\alpha - \phi')}$$

Therefore for

$$\begin{aligned}
\alpha = 56°, \quad &P_h = 131.0 \text{ kN/m} \\
\alpha = 58°, \quad &P_h = 132.1 \text{ kN/m} \\
\alpha = 59°, \quad &P_h = 132.1 \text{ kN/m} \\
\alpha = 60°, \quad &P_h = 131.9 \text{ kN/m} \\
\alpha = 62°, \quad &P_h = 130.6 \text{ kN/m}
\end{aligned}$$

Thus $\alpha_{\text{crit}} \approx 59°$, whence $P_h \Rightarrow P_{ha} = \underline{132.1 \text{ kN/m}}$ and $X_a = 132.1 \tan 25° = \underline{61.6 \text{ kN/m}}$.

Alternatively, we may use the active earth pressure equation $\sigma'_{ha} = \sigma'_v K'_a$ with K'_a defined by Eq. (6.26). Thus, with $\phi' = 35°$ and $\delta' = 25°$ we obtain $K'_a = 0.2215$ and therefore

$$P_{ha} = \tfrac{1}{2}\rho_s gH^2 K'_a = \tfrac{1}{2} \times 1.90 \times 9.81 \times 8^2 \times 0.2215 = \underline{132.1 \text{ kN/m}}$$

as above.

If no drainage system were to be provided, with the water table subsequently rising to the ground surface, the distribution of σ'_{ha} and σ_{ha} on the back of the wall would be as shown in Fig. 6.14c, from which we obtain

$$P_{ha} = P'_{ha} + P_{hw}$$

$$= \tfrac{1}{2}\rho' gH^2 K'_a + \tfrac{1}{2}\rho_w gH^2$$

$$= \tfrac{1}{2} \times 0.9 \times 9.81 \times 8^2 \times 0.2215 + \tfrac{1}{2} \times 1 \times 9.81 \times 8^2$$

$$= 62.58 + 313.92 = \underline{376.50 \text{ kN/m}}$$

and $$X_a = P'_{ha} \tan \delta' = 62.58 \tan 25° = \underline{29.18 \text{ kN/m}}$$

We see then the importance of providing and maintaining adequate wall drainage.

Example 6.3 A gravity wall, 10 m high and having a vertical back, is to retain a saturated overconsolidated clay level with the top of the wall, as shown in Fig. 6.15a. Calculate the horizontal and vertical components of active thrust on the back of the wall immediately after

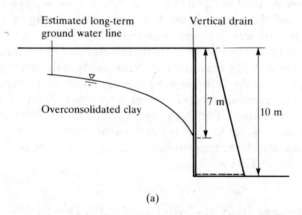

(a)

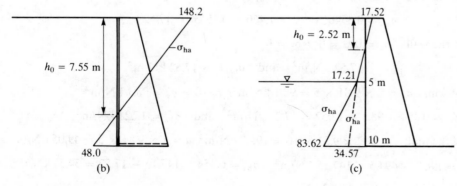

(b)   (c)

Figure 6.15 Example 6.3.

construction and a long time after construction given that the properties of the clay are $\rho_s = 2.0 \text{ Mg/m}^3$, $c_u = 56 \text{ kN/m}^2$, $c_w = 42 \text{ kN/m}^2$, $\phi' = 24°$, $c' = 12 \text{ kN/m}^2$. $\delta' = 18°$ and $c'_w = 9 \text{ kN/m}^2$. Assume for the long-term case that the effects of steady state seepage flow to the vertical drain are equivalent to a static water level at the mid-height of the wall.

SOLUTION Assuming that there has been no dissipation of excess porewater pressure by the end of construction, then the clay is undrained and the immediate active thrust on the wall may be determined based on a total stress analysis. From Eq. (6.35b) the distribution of σ_{ha} is then given by

$$\sigma_{ha} = \sigma_v - 2c_u\sqrt{1 + \frac{c_w}{c_u}} = \sigma_v - 2 \times 56\sqrt{1 + \frac{42}{56}} = \sigma_v - 148.2$$

At the top of the wall: $\sigma_v = 0 \Rightarrow \sigma_{ha} = -148.2 \text{ kN/m}^2$
At the base of the wall: $\sigma_v = 2 \times 9.81 \times 10 = 196.2 \text{ kN/m}^2 \Rightarrow \sigma_{ha} = 196.2 - 148.2 = 48 \text{ kN/m}^2$

The distribution of σ_{ha} on the wall is then as shown in Fig. 6.15b. The depth of the tension crack h_0 may be calculated directly from the geometry of the pressure diagram, whence we obtain $h_0 = 7.55$ m. Thus

$$P_{ha} = \tfrac{1}{2} \times 48 \times 2.45 = \underline{58.8 \text{ kN/m}}$$

and $$X_a = c_w(H - h_0) = 42 \times 2.45 = \underline{102.9 \text{ kN/m}}$$

Note that if no wall drain is provided and the ground surface is unpaved, the tension crack behind the wall can readily fill up with rain water and subject the wall to an additional hydrostatic thrust, which herein would be equal to $\tfrac{1}{2} \times 1 \times 9.81 \times 7.55^2 = 279.6 \text{ kN/m}$. This is substantially greater than the short-term thrust from the clay. This again indicates the importance of providing adequate wall drainage at all times.

With the passage of time, the porewater pressures in the retained clay slowly adjust until they are everywhere in equilibrium with the resulting long-term steady state seepage flow to the vertical wall drain. The clay is then fully drained (in the sense that there are no excess porewater pressures) and consequently the determination of the long-term active thrust on the wall must be based on an effective stress analysis. For this purpose the effects of the seepage flow are closely approximated by a static water level at the mid-height of the wall (Fig. 6.15c). This simplifies the analysis considerably, since the distribution of σ_{ha} on the back of the wall is then defined throughout by Eq. (6.36). That is

$$\sigma'_{ha} = \sigma'_v K'_{a1} - c' K'_{a2}$$

where K'_{a1} and K'_{a2} are given respectively by Eqs (6.37) and (6.38). Thus for $\phi' = 24°$, $\delta' = 18°$, $c' = 12 \text{ kN/m}^2$ and $c'_w = 9 \text{ kN/m}^2$ we obtain $K'_{a1} = 0.354$ and $K'_{a2} = 1.460$. Hence

$$\sigma'_{ha} = 0.354\sigma'_v - 12 \times 1.460 = 0.354\sigma'_v - 17.52$$

At the top of the wall: $\sigma_v = 0, u = 0 \Rightarrow \sigma'_v = 0$

$$\sigma'_{ha} = -17.52 \text{ kN/m}^2 \quad \text{and} \quad \sigma_{ha} = -17.52 \text{ kN/m}^2$$

At a depth of 5 m: $\sigma_v = 2 \times 9.81 \times 5 = 98.1 \text{ kN/m}^2$, $u = 0 \Rightarrow \sigma'_v = 98.1 \text{ kN/m}^2$

$$\sigma'_{ha} = 0.354 \times 98.1 - 17.52 = 17.21 \text{ kN/m}^2 \quad \text{and} \quad \sigma_{ha} = 17.21 \text{ kN/m}^2$$

At the base of the wall: $\sigma_v = 2 \times 9.81 \times 10 = 196.2 \text{ kN/m}^2$, $u = 1 \times 9.81 \times 5 = 49.05 \text{ kN/m}^2$

$\Rightarrow \qquad \sigma'_v = 196.2 - 49.05 = 147.15 \text{ kN/m}^2$, $\sigma'_{ha} = 0.354 \times 147.15 - 17.52 = 34.57 \text{ kN/m}^2$

and $\qquad \sigma_{ha} = 34.57 + 49.05 = 83.62 \text{ kN/m}^2$

The distributions of σ'_{ha} and σ_{ha} are then as shown in Fig. 6.15c from which we obtain:

$$h_0 = 2.522 \text{ m}$$

$$P'_{ha} = \tfrac{1}{2} \times 17.21 \times 2.478 + \tfrac{1}{2}(17.21 + 34.57)5 = \underline{150.77 \text{ kN/m}}$$

$$P_{hw} = \tfrac{1}{2}(83.62 - 34.57)5 = \underline{122.63 \text{ kN/m}}$$

$$P_{ha} = P'_{ha} + P_{hw} = 150.77 + 122.63 = \underline{273.40 \text{ kN/m}}$$

and $\quad X_a = c'_w(H - h_0) + P'_{ha} \tan \delta' = 9 \times 7.478 + 150.77 \tan 18° = \underline{116.29 \text{ kN/m}}$

Passive Earth Pressure

Sand Figure 6.16a shows the foundation part of a gravity wall with sand against the buried face. The contact face is taken to be vertical, the surface of the sand horizontal and the water table below the base. As the wall yields under the active thrust from the soil on the retained side, the sand against the face is compressed, giving rise to passive resistance. The form of the slip surface is as indicated (and as previously determined), being distinctly curved over its initial part. This is closely approximated by either a log spiral or a circular arc, and for given values of ϕ' and δ' is drawn in to satisfy $\theta' = \theta'_p$ at the toe of the wall [Eq. (6.22)] and $\theta' = 0$ at point C. The soil mass over the curved portion is then divided into a number of vertical slices. If these are sufficiently close, the boundary surface at the base of each slice may be replaced by a straight line. The forces acting on a particular slice are then as shown, wherein α is the inclination of the base, S_f and N are the shear resistance and normal reaction on the base, E is the lateral force on the right-hand face of the slice which changes an incremental amount to become $E + \Delta E$ on the left-hand side, X and $X + \Delta X$ are the corresponding vertical shear forces, Δb is the breadth of the slice, and ΔW is the total weight. Resolving horizontally and vertically gives the change in lateral force as

$$\Delta E = (\Delta W + \Delta X) \tan (\alpha + \phi')$$

On the shearless vertical plane CE, $\sigma'_{hp} = \sigma'_v \tan^2 (45 + \phi'/2)$ [(Eq. (6.5)], whence

$$E_0 = \tfrac{1}{2}\rho g h_{CE}^2 \tan^2 \left(45 + \frac{\phi'}{2}\right)$$

For horizontal equilibrium of the soil mass

$$P_{hp} = E_0 + \sum_C^B \Delta E$$

whence $\quad P_{hp} = \tfrac{1}{2}\rho g h_{CE}^2 \tan^2 \left(45 + \frac{\phi'}{2}\right) + \sum_C^B \Delta W \tan (\alpha + \phi') + \sum_C^B \Delta X \tan (\alpha + \phi') \quad (6.42)$

Now the vertical shear force at the soil–wall interface is equal to $P_{hp} \tan \delta'$, and this is dissipated through the mass to a value of zero at CE. The precise form of the distribution is not easily definable and therefore to develop Eq. (6.42) further we seek that particular distribution which makes the minimum contribution to the passive resistance. Consider then that all the shear change occurs at the wall so that $\Delta X = P'_{ph} \tan \delta'$ at B and thereafter the shear force on all vertical planes is zero. The last term in Eq. (6.42) then reduces to

$$\sum_C^B \Delta X \tan (\alpha + \phi') = P_{hp} \tan \delta' \tan (\alpha_B + \phi') \quad (6.43)$$

Since α is a maximum negative value at B, then we see that this assumption results in the shear

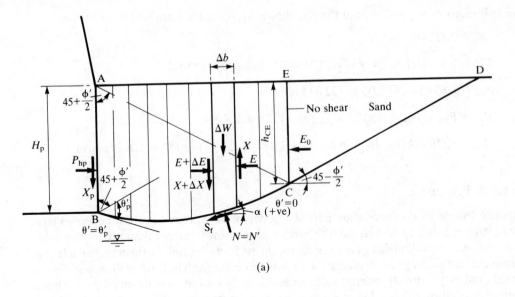

(a)

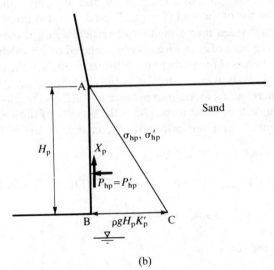

(b)

Figure 6.16 Gravity wall in sand: (a) forces on typical slice of failure mass, (b) passive earth pressure distribution.

term making the minimum contribution to the passive resistance. Thus, substituting Eq. (6.43) in Eq. (6.42) and rearranging

$$P_{hp}(= P'_{hp}) = \tfrac{1}{2}\rho g H_p^2 K'_p \tag{6.44}$$

where H_p = height of soil against the face

and

$$K'_p = \frac{(h_{CE}^2/H_p^2)\tan^2(45 + \phi'/2) + \sum_{C}^{B}(2\,\Delta W/\rho g H_p^2)\tan(\alpha + \phi')}{1 - \tan\delta'\tan(\alpha_B + \phi')} \tag{6.45}$$

The equation for K'_p may be integrated either numerically or analytically for a particular shape of failure surface. Table 6.3 gives the values obtained for a log spiral which is found to be marginally the most critical form.

Table 6.3 Values of K'_p

δ'/ϕ'	ϕ'							
	5°	10°	15°	20°	25°	30°	35°	40°
0	1.19	1.42	1.70	2.04	2.46	3.00	3.69	4.60
$\frac{1}{4}$	1.22	1.48	1.82	2.26	2.84	3.62	4.70	6.26
$\frac{1}{2}$	1.23	1.53	1.92	2.43	3.13	4.13	5.58	7.80
$\frac{3}{4}$	1.24	1.56	1.98	2.55	3.36	4.52	6.31	9.18
1	1.26	1.60	2.06	2.70	3.63	5.03	7.25	11.03

Although the precise form of the shear distribution through the mass is not easily defined, an assessment of the likely form of the distribution, and its consequent influence on the passive resistance of the soil, may be made on the condition that Mohr's circle of stress is satisfied at all points around the failure surface. For the typical data $\delta'/\phi' = \frac{3}{4}$ with $\phi' = 30°$ and $40°$, analysis then gives $K'_p = 5.65$ and 13.95 respectively. The coefficient is thus increased by 25–52 per cent. In practice, however, these higher values are not achieved because the deformation to passive failure results either in considerable progressive failure or large and unacceptable displacement (Rowe and Peaker, 1965).

Equation (6.44) implies the linear effective passive earth pressure equation

$$\sigma'_{hp} = \sigma'_v K'_p \qquad (6.46)$$

The distribution of σ'_{hp} over the buried face is then as shown in Fig. 6.16b, varying from zero at the soil surface to $\rho g H_p K'_p$ at the toe. This is also the distribution of σ_{hp}, and the area of the pressure diagram defines both P'_{hp} and P_{hp}, re-establishing Eq. (6.44).

Undrained saturated clay We are concerned here with the short-term passive resistance of a saturated clay while it remains undrained, for which condition a total stress analysis may be employed. It is again assumed that the soil–wall interface is vertical and the ground surface horizontal (Fig. 6.17).

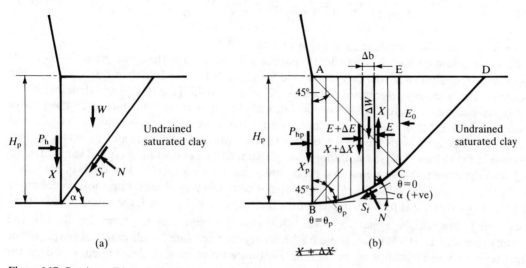

Figure 6.17 Gravity wall in undrained saturated clay: (a) straight slip plane, (b) curved slip surface.

If c_w denotes the adhesion between the soil and the wall, it may be shown that the slip plane at the toe is shifted clockwise through an angle θ_p defined by

$$\theta_p = \frac{1}{2} \sin^{-1} \frac{c_w}{c_u} \tag{6.47}$$

For a typical value of $c_w/c_u = \frac{3}{4}$, this gives $\theta_p = 24.3°$ from which it is evident that the influence of wall shear is not too great and in consequence we may reasonably assume a straight slip plane (Fig. 6.17a). However, for $c_w/c_u = 1$, $\theta_p = 45°$ and curvature of the slip surface is more pronounced (Fig. 6.17b). It is desirable, therefore, to consider both possibilities.

For a *straight* slip plane, the forces acting on the clay wedge are as shown in Fig. 6.17a. The sequence of steps involved in the analysis follow those presented earlier for the determination of the active thrust of an undrained clay and lead to the result

$$P_{hp} = \tfrac{1}{2}\rho_s g H_p^2 + c_u H_p K_{p2} \tag{6.48}$$

where

$$K_{p2} = 2\sqrt{1 + \frac{c_w}{c_u}} \tag{6.49}$$

For a *curved* failure surface, the forces acting on an elemental vertical slice of the mass are as shown in Fig. 6.17b. Resolving horizontally and vertically gives the change in lateral force as

$$\Delta E = (\Delta W + \Delta X) \tan \alpha + c_u \, \Delta b \sec^2 \alpha$$

Summating over the whole of the failure surface defines the total passive force against the face. The required integration may be performed analytically for a given shape of failure surface. As $\phi_u = 0$, the equation of a log spiral reduces to that of a circular arc and a common expression is obtained for P_{hp}. This is of the same form as Eq. (6.48) for a straight slip plane but where we now find, for the assumption that the wall shear is fully dissipated at the face

$$K_{p2} = 1 + \tan\frac{\theta_p}{2} + \frac{1}{\sqrt{2} \sin \theta_p} \ln \frac{\tan 67\tfrac{1}{2}°}{\tan (67\tfrac{1}{2} - \theta_p/2)} + \frac{c_w}{c_u} \tan (45 - \theta_p) \tag{6.50}$$

and for the wall shear dissipated through the mass

$$K_{p2} = 1 + \tan\frac{\theta_p}{2} + \frac{1}{\sqrt{2} \sin \theta_p} \ln \frac{\tan 67\tfrac{1}{2}°}{\tan (67\tfrac{1}{2} - \theta_p/2)} + \sum_{C}^{B} \left(\frac{c_{w_{n+1}}}{c_u} \frac{h_{n+1}}{H_p} - \frac{c_{w_n}}{c_u} \frac{h_n}{H_p} \right) \tan \alpha \tag{6.51}$$

A comparison of the coefficients is given in Table 6.4.

We see in column 3 that the coefficient is particularly sensitive to the assumption that the wall shear is fully dissipated at the face, the value for $c_w/c_u = 1$ being less than for $c_w/c_u = \frac{3}{4}$. The reason for this is readily determined since for $c_w/c_u = 1$, $\theta_p = 45°$ [Eq. (6.47)] and therefore in Eq. (6.50) the shear term $(c_w/c_u) \tan (45 - \theta_p) = 0$, and thus makes no contribution to the passive resistance. This anomalous result does not arise for the more realistic assumption that the wall shear is dissipated through the mass (column 4). Also, this assumption results in only a modest increase in the values of K_{p2}, amounting to approximately 8 per cent for a typical value of $c_w/c_u = \frac{3}{4}$, and therefore it is considered that these values are more acceptable than those in column 3. We further see that the values for K_{p2} in column 4 compare very closely with those in column 2 predicted by a straight slip plane. In fact for the limiting case of $c_w/c_u = 1$, the values are identical, both being numerically equal to $2\sqrt{2}$. This may be seen directly from Eq. (6.49) and demonstrated for Eq. (6.51) with some further analysis. Therefore for all practical purposes the short-term passive resistance of an undrained saturated clay may be determined, based on the simplified assumption of a straight slip plane.

Table 6.4 Values of K_{p2}

$\dfrac{c_w}{c_u}$	Straight slip plane [Eq. (6.49)]	Log spiral, Circular arc [Eq. (6.50)]†	Log spiral, Circular arc [Eq. (6.51)]‡	Code §
0	2	2	2	2
$\frac{1}{4}$	2.236	2.203	2.226	
$\frac{1}{2}$	2.449	2.328	2.414	2.4
$\frac{3}{4}$	2.646	2.378	2.577	
1	2.828	2.296	2.828	2.6

† Wall shear fully dissipated at the face.
‡ Wall shear dissipated through the mass.
§ *Code of Practice No. 2 (1951) Earth Retaining Structures* (under review).

Equation (6.48) implies the linear passive earth pressure equation:

$$\sigma_{hp} = \sigma_v + c_u K_{p2} \qquad (6.52)$$

Drained clay We are concerned here with the long-term passive resistance of a clay when it is fully drained. For this condition we require an effective stress analysis. The approach is similar to that demonstrated for a sand and for a vertical soil–wall interface and horizontal ground surface the following effective passive earth pressure equation is obtained:

$$\sigma'_{hp} = \sigma'_v K'_{p1} + c' K'_{p2} \qquad (6.53)$$

Values of the coefficients K'_{p1} and K'_{p2} are given in Table 6.5 for the assumptions of a log spiral failure surface and wall shear dissipated at the face.

Table 6.5 Values of K'_{p1} and K'_{p2}

Coefficient	$\dfrac{c'_w}{c'}$	$\dfrac{\delta'}{\phi'}$	ϕ' 5°	10°	15°	20°	25°	30°
K'_{p1}		0	1.19	1.42	1.70	2.04	2.46	3.00
		$\frac{1}{4}$	1.22	1.48	1.82	2.26	2.84	3.62
		$\frac{1}{2}$	1.23	1.53	1.92	2.43	3.13	4.13
		$\frac{3}{4}$	1.24	1.56	1.98	2.55	3.36	4.52
		1	1.26	1.60	2.06	2.70	3.63	5.03
K'_{p2}	0	0	2.18	2.38	2.61	2.86	3.14	3.46
	$\frac{1}{4}$	$\frac{1}{4}$	2.45	2.73	3.06	3.45	3.92	4.50
	$\frac{1}{2}$	$\frac{1}{2}$	2.61	2.94	3.33	3.81	4.40	5.15
	$\frac{3}{4}$	$\frac{3}{4}$	2.67	3.02	3.43	3.94	4.58	5.39
	1	1	2.57	2.89	3.26	3.73	4.30	5.04

Example 6.4 Figure 6.18 shows the details of a gravity wall retaining an overconsolidated clay. Calculate the maximum available long-term passive resistance against the face given that the properties of the clay are $\rho_s = 2.1$ Mg/m³, $c' = 8$ kN/m², $\phi' = 20°$, $c'_w = 6$ kN/m² and $\delta' = 15°$. Calculate also the decrease in passive resistance if c' were to decrease to zero with time.

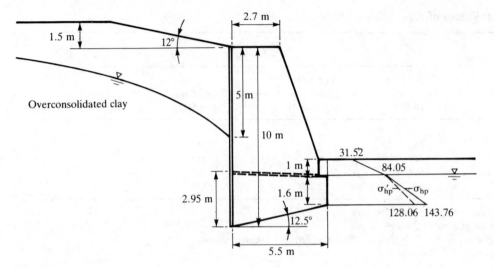

Figure 6.18 Example 6.4.

SOLUTION We require an effective stress analysis and thus from Eq. (6.53)

$$\sigma'_{hp} = \sigma'_v K'_{p1} + c' K'_{p2}$$

With $\phi' = 20°$ and $c'_w/c' = \delta'/\phi' = \frac{3}{4}$, Table 6.5 gives $K'_{p1} = 2.55$ and $K'_{p2} = 3.94$ whence

$$\sigma'_{hp} = 2.55\sigma'_v + 8 \times 3.94 = 2.55\sigma'_v + 31.52$$

At the ground surface: $\sigma_v = 0$, $u = 0 \Rightarrow \sigma'_v = 0$, $\sigma'_{hp} = 31.52 \text{ kN/m}^2$ and $\sigma_{hp} = 31.52 \text{ kN/m}^2$

At a depth of 1 m: $\sigma_v = 2.1 \times 9.81 \times 1 = 20.6 \text{ kN/m}^2$, $u = 0 \Rightarrow \sigma'_v = 20.6 \text{ kN/m}^2$,

$$\sigma'_{hp} = 2.55 \times 20.6 + 31.52 = 84.05 \text{ kN/m}^2 \quad \text{and} \quad \sigma_{hp} = 84.05 \text{ kN/m}^2$$

At the toe of the wall: $\sigma_v = 2.1 \times 9.81 \times 2.6 = 53.56 \text{ kN/m}^2$,

$u = 1 \times 9.81 \times 1.6 = 15.70 \text{ kN/m}^2 \Rightarrow \sigma'_v = 53.56 - 15.70 = 37.86 \text{ kN/m}^2$,
$\sigma'_{hp} = 2.55 \times 37.86 + 31.52 = 128.06 \text{ kN/m}^2 \quad \text{and} \quad \sigma_{hp} = 128.06 + 15.70 = 143.76 \text{ kN/m}^2$

The distributions of σ'_{hp} and σ_{hp} on the face of the wall are then as shown in Fig. 6.18 from which

$$P'_{hp} = 31.52 \times 2.6 + \tfrac{1}{2}(84.05 - 31.52) \times 1 + (84.05 - 31.52) \times 1.6$$
$$+ \tfrac{1}{2}(128.06 - 84.05) \times 1.6 = \underline{227.47 \text{ kN/m}}$$

$$P_{hw} = \tfrac{1}{2}(143.76 - 128.06) \times 1.6 = \underline{12.56 \text{ kN/m}}$$

$$P_{hp} = 227.47 + 12.56 = \underline{240.03 \text{ kN/m}}$$

$$X_p = 6 \times 2.6 + 227.47 \tan 15° = \underline{76.55 \text{ kN/m}}$$

$$M_p = 31.52 \times 2.6 \times 1.3 + \tfrac{1}{2}(84.05 - 31.52) \times 1 \times 1.93 + (84.05 - 31.52) \times 1.6 \times 0.8$$
$$+ \tfrac{1}{2}(143.76 - 84.05) \times 1.6 \times 0.53 = \underline{250.03 \text{ kN m/m}}$$

and

$$l_p = \frac{M_p}{P_{hp}} = \frac{250.03}{240.03} = \underline{1.042 \text{ m}}$$

If $c' = 0$ then the governing effective passive earth pressure equation reduces to $\sigma'_{hp} = 2.55\sigma'_v$, whence we obtain

$$P'_{hp} = 145.52 \text{ kN/m} \quad P_{hw} = 12.56 \text{ kN/m} \qquad P_{hp} = 158.08 \text{ kN/m}$$
$$X_p = 38.99 \text{ kN/m} \quad M_p = 143.49 \text{ kN m/m} \quad \text{and} \quad l_p = 0.908 \text{ m}$$

Thus, if c' decreases to zero with time there is a very marked decrease in the maximum available passive resistance of the clay from 240.03 kN/m to 158.08 kN/m. That is, P_{hp} decreases by 34 per cent.

Stability

A gravity-type wall has to be stable against overturning, forward sliding along its base, and bearing failure under the toe. The design of a suitable wall section for these purposes requires certain dimensions to be assumed. This is referred to as *proportioning* and is aided by the typical geometries shown in Fig. 6.1. If for a particular section the stability checks are inadequate, the dimensions are modified and the new section reappraised. For walls founded on clay soils, a check should also be made on the possibility of shear failure along a deep-seated arc passing below the base. The method of analysis follows that for slopes considered in Chapter 7.

Figure 6.19a shows the forces acting on a gravity wall wherein S_m and P_{hpm} denote the mobilized base and passive resistances to maintain equilibrium of the wall. The problem is statically determinate and the required stability calculations can be effected from a resolution of forces and moments about a point. Thus, resolving parallel and normal to the base and taking moments about the heel

$$S_m = (P_{ha} - P_{hpm}) \cos \alpha - (W + X_a - X_{pm}) \sin \alpha \qquad (6.54)$$

$$N = (W + X_a - X_{pm}) \cos \alpha + (P_{ha} - P_{hpm}) \sin \alpha \qquad (6.55)$$

and

$$N\bar{y} = P_{ha}l_a + W\bar{x} - P_{hpm}l_{pm} - X_{pm}B \qquad (6.56)$$

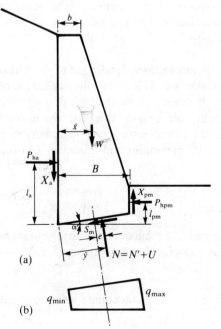

(a)

(b)

Figure 6.19 Forces on a gravity wall.

Forward sliding If u is the mean porewater pressure on the base of the wall, then the normal force U is

$$U = uB \sec \alpha$$

whence

$$N' = N - U$$

$$= (W + X_a - X_{pm}) \cos \alpha + (P_{ha} - P_{hpm}) \sin \alpha - uB \sec \alpha$$

If F is the factor of safety on shear strength, the *mobilized* shear resistance on the base is

$$S_m = \frac{S_f}{F} = \frac{1}{F} (c'_w B \sec \alpha + N' \tan \delta')$$

$$\therefore \quad S_m = \frac{1}{F} \{c'_w B \sec \alpha + [(W + X_a - X_{pm}) \cos \alpha + (P_{ha} - P_{hpm}) \sin \alpha - uB \sec \alpha] \tan \delta'\}$$

$$(6.57)$$

Equating Eqs (6.57) and (6.54) and rearranging

$$F = \frac{[(W + X_a - X_{pm} - uB) \tan \delta' + c'_w B] \sec \alpha}{(P_{ha} - P_{hpm}) \cos \alpha - (W + X_a - X_{pm}) \sin \alpha} + \tan \alpha \tan \delta' \quad (6.58)$$

Since the factor of safety is implicit in the value of P_{hpm}, Eq. (6.58) can only be solved by iteration (see Examples 6.5 and 6.6). In some cases it may be prudent to disregard the passive resistance if there is a possibility of future excavations near the wall face; F is then obtained directly. A further simplification arises if the base is horizontal (as is quite usual) since α is then zero. Also if the wall is founded on sand, the parameter c'_w is zero. For an undrained saturated clay we put $c'_w = c_w$, $\delta' = \delta_u = 0$ and we disregard the term in u since the porewater pressure does not appear explicitly in a total stress analysis; this gives

$$F = \frac{c_w B \sec \alpha}{(P_{ha} - P_{hpm}) \cos \alpha - (W + X_a - X_{pm}) \sin \alpha} \quad (6.59)$$

An alternative definition for the factor of safety is to compare the maximum available resisting force with the activating force in the direction of potential sliding. The ratio should not be less than 2 if the passive resistance is included, and not less than 1.5 if it is ignored.

Bearing pressure The determination of the factor of safety against forward sliding of the wall also establishes the value of the mobilized passive force against the face. This allows the evaluation of the normal reaction N on the base [Eq. (6.55)] and its distance $\bar{y}$ from the heel [Eq. (6.56)]. Assuming a linear distribution of bearing pressure q along the base of the wall, the normal reaction N must act within the middle third to ensure that the base pressures remain compressive over the entire width. From the principles of mechanics, the maximum and minimum bearing pressures are given by

$$q = \frac{N}{B \sec \alpha} \left(1 \pm \frac{6e}{B \sec \alpha}\right) \quad (6.60)$$

where e denotes the eccentricity of N (Fig. 6.19a). Generally, the maximum bearing pressure occurs under the toe (Fig. 6.19b) and should not exceed the allowable bearing pressure for the soil (Chapter 8).

Overturning If the middle third rule is complied with, there will be adequate safety against overturning of the wall.

Example 6.5 Figure 6.20a shows the gravity wall problem considered in the previous example, the properties of the overconsolidated clay being $\rho_s = 2.1$ Mg/m³, $c' = 8$ kN/m², $\phi' = 20°$, $c'_w = 6$ kN/m² and $\delta' = 15°$. For this data and position of the steady state groundwater line, the horizontal and vertical components of total active thrust on the back of the wall were computed to be $P_{ha} = 485.21$ kN/m and $X_a = 169.94$ kN/m acting at $l_a = 2.635$ m from the heel.

(a) Calculate the factor of safety against forward sliding of the wall and the bearing pressure under the base.
(b) Calculate the decrease in the factor of safety and the redistribution of bearing pressure if c' were to decrease to zero with time, given that P_{ha} increases to 622.26 kN/m, $X_a = 155.30$ kN/m and $l_a = 3.13$ m.

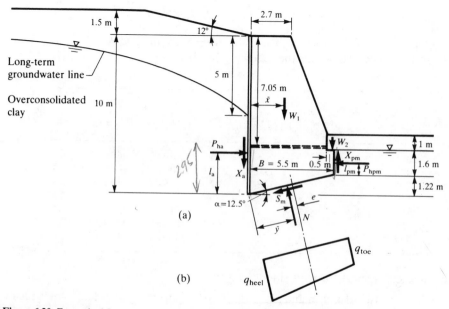

(a)

(b)

Figure 6.20 Example 6.5.

SOLUTION (a) From the data, $P_{ha} = 485.21$ kN/m, $X_a = 169.94$ kN/m and $l_a = 2.635$ m.

The maximum available passive resistance against the face was computed in Example 6.4 to be $P_{hp} = 240.03$ kN/m, $X_p = 76.55$ kN/m and $l_p = 1.042$ m. For a stable wall, however, only part of this maximum available passive resistance will be mobilized to maintain equilibrium. Thus, if c'_m and ϕ'_m denote the *mobilized* effective cohesion and friction of the soil in front of the face then

$$c'_m = \frac{c'}{F} \quad \text{and} \quad \tan \phi'_m = \frac{\tan \phi'}{F}$$

Thus, for a particular value of F, the mobilized shear strength parameters are determined. Assuming that at the soil–wall interface, $c'_{wm}/c'_m = c'_w/c'$ and $\delta'_m/\phi'_m = \delta'/\phi'$ where herein $c'_w/c' = \delta'/\phi' = \frac{3}{4}$, the associated values of K'_{p1m} and K'_{p2m} are obtained from Table 6.5. The *mobilized* passive force P_{hpm} against the face is then determined in a similar manner to that illustrated in Example 6.4 for P_{hp}. The forces acting on the wall are then as shown in Fig. 6.20a.

The factor of safety (on shear strength) against forward sliding of the wall is given by Eq. (6.58) as

$$F = \frac{[(W + X_a - X_{pm} - uB)\tan\delta' + c_w'B]\sec\alpha}{(P_{ha} - P_{hpm})\cos\alpha - (W + X_a - X_{pm})\sin\alpha} + \tan\alpha\tan\delta'$$

The weight of the wall $W_1 = [\frac{1}{2}(2.7 + 5)6.18 + 5 \times 1 + \frac{1}{2}(1.6 + 2.82)5.5]2.4 \times 9.81$
$$= 964.08 \text{ kN/m}$$

Weight of soil on wall ledge $W_2 = 1 \times 0.5 \times 2.1 \times 9.81 = 10.30 \text{ kN/m}$

Therefore total $W = 964.08 + 10.30 = 974.38 \text{ kN/m}$.

The mean porewater pressure u on the base of the wall is given by

$$u = \frac{1}{2}(2.95 + 1.6) \times 1 \times 9.81 = 22.32 \text{ kN/m}^2$$

Assume the base of the wall to be rough, whence $c_w' = c' = 8 \text{ kN/m}^2$ and $\delta' = \phi' = 20°$. Thus, with $B = 5.5$ m and $\alpha = 12\frac{1}{2}°$ we obtain the following results:

Assumed F	c_m' (kN/m²)	ϕ_m' (°)	$\dfrac{c_{wm}'}{c_m'}$	$\dfrac{\delta_m'}{\phi_m'}$	K_{p1m}'	K_{p2m}'	P_{hpm} (kN/m)	X_{pm} (kN/m)	Calculated F
1	8	20	$\frac{3}{4}$	$\frac{3}{4}$	2.55	3.94	240.03	76.55	48.24
48.24	0.17	0.43	$\frac{3}{4}$	$\frac{3}{4}$	1.00	2.42	70.67	0.65	2.79
2.79	2.87	7.43	$\frac{3}{4}$	$\frac{3}{4}$	1.39	2.82	112.91	15.39	3.61
3.61	2.22	5.76	$\frac{3}{4}$	$\frac{3}{4}$	1.28	2.70	101.17	11.01	3.33
3.33	2.40	6.24	$\frac{3}{4}$	$\frac{3}{4}$	1.31	2.75	104.50	12.21	3.41
3.41	2.35	6.09	$\frac{3}{4}$	$\frac{3}{4}$	1.30	2.74	103.46	11.84	3.38
3.38	2.37	6.15	$\frac{3}{4}$	$\frac{3}{4}$	1.30	2.74	103.61	11.97	3.39

Thus the factor of safety against forward sliding = 3.39.

With $F = 3.39$, $P_{hpm} = 103.61$ kN/m and acts at $l_{pm} = 0.95$ m from the toe. The total value of X_{pm} on the front face $= 11.97$ kN/m. Of this, 3.38 kN/m acts on the upper part of the face above the ledge and 8.59 kN/m on the lower part below the ledge. The horizontal distance of the centre of gravity of the wall from the rear face is found to be 2.20 m. Thus with reference to Fig. 6.20a:

Resolving normal to the base of the wall

$$N = (W_1 + W_2 + X_a - X_{pm})\cos\alpha + (P_{ha} - P_{hpm})\sin\alpha$$
$$= (964.08 + 10.30 + 169.94 - 3.38 - 8.59)\cos 12\frac{1}{2}° + (485.21 - 103.61)\sin 12\frac{1}{2}°$$
$$= 1188.10 \text{ kN/m}$$

and taking moments about the heel

$$N\bar{y} = P_{ha}l_a + W_1\bar{x} + W_25.25 - P_{hpm}(l_{pm} + 1.22) - 3.38 \times 5 - 8.59 \times 5.5$$

$$\therefore \quad 1188.10\bar{y} = 485.21 \times 2.635 + 964.08 \times 2.20 + 10.30 \times 5.25 - 103.61 \times 2.17$$
$$- 3.38 \times 5 - 8.59 \times 5.5$$

giving $\bar{y} = \underline{2.664 \text{ m}}$.

Thus, eccentricity $e = \frac{1}{2} \times 5.5 \sec 12\frac{1}{2}° - 2.664 = 0.153$ m. This is less than $\frac{1}{6} \times 5.5 \sec 12\frac{1}{2}° = 0.939$ m, so that N acts within the middle third and the distribution of bearing pressure is trapezoidal with the maximum value occurring under the *heel* (Fig. 6.20b). From Eq. (6.60) we then obtain

$$q = \frac{1188.10}{5.5 \sec 12\tfrac{1}{2}°} \left(1 \pm \frac{6 \times 0.153}{5.5 \sec 12\tfrac{1}{2}°}\right) = \underline{245.26 \text{ kN/m}^2} \quad \text{(heel)}$$

$$= \underline{176.53 \text{ kN/m}^2} \quad \text{(toe)}$$

The maximum bearing pressure of 245.26 kN/m² under the heel should be satisfactory for a stiff overconsolidated clay.

(b) If c' decreases to zero with time, there is a marked increase in active thrust on the back of the wall, wherein from the data given we now have

$$P_{ha} = 622.26 \text{ kN/m}, \quad X_a = 155.30 \text{ kN/m} \quad \text{and} \quad l_a = 3.13 \text{ m}$$

Correspondingly, there is a marked decrease in the maximum available passive resistance against the face, as evaluated in Example 6.4, wherein we now have

$$P_{hp} = 158.08 \text{ kN/m} \quad \text{and} \quad X_p = 38.99 \text{ kN/m}$$

It follows that there will be a marked reduction in the factor of safety against forward sliding of the wall, and in a similar manner to the above we now find $F = 1.53$. That is, F decreases by approximately 50 per cent. The maximum bearing pressure is now found to be under the toe, analysis giving $q_{toe} = 290.21 \text{ kN/m}^2$ and $q_{heel} = 133.92 \text{ kN/m}^2$. These bearing pressures should still be satisfactory for the clay.

Example 6.6 Figure 6.21 shows the details of a cantilever wall retaining a dense sand having $\rho = 1.80 \text{ Mg/m}^3$, $\phi' = 36°$ and water table below the base. Calculate the factor of safety against forward sliding of the wall and the bearing pressure under the base. Take $\delta' = 27°$ on the base of the wall.

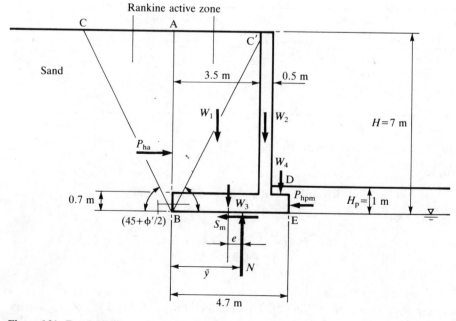

Figure 6.21. Example 6.6.

SOLUTION Cantilever walls are clearly more economical than gravity walls since a large proportion of the overall dead weight required for stability is provided by the weight of backfill on the heel slab. If the wall yields under the thrust from the earth pressures, the backfill fails along the two shear planes BC and BC′ inclined at $45 + \phi'/2$ to the horizontal (Fig. 6.21). This follows since the conjugate slip plane BC′ passes very close to the top of the wall and is therefore largely uninfluenced by the presence of the wall. The mass of sand between the two planes is thus essentially in a Rankine active failure state, there being no shear stress on any vertical plane within the wedge. The distribution of σ'_{ha} on the vertical plane AB through the heel is then defined by $\sigma'_{ha} = \sigma'_v \tan^2(45 - \phi'/2)$ (Eq. 6.1), and with $u = 0$ throughout the backfill we obtain

$$P_{ha} = P'_{ha} = \tfrac{1}{2}\rho g H^2 \tan^2(45 - \phi'/2)$$
$$= \tfrac{1}{2} \times 1.8 \times 9.81 \times 7^2 \times \tan^2(45 - 36/2) = 112.32 \text{ kN/m}$$

It is also conservative to assume $\delta' = 0$ on the vertical plane DE through the toe, so that $P_{hpm} = \tfrac{1}{2}\rho g H_p^2 \tan^2(45 + \phi'_m/2)$.

The factor of safety against forward sliding of the wall is defined by Eq. (6.58). With $c'_w = 0$, $u = 0$, $X_a = 0$, $X_{pm} = 0$ and $\alpha = 0$ this becomes

$$F = \frac{W \tan \delta'}{P_{ha} - P_{hpm}}$$

Weight of sand above heel slab $W_1 = 1.8 \times 9.81 \times 6.3 \times 3.5 = 389.36 \text{ kN/m}$
Weight of wall stem $W_2 = 2.4 \times 9.81 \times 6.3 \times 0.5 = 74.16 \text{ kN/m}$
Weight of wall base $W_3 = 2.4 \times 9.81 \times 0.7 \times 4.7 = 77.46 \text{ kN/m}$
Weight of sand above toe slab $W_4 = 1.8 \times 9.81 \times 0.3 \times 0.7 = 3.71 \text{ kN/m}$
Total weight W $= 544.69 \text{ kN/m}$

With $\delta' = 27°$, the following results obtain:

Assumed F	ϕ'_m (°)	P_{hpm} (kN/m)	Calculated F
1	36	34.01	3.54
3.54	11.60	13.27	2.80
2.80	14.55	14.75	2.84
2.84	14.35	14.65	2.84

Thus the factor of safety against forward sliding = 2.84

Resolving vertically

$$N = W_1 + W_2 + W_3 + W_4 = W = 544.69 \text{ kN/m}$$

Moments about the heel

$$544.69\bar{y} = 389.36 \times 1.75 + 74.16 \times 3.75 + 77.46 \times 2.35 + 3.71 \times 4.35$$
$$+ 112.32 \times 2.33 - 14.65 \times 0.33$$

giving $\bar{y} = 2.597 \text{ m}$

Thus, eccentricity $e = 2.597 - 2.35 = 0.247 \text{ m}$. This is less than $\tfrac{1}{6} \times 4.7 = 0.783 \text{ m}$, so that N acts within the middle third and the distribution of bearing pressure is trapezoidal with the maximum value occurring under the toe. From Eq. (6.60) we then obtain

$$q = \frac{544.69}{4.7}\left(1 \pm \frac{6 \times 0.247}{4.7}\right) = \underline{152.43 \text{ kN/m}^2} \quad \text{(toe)}$$

$$= \underline{79.35 \text{ kN/m}^2} \quad \text{(heel)}$$

These bearing pressures should be acceptable for a dense sand.

6.5 CRIB WALLS

The nature of a crib wall has been outlined in Sec. 6.1 and illustrated in Fig. 6.2a. The structural framework of stringers and ties are generally of precast reinforced concrete units but may also be in metal or timber. The wall is built with the framework advancing at a small height (<1 m) above the level of the compacted granular in-fill. For low walls of 1–2 m the face may be vertical, but for higher walls it is usual to have a batter of at least 1 on 5. The vertical spacing between the stringers should not be greater than 200 mm in order to retain the fill properly.

For design purposes, the stringers are treated as simply supported beams spanning between the ties. The front members are subject to at-rest pressures from the soil inside the crib, while the back members have to resist the difference between the inside at-rest pressures and the outside active pressures from the backfill. The computations for safety against forward sliding and bearing pressure follow those described for gravity walls. In this respect though it should be noted that the full weight of the enclosed soil is not wholly effective in aiding stability since the in-fill and the structural framework do not act as an integral unit (Winterkorn and Fang, 1975).

6.6 GABION WALLS

The essential details of a gabion wall system have been presented in Sec. 6.1 and consist of a stacked arrangement of rock or aggregate filled metal cages, commonly 1 m × 1 m in cross-section and up to 2 m in length (Fig. 6.2b). Stability of the individual blocks needs to be considered as well as overall stability of the structure. Some examples of the use of such walls have been discussed by Audova (1978).

6.7 REINFORCED EARTH WALLS

A reinforced earth retaining wall is formed of compacted granular soil with the placement of reinforcing strips at regular horizontal and vertical intervals (Fig. 6.22). The strips are usually galvanized steel but may also be stainless steel, aluminium, plastic or non-biodegradable fabrics. The main consideration for design purposes concerns their frictional properties and tensile strength since the mass is stabilized by the frictional resistance developed between the strips and the surrounding soil, the action of which simultaneously places the strips in tension. The facing skin prevents the local spillage of soil and is formed of individual units, either relatively flexible C-shaped steel sections or thin precast concrete slabs, each attached to a reinforcing strip. The structure possesses considerable inherent flexibility and can tolerate appreciable differential settlements. It also tends to be the most economical form of wall for heights greater than 10–12 m (Lee *et al.*, 1973). Current design methods are rather simplistic, but no doubt will be refined with increasing experience from observation of the actual performance of field structures.

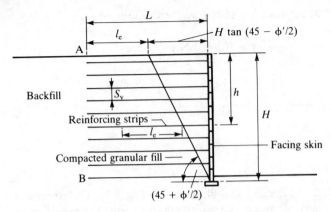

Figure 6.22 Reinforced earth wall.

It is essential for the water table to be maintained below the base of the structure. On this basis consider a particular reinforcing strip at depth h below the soil surface. The tensile force developed in the strip arising from the transfer of active thrust from the soil to the element is given by

$$T = (\rho g h K'_a)(S_V S_H) \qquad (6.61)$$

where the active coefficient K'_a is taken as the Rankine value $[= \tan^2 (45 - \phi'/2)]$ and S_V and S_H are respectively the vertical and horizontal spacing of the strips. The maximum force occurs in the bottommost tie at $h = H$. That is

$$T_{max} = (\rho g H K'_a)(S_V S_H) \qquad (6.62)$$

The reinforcing strips may fail either in tension or by pullout.

Tensile failure If w is the width of the strip, t the thickness and f_y the yield stress, the factor of safety against tensile failure is given by

$$F_T = \frac{f_y w t}{\rho g H K'_a S_V S_H} \qquad (6.63)$$

F_T is normally taken as 3, and therefore for a specified strip width w the required thickness t may be calculated.

Tie pullout The reinforcing strips at any depth h may fail by pullout if the frictional resistance developed over their embedded length l_e in the 'stable' zone (Fig. 6.22) is less than the tensile force to which they are subjected. Considering only the top and bottom surfaces of the elements, the maximum frictional resistance R that can be realized is given by

$$R = 2\rho g h w l_e \tan \delta' \qquad (6.64)$$

Hence the factor of safety against pullout is given by

$$F_P = \frac{R}{T} = \frac{2w l_e \tan \delta'}{K'_a S_V S_H} \qquad (6.65)$$

F_P is usually specified as 3, and with δ' determined either from direct shear tests or full-scale pullout tests the required constant anchorage length l_e may be calculated. In construction, the total length L of the strips is kept the same. With reference to Fig. 6.22, this is then given by

$$L = H \tan\left(45 - \frac{\phi'}{2}\right) + \frac{F_P K_a' S_V S_H}{2w \tan \delta'} \qquad (6.66)$$

A reinforced earth wall is a gravity structure and the design criteria for overall stability of such walls apply. For this purpose, the back of the wall is taken as the vertical plane AB at the inner end of the ties (Fig. 6.22) and the active thrust from the backfill determined based on the Rankine theory. The wall must then be stable against forward sliding along its base, and the bearing pressures must be wholly compressive and not exceed the allowable bearing pressure for the foundation soil.

Example 6.7 A reinforced earth retaining wall is to be built to a height of 10 m. The fill is to be compacted sandy gravel ($\rho = 1.75$ Mg/m^3, $\phi' = 36°$) and the reinforcing strips galvanized steel ($\delta' = 25°, f_y = 240\,000$ kN/m^2). The water table will be maintained below the base of the wall. Determine a suitable size and spacing of the reinforcement if the factors of safety against tensile failure and pullout are not to be less than 3. Assume the rate of corrosion to be 0.025 mm/yr and the design life of the structure 50 years.

SOLUTION From Eq. (6.63), thickness of reinforcing strip is given by

$$t = \frac{F_T \rho g H K_a' S_V S_H}{f_y w}$$

Assume a strip width w of 75 mm and vertical and horizontal spacings of $S_V = 0.5$ m and $S_H = 1$ m. Thus

$$t = \frac{3 \times 1.75 \times 9.81 \times 10 \times \tan^2(45 - 36/2) \times 0.5 \times 1}{240\,000 \times 0.075} = 0.00371 \text{ m} = 3.71 \text{ mm}$$

For a corrosion rate of 0.025 mm/yr and design life of 50 years

$$\text{actual required thickness} = 3.71 + 0.025 \times 50 \simeq \underline{5 \text{ mm}}$$

From Eq. (6.66), required length of strips is given by

$$L = H \tan\left(45 - \frac{\phi'}{2}\right) + \frac{F_P K_a' S_V S_H}{2w \tan \delta'}$$

$$= 10 \tan(45 - 36/2) + \frac{3 \times \tan^2(45 - 36/2) \times 0.5 \times 1}{2 \times 0.075 \times \tan 25°}$$

$$= 5.10 + 5.57 = \underline{10.67 \text{ m}}$$

So 75 mm wide $\times$ 5 mm thick $\times$ 10.67 m long strips spaced 0.5 m vertically and 1 m horizontally would be satisfactory.

6.8 SHEET-PILE WALLS

Anchored Walls

Anchored sheet-pile walls (also known as anchored bulkheads) are the most common type of retaining wall used in waterfront construction, being generally more economical than gravity walls. The wall is formed by driving the sheet-piles on the required line and then either excavating soil from in front of the sheeting (driven and dredged) or backfilling behind it (driven and backfilled). Lateral support near the top of the wall is usually provided by a system of tie rods and anchor blocks. The blocks rely on passive resistance and therefore should be kept back from the wall active zone. The behaviour of the wall is very complex because of soil–structure interaction resulting from the flexibility of the piling, and various design methods have been proposed [Free Earth Support (followed from 19th Century classical earth pressure distributions on stiff walls); Danish Society of Engineers (1926); Stroyer (1935); Fixed Earth Support (Krey, 1936; Pennoyer, 1933); Equivalent Beam Method (Blum, 1930; Tschebotarioff, 1951); Flexibility Method (Rowe, 1952, 1955a, 1955b, 1956, 1957a, 1957b; Hansen, 1953; Terzaghi, 1954)].

Flexibility method of design Of the various design approaches, Rowe's flexibility method is considered the most rational. This has as its starting point a consideration of an *infinitely stiff* pile. Assuming that the anchor and subsoil yield by approximately the same amount, such a wall will translate away from the retained soil and into the soil below the dredge level. This is the *free earth support* condition and the equations governing the pressure distribution on gravity walls apply. Factored soil properties are used on the passive side, and taking moments of the active and passive forces about the anchorage point gives an equation for the penetration depth D from which D is determined. This is the correct embedment length required even if the pile is flexible, since at failure in penetration there can be no fixity below the dredge level. Resolving horizontally allows the determination of the free earth support tie force T_{FES} and taking moments at various points down the sheeting yields the maximum free earth support moment M_{FES}. The actual maximum moment M acting on the sheeting is less than M_{FES} since a pile is not infinitely stiff and some fixity develops below the dredge level. The fixity increases with increasing flexibility of the pile *relative* to the compressibility of the soil and in consequence M decreases. Figure 6.23 shows the moment reduction curves obtained by Rowe (1952) for a sheet-pile wall embedded in sand and retaining sand: α is the ratio depth of dredge level to total length H of the pile and ρ is the flexibility number defined by

$$\rho = \frac{H^4}{EI} \tag{6.67}$$

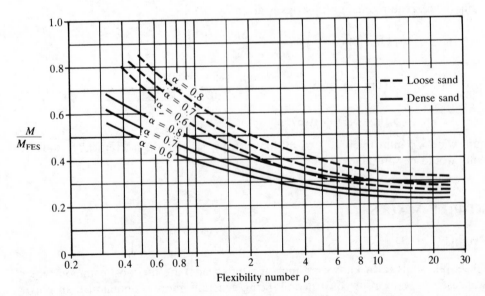

Figure 6.23 Moment reduction curves for sheet-pile walls in sand. (After Rowe, 1952.)

To design the wall we require to determine a pile section such that the resulting moment on the wall stresses the sheeting to its specified allowable stress f_{all}. For this purpose choose a particular section from published tables of commercial sheet pile sections (such as Frodingham, Larssen or US Steel Corporation), calculate ρ and obtain the ratio M/M_{FES} from Fig. 6.23. Hence calculate M and thus the actual stress f in the sheeting from actual stress f = moment M/section modulus. Compare f and f_{all} and repeat the process until agreement is obtained.

Figure 6.24 shows the moment reduction curves obtained by Rowe (1957a) for a sheet-pile wall embedded in clay and retaining sand. The stability number S is defined by

$$S = \frac{c_u\sqrt{1 + c_w/c_u}}{\sigma_{vn}} \tag{6.68}$$

where σ_{vn} is the difference in total vertical pressure between the active and passive sides of the wall

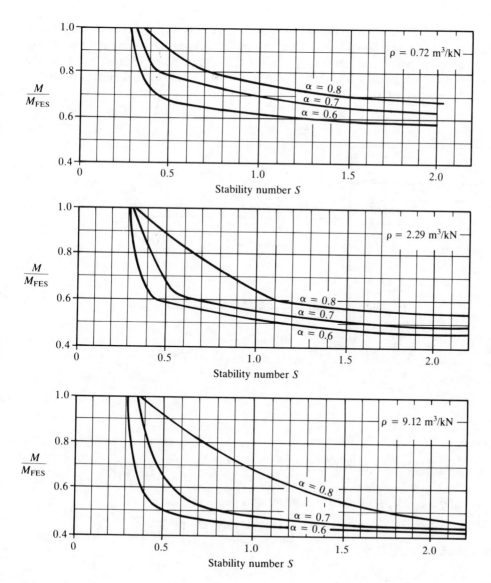

Figure 6.24 Moment reduction curves for sheet-pile walls in clay. (From Rowe, 1957a.)

at the dredge level. The wall cannot stand if $S < \frac{1}{4}$ since there is then no resultant pressure on the sheeting below the dredge level. To use the design curves, calculate S and for the relevant value of α obtain the values of M/M_{FES} for the three cases given. Hence plot a graph of M/M_{FES} versus ρ and proceed as described for a pile in sand.

The actual force T in the tie rod is greater than the free earth support value. For a typical geometry, T/T_{FES} is of the order of 1.2 for walls in sand and 1.3 for walls in clay. If the wall is tied back to an unyielding structure, take $T = 1.4T_{FES}$. Ties may also receive extra load from the weight of overburden, causing them to bend and overstress. Hence it may be necessary to protect them in reinforced concrete boxes. They should also be well tarred and wrapped to protect them against corrosion. In designing the anchor plates take $\delta' = 0$ on K'_p and full δ' on K'_a. The length of the bars should be such that the passive zone of the plate does not overlap with the active zone of the wall. For walls in clay check overall stability against a potential deep-seated slip surface (Chapter 7).

Example 6.8 Figure 6.25 shows an anchored sheet-pile wall in a dense sand. The depth of water against the face is tidal and a lag of 1 m between the inside and outside levels can be expected. Calculate the required penetration depth for a factor of safety of 1.5 on shear strength on the passive side of the wall, a suitable pile section and size of anchor bars if these are to be at 3 m centres. The properties of the sand are $\rho = 1.75 \text{ Mg/m}^3$, $\rho_s = 2.0 \text{ Mg/m}^3$, $\phi' = 37°$ and $\delta' = 25°$.

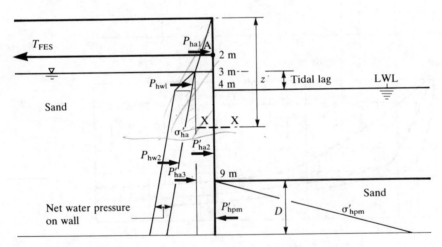

Figure 6.25 Example 6.8.

SOLUTION

Active pressure

$$\sigma'_{ha} = \sigma'_v K'_a \quad \text{wherein} \quad K'_a = \left[\frac{\cos \phi'}{1 + \sin \phi' \sqrt{1 + \tan \delta'/\tan \phi'}} \right]^2$$

For $\phi' = 37°$ and $\delta' = 25°$, $K'_a = 0.20$. Therefore at a depth of 3 m,

$$\sigma'_{ha} = (1.75 \times 9.81 \times 3)0.2 = 10.30 \text{ kN/m}^2$$

and at the toe of the wall,

$$\sigma'_{ha} = 10.30 + [1 \times 9.81(6 + D)]0.2$$
$$= 10.30 + 1.96(6 + D) \text{ kN/m}^2$$

Thus
$$P'_{ha1} = \tfrac{1}{2} \times 10.3 \times 3 = 15.45 \text{ kN/m}$$
$$P'_{ha2} = 10.3(6 + D) \text{ kN/m}$$
$$P'_{ha3} = \tfrac{1}{2} \times 1.96(6 + D)(6 + D) = 0.98(6 + D)^2 \text{ kN/m}$$

Differential water level On the ebb tide, the water level on the outside of the pile falls faster than the inside and the lag of 1 m represents a differential water pressure of 9.81 kN/m^2 acting on the sheeting. It is conservative to assume this differential acts down to the base of the pile (Fig. 6.25) even though there can be no differential pressure at the toe. This offsets the effects of seepage flow which slightly increase the active thrust and decrease the passive resistance. Where, however, the differential pressure is likely to be much greater, as for example in a dry dock, it is important that the effect of seepage flow is taken into account (Terzaghi, 1954). From Fig. 6.25

$$P_{hw1} = \tfrac{1}{2} \times 9.81 \times 1 = 4.91 \text{ kN/m}$$
$$P_{hw2} = 9.81(5 + D) \text{ kN/m}$$

Passive pressure Assuming a factor of safety of 1.5 on shear strength

$$\tan \phi'_m = \frac{\tan 37°}{1.5} \quad \text{and} \quad \tan \delta'_m = \frac{\tan 25°}{1.5}$$

giving $\phi'_m = 26.7°$ and $\delta'_m = 17.3°$. Interpolating from Table 6.3, $K'_{pm} = 3.64$. Thus

$$\sigma'_{hpm} = \sigma'_v K'_{pm} = 3.64\sigma'_v$$

Therefore, at the toe of the pile $\sigma'_{hpm} = 3.64(1 \times 9.81 \times D) = 35.71D$ kN/m^2

and
$$P'_{hpm} = \tfrac{1}{2} \times 35.71D \times D = 17.86D^2 \text{ kN/m}$$

Penetration depth Taking moments about anchorage point A:

$$10.3(6 + D)[\tfrac{1}{2}(6 + D) + 1] + 0.98(6 + D)^2[\tfrac{2}{3}(6 + D) + 1] + 4.91 \times 1\tfrac{2}{3}$$
$$+ 9.81(5 + D)[\tfrac{1}{2}(5 + D) + 2] = 17.86D^2(7 + \tfrac{2}{3}D)$$

from which
$$D^3 + 9.08D^2 - 19.81D - 57.95 = 0$$

By trial
$$D = \underline{3.14 \text{ m}}$$

This is the required penetration depth.

Free earth support tie force Resolving horizontally:

$$T_{FES} + 17.86(3.14)^2 = 15.45 + 10.3(6 + 3.14) + 0.98(6 + 3.14)^2 + 4.91 + 9.81(5 + 3.14)$$

giving
$$T_{FES} = \underline{100.13 \text{ kN/m}}$$

Maximum free earth support bending moment Maximum bending moment usually occurs between $0.5H$ and $0.6H$ below the coping. Thus take moments about section XX through the sheeting, distance z below top of wall where 4 m $< z <$ 9 m. Hence.

$$M_z = 100.13(z - 2) - 15.45(z - 2) - 10.3(z - 3) \times \tfrac{1}{2}(z - 3)$$
$$- [1 \times 9.81(z - 3)] \times 0.2 \times \tfrac{1}{2}(z - 3) \times \tfrac{1}{3}(z - 3) - 4.91[\tfrac{1}{3} + (z - 4)]$$
$$- 9.81(z - 4) \times \tfrac{1}{2}(z - 4)$$

$$\frac{dM_z}{dz} = 100.13 - 15.45 - 10.3(z - 3) - 0.98(z - 3)^2 - 4.91 - 9.81(z - 4)$$

$$= 0 \text{ for a maximum}$$

Hence
$$z^2 + 14.52z - 143.97 = 0$$

from which
$$z = \underline{6.76 \text{ m}}$$

Back substitution then gives the maximum free earth support bending moment as

$$M_{\text{FES}} = \underline{260.33 \text{ kN m/m}}$$

Sheet-pile section The total length of pile $H = 12.14$ m and $\alpha = 9/12.14 = 0.74$. The determination of a suitable section is illustrated with reference to steel sheet piling produced by the United States Steel Corporation and the relevant calculations are set out in the following table. For this purpose $E = 207 \times 10^6$ kN/m^2 and $f_{\text{all}} = 172\,500$ kN/m^2.

Section (US Steel Corporation)	I (m^4/m)	$\rho = \dfrac{H^4}{EI}$ (m^3/kN)	$\dfrac{M}{M_{\text{FES}}}$ (Fig. 6.23)	M (kN m/m)	Section modulus (m^3/m)	$f = \dfrac{\text{Moment } M}{\text{Sec. mod.}}$ (kN/m^2)	f_{all} (kN/m^2)
PZ–27	251.43×10^{-6}	0.42	0.60	156.20	162.17×10^{-5}	96 317	172 500
PDA–27	54.33×10^{-6}	1.93	0.38	98.93	57.46×10^{-5}	172 172	172 500

Therefore, use US Steel Corporation section <u>PDA–27</u>. Equivalent sections for Frodingham and Larssen steel sheet piling may also readily be determined.

Anchor bars Take $T/T_{\text{FES}} = 1.2$. Hence $T = 1.2 \times 100.13 = 120.16$ kN/m. For tie rods at 3 m centres, total tie force to be resisted $= 120.16 \times 3 = 360.48$ kN. Assuming a factor of safety of 2 on the yield stress to provide extra margin for possible overtightening of anchor bars (i.e., taking $f_{\text{all}} = 132\,500$ kN/m^2), the required diameter d of tie rod is given by

$$d = \sqrt{\frac{4 \times 360.48}{\pi \times 132\,500}} = 0.059 \text{ m} = \underline{59 \text{ mm}}$$

Example 6.9 Figure 6.26 shows an anchored sheet-pile wall embedded in a firm clay and retaining a dense sand bearing a uniform surcharge of 20 kN/m^2. The water level is constant at the position shown. Calculate the required penetration depth assuming a factor of safety of 1.5 on the undrained shear strength of the clay. Also determine a suitable pile section and size of anchor bars if these are to be at 3 m centres. The properties of the sand are $\rho = 1.75$ Mg/m^3, $\rho_s = 2.0$ Mg/m^3, $\phi' = 37°$, $\delta' = 25°$, and for the clay $c_u = 45$ kN/m^2, $c_w = 25$ kN/m^2.

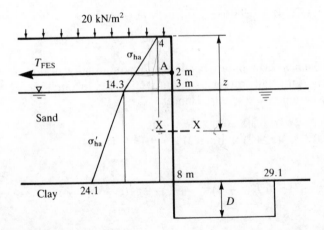

Figure 6.26 Example 6.9.

SOLUTION

Active pressure above dredge level

$$\sigma'_{ha} = \sigma'_v K'_a \quad \text{wherein} \quad K'_a = \left[\frac{\cos \phi'}{1 + \sin \phi' \sqrt{1 + \tan \delta'/\tan \phi'}} \right]^2$$

For $\phi' = 37°$ and $\delta' = 25°$, $K'_a = 0.20$. Therefore:

At the coping $\quad \sigma'_{ha} = 20 \times 0.2 = 4.0 \text{ kN/m}^2$

At a depth of 3 m $\quad \sigma'_{ha} = (20 + 1.75 \times 9.81 \times 3)0.2 = 14.30 \text{ kN/m}^2$

At a depth of 8 m $\quad \sigma'_{ha} = (20 + 1.75 \times 9.81 \times 3 + 1 \times 9.81 \times 5)0.2 = 24.11 \text{ kN/m}^2$

The water levels on both sides of the pile are the same, and therefore there is no nett water pressure acting on the sheeting.

Nett pressure below dredge level For a factor of safety F on the undrained shear strength of the clay:

Nett pressure on sheeting at dredge level

$$= \sigma_{hp} - \sigma_{ha}$$

$$= \left[\sigma_{vp} + 2\frac{c_u}{F} \sqrt{1 + \frac{c_w}{c_u}} \right] - \left[\sigma_{va} - 2\frac{c_u}{F} \sqrt{1 + \frac{c_w}{c_u}} \right]$$

$$= 4\frac{c_u}{F} \sqrt{1 + \frac{c_w}{c_u}} - (\sigma_{va} - \sigma_{vp})$$

$$= \frac{4 \times 45\sqrt{1 + 25/45}}{1.5} - (20 + 1.75 \times 9.81 \times 3 + 2 \times 9.81 \times 5 - 1 \times 9.81 \times 5)$$

$$= 29.11 \text{ kN/m}^2$$

Since the rate of increase of active and passive pressures below the dredge level are the same, the pressure difference is constant with depth.

Penetration depth Taking moments about anchorage point A:

$$4 \times 8 \times 2 + 10.3 \times 5 \times 3.5 + \tfrac{1}{2} \times 9.81 \times 5 \times 4.33 = 29.11 \times D \times (6 + \tfrac{1}{2}D)$$

from which $\quad D^2 + 12.0D - 24.07 = 0$

giving $\quad D = \underline{1.75 \text{ m}}$

This is the required penetration depth.

Free earth support tie force Resolving horizontally

$$T_{FES} + 29.11 \times 1.75 = 4 \times 8 + \tfrac{1}{2} \times 10.3 \times 3 + 10.3 \times 5 + \tfrac{1}{2} \times 9.81 \times 5$$

giving $\quad T_{FES} = \underline{72.53 \text{ kN/m}}$

Maximum free earth support bending moment Take moments about section XX through the sheeting, distance z below top of wall where 3 m $< z <$ 8 m.

$$M_z = 72.53(z-2) - 4z \times \tfrac{1}{2}z - \tfrac{1}{2} \times 10.3 \times 3(z-2) - 10.3(z-3) \times \tfrac{1}{2}(z-3)$$
$$- [1 \times 9.81 \times (z-3)]0.2 \times \tfrac{1}{2}(z-3) \times \tfrac{1}{3}(z-3)$$

$$\frac{dM_z}{dz} = 72.53 - 4z - 15.45 - 10.3(z-3) - 0.98(z-3)^2 = 0 \text{ for a maximum}$$

Hence
$$z^2 + 8.59z - 80.78 = 0$$

from which
$$z = \underline{5.67 \text{ m}}$$

Back substitution then gives the maximum free earth support bending moment as

$$M_{\text{FES}} = \underline{102.25 \text{ kN m/m}}$$

Sheet-pile section The total length of pile $H = 9.75$ m and $\alpha = 8/9.75 = 0.82$. From Eq. (6.68) the stability number is given by:

$$S = \frac{c_u\sqrt{1 + c_w/c_u}}{\sigma_{vn}} = \frac{45\sqrt{1 + 25/45}}{(20 + 1.75 \times 9.81 \times 3 + 2 \times 9.81 \times 5 - 1 \times 9.81 \times 5)} = 0.46$$

From Fig. 6.24 we see that for these parameters M/M_{FES} is essentially independent of ρ, being approximately 0.925. The following results obtain:

Section (US Steel Corporation)	I (m⁴/m)	$\rho = \dfrac{H^4}{EI}$ (m³/kN)	$\dfrac{M}{M_{\text{FES}}}$ (Fig. 6.24)	M (kN m/m)	Section modulus (m³/m)	$f = \dfrac{M}{\text{Sec. mod.}}$ (kN/m²)	f_{all} (kN/m²)
PDA–27	54.33×10^{-6}	0.80	0.925	94.58	57.46×10^{-5}	164 603	172 500
PMA–22	18.70×10^{-6}	2.33	0.925	94.58	29.00×10^{-5}	326 142	172 500

Therefore use US Steel Corporation section $\underline{\text{PDA–27}}$.

Anchor bars Take $T/T_{\text{FES}} = 1.3$. Hence $T = 1.3 \times 72.53 = 94.29$ kN/m. For tie rods at 3 m centres, total tie force to be resisted $= 94.29 \times 3 = 282.87$ kN. Assuming again a factor of safety of 2 on the yield stress (i.e., $f_{\text{all}} = 132\,500$ kN/m²) the required diameter of tie rod is given by

$$d = \sqrt{\frac{4 \times 282.87}{\pi \times 132\,500}} = 0.052 \text{ m} = \underline{52 \text{ mm}}$$

Cantilever Walls

Cantilever walls are used mainly for temporary works where the free height is generally less than 6 m. Considering a stiff wall in sand, the pile rotates outwards about a point near its base, giving rise to passive pressure on the *inside* face below the rotation point. As failure in penetration is approached, the point of rotation approaches the toe of the pile and the pressure distribution on the sheeting tends to the classical form. With an adequate factor of safety on shear strength on the passive side ($F = 3$ recommended), the required penetration depth is obtained by taking moments about the toe. At safe penetration the actual maximum moment acting on the pile is less than the free earth support value, and for a typical value of $\alpha = 0.5$, $M/M_{\text{FES}} \approx 0.65$ for all values of flexibility number ρ (Rowe, 1951).

Example 6.10 Figure 6.27 shows a cantilever sheet-pile wall embedded in a dense sand and retaining a loose sand sustaining a surcharge of 20 kN/m². No water problems are envisaged because of a very low water table. Calculate the required penetration depth for a factor of safety of 3 on shear strength on the passive side and a suitable pile section, given that the properties of the dense sand are $\rho = 1.80$ Mg/m³, $\phi' = 40°$, $\delta' = 27°$, and for the loose sand $\rho = 1.60$ Mg/m³, $\phi' = 33°$, $\delta' = 22°$.

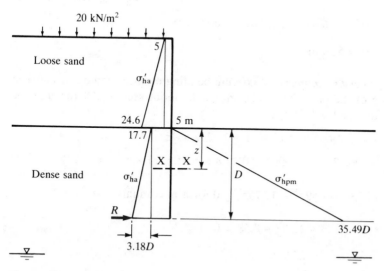

Figure 6.27 Example 6.10.

SOLUTION

Active pressure

$$\sigma'_{ha} = \sigma'_v K'_a \quad \text{wherein} \quad K'_a = \left[\frac{\cos \phi'}{1 + \sin \phi' \sqrt{1 + \tan \delta'/\tan \phi'}} \right]^2$$

This gives for the loose sand with $\phi' = 33°$ and $\delta' = 22°$, $K'_a = 0.25$ and for the dense sand with $\phi' = 40°$ and $\delta' = 27°$, $K'_a = 0.18$.

At the top of the wall: $\sigma'_{ha} = 20 \times 0.25 = 5$ kN/m²

At a depth of 5 m:
for the loose sand $\sigma'_{ha} = (20 + 1.6 \times 9.81 \times 5)0.25 = 24.62$ kN/m²
and for the dense sand $\sigma'_{ha} = (20 + 1.6 \times 9.81 \times 5)0.18 = 17.73$ kN/m²

At the toe of the wall: $\sigma'_{ha} = 17.73 + (1.8 \times 9.81 \times D)0.18 = 17.73 + 3.18D$ kN/m²

Passive pressure For a factor of safety of 3 on shear strength

$$\tan \phi'_m = \frac{\tan 40°}{3} \quad \text{and} \quad \tan \delta'_m = \frac{\tan 27°}{3}$$

giving $\phi'_m = 15.6°$ and $\delta'_m = 9.6°$. Interpolating from Table 6.3, $K'_{pm} = 2.01$. Thus

$$\sigma'_{hpm} = \sigma'_v K'_{pm} = 2.01\sigma'_v$$

Therefore at the toe of the pile $\sigma'_{hpm} = 2.01(1.8 \times 9.81 \times D) = 35.49D$ kN/m². The pressure distribution on the sheeting is then as shown in Fig. 6.27. The force R denotes the passive resistance developed on the inside face of the pile below the point of rotation, taken to be the toe.

Penetration depth Taking moments about the toe

$$5 \times 5 \times (2\tfrac{1}{2} + D) + \tfrac{1}{2} \times 19.62 \times 5 \times (1\tfrac{2}{3} + D) + 17.73D \times \tfrac{1}{2}D + \tfrac{1}{2} \times 3.18D \times D \times \tfrac{1}{3}D$$
$$= \tfrac{1}{2} \times 35.49D \times D \times \tfrac{1}{3}D$$

from which
$$D^3 - 1.65D^2 - 13.74D - 26.76 = 0$$

By trial
$$D = \underline{5.24 \text{ m}}$$

Maximum free earth support bending moment Maximum bending moment will occur between the dredge line and the toe of the pile. Thus, take moments about section XX through the sheeting, distance z below dredge level. Hence

$$M_z = 5 \times 5(2\tfrac{1}{2} + z) + \tfrac{1}{2} \times 19.62 \times 5(1\tfrac{2}{3} + z) + 17.73z \times \tfrac{1}{2}z$$
$$+ (1.8 \times 9.81 \times z)0.18 \times \tfrac{1}{2}z \times \tfrac{1}{3}z - 2.01(1.8 \times 9.81 \times z) \times \tfrac{1}{2}z \times \tfrac{1}{3}z$$

$$\frac{dM_z}{dz} = 25 + 49.05 + 17.73z + 1.59z^2 - 17.75z^2 = 0 \text{ for a maximum}$$

This gives
$$z^2 - 1.10z - 4.58 = 0$$

from which
$$z = \underline{2.76 \text{ m}}$$

Back substitution gives the maximum free earth support bending moment as

$$M_{\text{FES}} = \underline{302.93 \text{ kN m/m}}$$

Sheet-pile section Total length of pile $H = 5 + 5.24 = 10.24$ m. Thus $\alpha = 5/10.24 = 0.49$ and $M/M_{\text{FES}} \approx 0.65$. Hence

$$M = 0.65 \times 302.93 = \underline{196.90 \text{ kN m/m}}$$

Thus required section modulus $= \dfrac{196.90}{172\,500} = 114 \times 10^{-5} \text{ m}^3/\text{m}$

Therefore use, for example, US Steel Corporation section $\underline{\text{PZ–27}}$ (section modulus $= 162 \times 10^{-5} \text{ m}^3/\text{m}$).

Note the larger penetration depth and design bending moments for cantilever walls as compared with anchored walls.

6.9 BRACED EXCAVATIONS

Figure 6.28a shows a narrow trench in which the side walls are supported by a system of sheet piles and horizontal struts, referred to as a *braced excavation*. The trench is formed by first driving the sheet piles to the required depth and then excavating the soil from between the piles, the excavation being carried out in stages to suit the number of struts to be installed. The piles deflect progressively inwards with increasing excavation, the deflections taking place largely before the supporting struts are able to be placed in position. Little lateral movement occurs at the level of the first line of struts and the pressure on the sheeting over this initial depth will be close to the at-rest value. At the bottom of the trench where the inward movement of the piles is

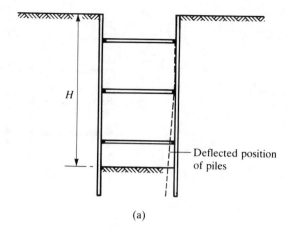

(a)

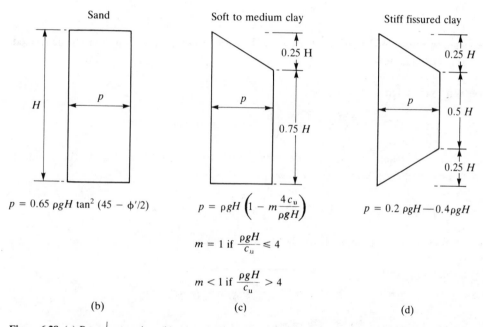

Sand

$$p = 0.65 \, \rho g H \tan^2 (45 - \phi'/2)$$

Soft to medium clay

0.25 H

0.75 H

$$p = \rho g H \left(1 - m \frac{4 c_u}{\rho g H}\right)$$

$$m = 1 \text{ if } \frac{\rho g H}{c_u} \leqslant 4$$

$$m < 1 \text{ if } \frac{\rho g H}{c_u} > 4$$

Stiff fissured clay

0.25 H

0.5 H

0.25 H

$$p = 0.2 \, \rho g H - 0.4 \rho g H$$

(b)   (c)   (d)

Figure 6.28 (a) Braced excavation; (b), (c) and (d) apparent pressure envelopes. (From Terzaghi and Peck, 1967.)

more pronounced the pressure is more likely to approximate to the active value. The pressure distribution on the sheeting is therefore not of the classical form and the lateral force generally exceeds the active thrust by about 15 per cent. Based on field observations, Terzaghi and Peck (1967) recommend the use of the simplified pressure diagrams shown in parts b, c and d of Fig. 6.28, sometimes referred to as *apparent pressure envelopes*. The computation of the strut loads from these pressure diagrams is illustrated in the following example. For cuts in clays it is also necessary to consider a potential base heave (Chapter 8), and for excavations in sand with a high water table the piles should be driven deep enough below the base of the trench to avoid the possibility of a piping failure (Chapter 3).

Example 6.11 Figure 6.29a shows a proposed braced excavation which is to be made to a depth of 9 m in a soft deposit of saturated clay having a density of 1.80 Mg /m³ and an average

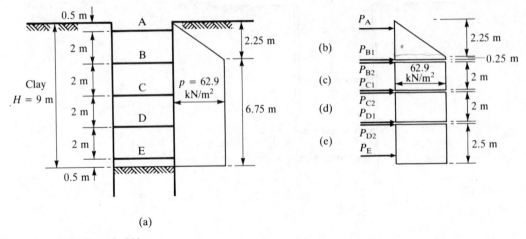

(a)

Figure 6.29 Example 6.11.

undrained shear strength of 30 kN/m². Calculate the forces in the struts if these are to be spaced at 3 m intervals along the length of the trench.

SOLUTION With reference to Fig. 6.28c:

$$\frac{\rho g H}{c_u} = \frac{1.80 \times 9.81 \times 9}{30} = 5.30 > 4$$

Hence $m < 1$. Limited field measurements indicate m ranges from 1 to 0.4. As the value of $\rho g H/c_u$ is not excessively greater than 4, take $m = 0.8$ whence

$$p = 1.8 \times 9.81 \times 9\left(1 - 0.8 \times \frac{4 \times 30}{1.8 \times 9.81 \times 9}\right) = 62.9 \text{ kN/m}^2$$

The design pressure envelope is then as shown in Fig. 6.29a.
With reference to Fig. 6.29b:
  Taking moments about P_{B1}

$$2P_A = \tfrac{1}{2} \times 62.9 \times 2.25 \times 1 + 62.9 \times 0.25 \times 0.125$$

$$\therefore \qquad P_A = 36.4 \text{ kN/m}$$

and resolving horizontally

$$P_{B1} = \tfrac{1}{2}(0.25 + 2.5)62.9 - 36.4 = 50.1 \text{ kN/m}$$

With reference to parts c and d of Fig. 6.29:

$$P_{B2} = P_{C1} = P_{C2} = P_{D1} = \tfrac{1}{2} \times 62.9 \times 2 = 62.9 \text{ kN/m}$$

With reference to Fig. 6.29e:
  Taking moments about P_{D2}

$$2P_E = 62.9 \times 2.5 \times 1.25$$

$$\therefore \qquad P_E = 98.3 \text{ kN/m}$$

and resolving horizontally

$$P_{D2} = 62.9 \times 2.5 - 98.3 = 59.0 \text{ kN/m}$$

Thus
$$P_A = 36.4 \text{ kN/m}$$
$$P_B = P_{B1} + P_{B2} = 50.1 + 62.9 = 113.0 \text{ kN/m}$$
$$P_C = P_{C1} + P_{C2} = 62.9 + 62.9 = 125.8 \text{ kN/m}$$
$$P_D = P_{D1} + P_{D2} = 62.9 + 59.0 = 121.9 \text{ kN/m}$$

and
$$P_E = 98.3 \text{ kN/m}$$

If the struts are spaced at 3 m intervals along the length of the trench, then the design loads are

$$\text{Strut A} = \underline{109.2 \text{ kN}}$$

$$\text{Strut B} = \underline{339.0 \text{ kN}}$$

$$\text{Strut C} = \underline{377.4 \text{ kN}}$$

$$\text{Strut D} = \underline{365.7 \text{ kN}}$$

and

$$\text{Strut E} = \underline{294.9 \text{ kN}}$$

6.10 DIAPHRAGM WALLS

The use of diaphragm walls for the construction of basements, underpasses and other underground structures has been outlined in Sec. 6.1. Such walls are normally tied-back by ground anchors. The resulting distribution of lateral pressure on the wall then depends on the type of wall movement. For a single line of ties near the top of the wall it is likely that the distribution will be triangular whereas for multiple rows of ties over the height of the wall it is probable that the distribution will be of the form indicated in Fig. 6.28b, c, d. The wall is then designed as a continuous beam.

Trench Stability

Of particular interest in the construction of a diaphragm wall is the stability of the slurry trench. For this purpose consider a trench formed to some depth H in a deposit of sand, the groundwater level being at ηH below the soil surface (Fig. 6.30). The forces acting on a potential failure wedge of the side wall are then as shown. If ρ_c denotes the density of the bentonite clay slurry, the hydrostatic thrust against the trench face is given by

$$P = \tfrac{1}{2}\rho_c g H^2$$

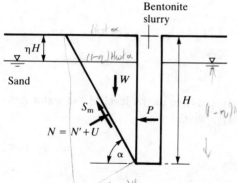

Figure 6.30 Stability of slurry trench.

No shear stress acts on the face and therefore the potential failure plane is inclined at

$$\alpha = 45 + \frac{\phi'_m}{2}$$

The weight of the wedge is $W = \rho_s g \frac{1}{2}(1-\eta) H \cot \alpha (1-\eta) H + \rho g \frac{1}{2}[H \cot \alpha + (1-\eta) H \cot \alpha] \eta H$

$$W = \tfrac{1}{2}\rho_s g(1 - \eta)^2 H^2 \cot \alpha + \tfrac{1}{2}\rho g(2 - \eta)\eta H^2 \cot \alpha$$

On the potential failure plane the mobilized shear resistance is

$$S_m = N' \tan \phi'_m$$

and the normal water force

$$U = \tfrac{1}{2}\rho_w g(1 - \eta)^2 H^2 \operatorname{cosec} \alpha$$

Resolving horizontally

$$P = N \sin \alpha - S_m \cos \alpha = (N' + U) \sin \alpha - N' \tan \phi'_m \cos \alpha$$

∴ $$P - U \sin \alpha = N' \cos \alpha(\tan \alpha - \tan \phi'_m) \qquad (6.69)$$

Resolving vertically

$$W = N \cos \alpha + S_m \sin \alpha = (N' + U) \cos \alpha + N' \tan \phi'_m \sin \alpha$$

∴ $$W - U \cos \alpha = N' \cos \alpha(1 + \tan \alpha \tan \phi'_m) \qquad (6.70)$$

Dividing Eq. (6.69) by (6.70)

$$\frac{P - U \sin \alpha}{W - U \cos \alpha} = \tan (\alpha - \phi'_m)$$

Substituting for P, W, U and $\alpha = 45 + \phi'_m/2$ gives

$$\tan^2 \left(45 - \frac{\phi'_m}{2}\right) = \frac{\rho_c - \rho_w(1 - \eta)^2}{\rho'(1 - \eta)^2 + \rho(2 - \eta)\eta}$$

whence $$\phi'_m = 90 - 2 \tan^{-1}\left[\frac{\rho_c - \rho_w(1 - \eta)^2}{\rho'(1 - \eta)^2 + \rho(2 - \eta)\eta}\right]^{1/2}$$

Thus $$F = \frac{\tan \phi'}{\tan \phi'_m} = \frac{\tan \phi'}{\tan \left\{90 - 2 \tan^{-1}\left[\dfrac{\rho_c - \rho_w(1 - \eta)^2}{\rho'(1 - \eta)^2 + \rho(2 - \eta)\eta}\right]^{1/2}\right\}} \qquad (6.71)$$

For the typical data $\phi' = 35°$, $\rho_s = 2.0 \text{ Mg/m}^3$, $\rho = 1.8 \text{ Mg/m}^3$, $\rho_c = 1.22 \text{ Mg/m}^3$ and considering a relatively high water table (as is quite usual), we obtain for

$$\eta = 0.20, \qquad F = 1.71$$
$$\eta = 0.15, \qquad F = 1.51$$
$$\eta = 0.10, \qquad F = 1.30$$

and $$\eta = 0.05, \qquad F = 1.08$$

The stability of the trench face is therefore particularly sensitive to the level of the water table. For an undrained saturated clay a total stress analysis gives

$$F = \frac{4c_u}{\rho_s g H(1 - \rho_c/\rho_s)} \qquad (6.72)$$

PROBLEMS

6.1 The soil profile at a flat site consists of 8 m of soft, normally consolidated, saturated clay overlying 2 m of sand resting on bedrock. The water table is at the ground surface and the piezometric level for the sand is 2 m above ground level. Assuming steady state conditions to obtain in the clay, calculate the ratio of c_u/σ_v' at any point in the deposit given that the properties of the clay are $\rho_s = 1.80$ Mg/m³, $c' = 0$, $\phi' = 24°$, $K_0' = 0.59$, $A_f = 1$ and $A = 0.5$. Hence calculate the value of c_u at a depth of 4 m below ground level.

If the piezometric level for the sand is lowered to the ground surface, calculate the long-term change in undrained shear strength at this depth of 4 m.
[Ans. 0.23; 5.0 kN/m²; 2.2 kN/m² (increase)]

6.2 A gravity wall 9 m high and having a vertical back retains 3 m of sandy gravel overlain by 6 m of granular fill. The surface of the fill is level with the top of the wall and supports a uniform surcharge of 30 kN/m². Wall drainage is provided and hence it can be assumed that groundwater level is at or below the base of the wall. Calculate the horizontal and vertical components of total active force on the wall, and also the associated overturning moment about the heel of the wall, given that the properties of the fill are $\rho = 1.65$ Mg/m³, $\phi' = 34°$, $\delta' = 30°$, and of the gravel are $\rho = 1.80$ Mg/m³, $\phi' = 37°$, $\delta' = 33°$.
[Ans. 192.6 kN/m; 117.6 kN/m; 685.7 kN m/m]

6.3 A gravity retaining wall 7 m high has a vertical back and retains 4 m of sand overlying 3 m of clay. The surface of the sand is level with the top of the wall and a vertical wall drain is provided over the depth of the clay. Calculate the horizontal and vertical components of total active force on the wall immediately after construction and a long time after construction, given that the properties of the sand are $\rho = 1.84$ Mg/m³, $\phi' = 38°$, $\delta' = 25°$, and of the clay are $\rho_s = 1.95$ Mg/m³, $c_u = 40$ kN/m², $\phi_u = 0$, $c_w = 20$ kN/m², $\delta_u = 0$, $c' = 0$, $\phi' = 26°$, $c_w' = 0$ and $\delta' = 20°$.

For the long-term case, assume that the effect of steady seepage to the vertical drain is equivalent to a static water table level with the sand/clay interface.
[Ans. 54.4 kN/m; 46.2 kN/m; 156.2 kN/m; 43.7 kN/m]

6.4 Figure P6.4 shows three options under consideration for a 10-m high masonry wall to support a drained sand, the surface of which slopes at 20° to the horizontal. For each case, calculate the overturning moment about the heel due to the total active force on the back of the wall given that the properties of the sand are $\rho = 1.70$ Mg/m³, $\phi' = 35°$ and $\delta' = 25°$.
[Ans. 1134 kN m/m; 814 kN m/m; 593 kN m/m]

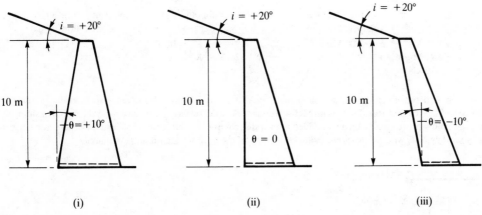

(i)   (ii)   (iii)

Figure P6.4

6.5 The gravity wall shown in Fig. P6.5 retains a sandy clay having a surface inclined at 15° to the horizontal. The wall is 9 m high and is founded on impervious bedrock underlying the clay. A vertical drain is provided down the back of the wall and the long-term steady seepage towards this drain is represented by the flow net shown in Fig. P6.5. Given that the critical slip path is inclined at 40° to the horizontal, determine the long-term horizontal and vertical components of total active force on the wall. The properties of the clay are $\rho_s = 1.98$ Mg/m³, $c' = 0$, $\phi' = 28°$, $c_w' = 0$ and $\delta' = 20°$.
[Ans. 378 kN/m; 138 kN/m]

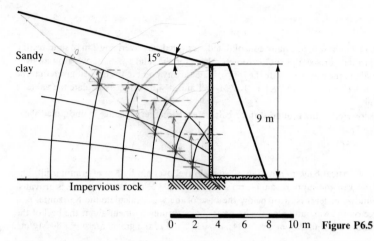

Figure P6.5

6.6 Figure P6.6 shows a cast-*in situ* concrete wall 6 m high founded on and retaining sand. The surface of the sand behind the wall carries a uniform surcharge of 35 kN/m², and provision of wall drainage ensures that groundwater level remains below the base of the wall. Calculate the factor of safety against forward sliding of the wall and the maximum bearing pressure under the base. The properties of the sand are $\rho = 1.90$ Mg/m³, $\phi' = 36°$ and $\delta' = 24°$, and for the wall material $\rho_c = 2.4$ Mg/m³.
[Ans. 2.30; 177 kN/m²]

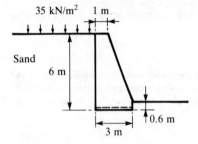

Figure P6.6

6.7 The mass concrete wall shown in Fig. P6.7 was constructed on a stiff boulder clay and retained 5 m of silty sand on which was placed 3 m of lightly compacted granular fill. The wall was designed on the basis of the following data

Granular fill: $\rho = 1.76$ Mg/m³, $\rho_s = 2.00$ Mg/m³, $\phi' = 32°$, $\delta' = 21°$ and $K_a' = 0.257$
Silty sand: $\rho = 1.91$ Mg/m³, $\rho_s = 2.10$ Mg/m³, $\phi' = 36°$, $\delta' = 24°$ and $K_a' = 0.215$
Boulder clay: $c_u = 110$ kN/m², $c' = 8$ kN/m² and $\phi' = 28°$
Weight of the wall = 577 kN/m

Some years after construction and following a prolonged period of high rainfall, it was observed that the ground surface in front of the wall had heaved upwards. Further inspection revealed that the surface of the fill behind the wall had slumped slightly, leaving shallow depressions which were filled with water. Suggest the most probable cause of these movements and support your diagnosis with calculations, using such items of the above design data as required.

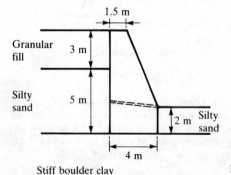

Figure P6.7

6.8 Figure P6.8 shows the details of a cantilever wall retaining a sand having $\rho = 1.75$ Mg/m^3, $\phi' = 35°$ and water table below the base. Calculate the factor of safety against forward sliding of the wall and the bearing pressure under the base. Take $\delta' = 25°$ on the base of the wall.

[Ans. 2.26; 183.56 kN/m^2 (under the toe); 73.89 kN/m^2 (under the heel)]

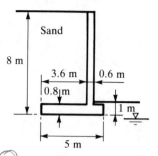

Figure P6.8

6.9 A reinforced earth retaining wall is to be built to a height of 12 m. The fill is to be compacted sand ($\rho = 1.75$ Mg/m^3, $\phi' = 35°$) and the reinforcing strips galvanized steel ($\delta' = 25°$, $f_y = 240\,000$ kN/m^2). The water table will be maintained below the base of the wall. Determine a suitable size and spacing of the reinforcement if the factors of safety against tensile failure and pullout are not to be less than 3. Assume the rate of corrosion to be 0.025 mm/yr and the design life of the structure 50 years.

[Ans. Use 100 mm wide × 5 mm thick × 10.61 m long strips spaced 0.5 m vertically and 1 m horizontally]

6.10 Figure P6.10 shows the details of an anchored sheet-pile wall which is to be used to support the sides of a temporary excavation in a deep deposit of sand ($\rho = 1.60$ Mg/m^3, $\phi' = 37°$ and $\delta' = 25°$). No water problems are envisaged because of a very low water table. Calculate the required penetration depth for a factor of safety of 1.5 on shear strength on the passive side of the wall, a suitable pile section, and size of anchor bars if these are to be at 3 m centres.

[Ans. 2.37 m; US Steel Corporation section PDA–27; 53 mm]

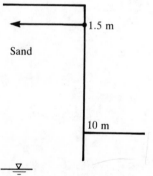

Figure P6.10

6.11 Figure P6.11 shows an anchored sheet-pile wall embedded in clay and retaining a sand bearing a uniform surcharge of 20 kN/m^2. The water level is constant at the position shown. Calculate the required penetration depth assuming a factor of safety of 1.5 on the undrained shear strength of the clay. Also determine a suitable pile section and size of anchor bars if these are to be at 3 m centres.

The properties of the sand are $\rho = 1.75$ Mg/m^3, $\rho_s = 2.0$ Mg/m^3, $\phi' = 37°$, $\delta' = 25°$, and for the clay $c_u = 35$ kN/m^2, $c_w = 20$ kN/m^2.

[Ans. 2.31 m; US Steel Corporation section PDA–27; 43 mm]

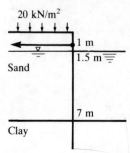

Figure P6.11

6.12 Figure P6.12 shows a proposed braced excavation which is to be made to a depth of 9.5 m in a deposit of saturated clay having a density of 1.90 Mg/m³ and an average undrained shear strength of 35 kN/m². Calculate the forces in the struts if these are to be spaced at 3 m intervals along the length of the trench. (Take $m = 0.9$.)
[Ans.   Strut A = 178.3 kN;   Strut B = 367.5 kN;   Strut C = 352.4 kN;   Strut D = 375.4 kN]

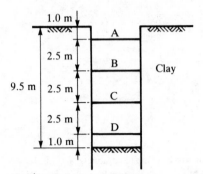

Figure P6.12

6.13 The soil conditions at a particular site consist of a deep deposit of sand with groundwater level at a depth of 1.5 m. As part of the proposed construction of a diaphragm wall, a trench, 1 m wide, is to be excavated to a depth of 10 m and supported by a bentonite clay slurry. Calculate the factor of safety against a shear failure of the trench face given that the properties of the sand are $\rho = 1.80$ Mg/m³, $\rho_s = 2.00$ Mg/m³, $\phi' = 35°$, and for the bentonite slurry $\rho = 1.22$ Mg/m³.
[Ans.   1.51]

STABILITY OF SLOPES

7.1 INTRODUCTION

The same principles of limiting equilibrium mechanics are used to analyse the stability of slopes (unretained soil masses) as for retained soil masses.

For purposes of analysis, slopes may be classed either as infinite or finite. In practice, a slope may be considered to be *infinite* where the soil properties at corresponding depths are the same and where the depth D to a hard stratum is constant and small compared with the overall length of the slope, as shown, for example, in Fig. 7.1. For this geometry, any mass movement or failure of

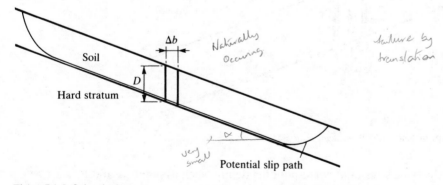

Figure 7.1 Infinite slope.

the slope usually involves the displacement of a soil mass having a length many times greater than its depth, as indicated by the potential slip path shown in Fig. 7.1. Neglecting end effects, a typical vertical slice through the soil of width Δb can be taken as representative of the whole failure mass, in which case a consideration of the simple statics governing equilibrium of the typical slice can be used to derive stability relationships for the slope.

A slope which is of *finite* extent is illustrated in Fig. 7.2. This represents the more general problem and in such slopes the statics of the whole failure mass must be considered. Because of

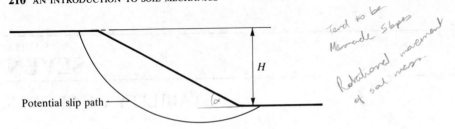

Figure 7.2 Finite slope.

this, the analysis of finite slopes is usually more complex than that for infinite slopes. This category includes cuttings for roads, railways, canals, etc., and embankments for roads and earth dams.

We will thus be concerned with the stability of infinite slopes, cuttings, embankments and earth dams.

7.2 STABILITY OF INFINITE SLOPES

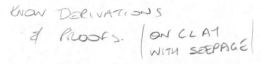

Infinite Slope of Sand without Seepage

Figure 7.3 shows an infinite slope of sand wherein the water table is at or below the base of the deposit so that the slope is not subject to the influence of any seepage flow.

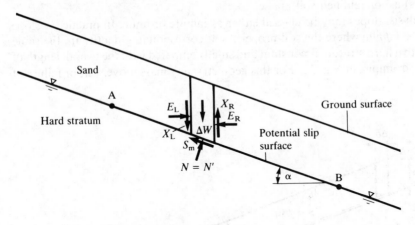

Figure 7.3 Infinite slope of sand without seepage.

For an infinite slope the stresses at corresponding depths, such as points A and B, must be the same. Thus, the stresses on the sides of the element in Fig. 7.3 are equal. That is $E_L = E_R$ and $X_L = X_R$. Hence: resolving parallel to the base of the element

$$S_m = \Delta W \sin \alpha \tag{7.1}$$

and resolving perpendicular to the base of the element

$$N = \Delta W \cos \alpha \tag{7.2}$$

As $u = 0$ throughout the mass, $N = N'$ whence we also have

$$N' = \Delta W \cos \alpha \tag{7.3}$$

For a stable slope, the shear resistance *mobilized* on the base of the element to maintain equilibrium is given by

$$S_m = \frac{S_f}{F} = \frac{N' \tan \phi'}{F}$$

Substituting for N' from Eq. (7.3)

$$S_m = \frac{1}{F} \Delta W \cos \alpha \tan \phi' \tag{7.4}$$

Equating Eqs (7.4) and (7.1) we then obtain

$$F = \frac{\tan \phi'}{\tan \alpha} \tag{7.5}$$

For a slope in limiting equilibrium $F = 1$, whence

$$\alpha = \phi' \tag{7.6}$$

Thus, we see that in the absence of any seepage flow, a slope in sand is stable to any height provided the slope angle α does not exceed the effective angle of friction ϕ'. In this case, failure does not occur on a deep-seated slip plane but occurs simultaneously at all points. Attempts to form a slope at an angle $\alpha > \phi'$ result in surface unravelling, until $\alpha = \phi'$ when the slope stabilizes. Governed by α not depth of soil

Infinite Slope of Sand subject to Steady Seepage

Consider an infinite slope of sand subject to steady seepage flow parallel to the ground surface (Fig. 7.4). In this case the effective stresses and porewater pressures at corresponding depths are the same. Thus, for the typical element shown

$$E_L = E_R, \ X_L = X_R$$

and

$$\Delta W = \rho g(D - D_w)\,\Delta b + \rho_s g D_w\,\Delta b \tag{7.7}$$

The porewater pressure u at all points on the base of the element is the same and is given by

$$u = \rho_w g D_w \cos^2 \alpha$$

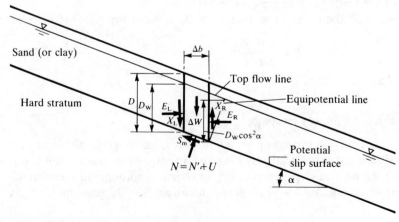

Figure 7.4 Infinite slope subject to steady seepage.

whence the water force U normal to the base of the element is given by

$$U = \rho_w g D_w \cos^2 \alpha \, \Delta b \sec \alpha = \rho_w g D_w \, \Delta b \cos \alpha \qquad (7.8)$$

Thus resolving parallel to the base of the element

$$S_m = \Delta W \sin \alpha \qquad (7.9)$$

Substituting for ΔW from Eq. (7.7)

$$S_m = [\rho g(D - D_w) \, \Delta b + \rho_s g D_w \, \Delta b] \sin \alpha \qquad (7.10)$$

Resolving perpendicular to the base of the element

$$N = \Delta W \cos \alpha$$

whence

$$N' = N - U = \Delta W \cos \alpha - U \qquad (7.11)$$

Substituting for ΔW and U from Eqs (7.7) and (7.8) then gives

$$N' = [\rho g(D - D_w) \, \Delta b + \rho' g D_w \, \Delta b] \cos \alpha \qquad (7.12)$$

The shear resistance mobilized on the base of the element to maintain equilibrium is given by

$$S_m = \frac{S_f}{F} = \frac{1}{F} N' \tan \phi'$$

Substituting for N' from Eq. (7.12) then gives

$$S_m = \frac{1}{F} [\rho g(D - D_w) \, \Delta b + \rho' g D_w \, \Delta b] \cos \alpha \tan \phi' \qquad (7.13)$$

Equating Eqs (7.13) and (7.10) we then obtain

$$F = \frac{[\rho(D - D_w) + \rho' D_w] \tan \phi'}{[\rho(D - D_w) + \rho_s D_w] \tan \alpha} \qquad (7.14)$$

If the top flow line is at the ground surface, then $D_w = D$ and Eq. (7.14) becomes

$$F = \frac{\rho'}{\rho_s} \frac{\tan \phi'}{\tan \alpha} \qquad (7.15)$$

Since the effective density ρ' is approximately half the saturated density ρ_s, we then see that the factor of safety for an infinite slope of sand subject to full steady seepage is approximately half that for an infinite slope of sand without seepage [Eq. (7.5)].

If the top flow line is level with the base of the sand, then $D_w = 0$ and Eq. (7.14) reduces to

$$F = \frac{\tan \phi'}{\tan \alpha} \qquad (7.16)$$

which re-establishes Eq. (7.5).

Infinite Slope of Clay subject to Steady Seepage

In the case of clay slopes which may be treated on an infinite basis, we are generally concerned with the stability of natural slopes that are relatively long and, in some cases, quite shallow (for example, slopes of 6° or so). All natural slopes exist in the long-term condition and therefore we require an effective stress analysis. Figure 7.4 is also relevant here and, as in the previous analysis, we have

$$E_L = E_R, \; X_L = X_R$$

and
$$U = \rho_w g D_w \, \Delta b \cos \alpha \qquad (7.8 \text{ bis})$$

Herein
$$\Delta W = \rho_s g D \, \Delta b \qquad (7.17)$$

and therefore substituting in Eq. (7.9)

$$S_m = \rho_s g D \, \Delta b \sin \alpha \qquad (7.18)$$

Substituting for ΔW and U in Eq. (7.11)

$$N' = \rho_s g D \, \Delta b \cos \alpha \left(1 - \frac{\rho_w}{\rho_s} \frac{D_w}{D} \right)$$

The shear resistance mobilized on the base of the element to maintain equilibrium is given by

$$S_m = \frac{1}{F} (c' \, \Delta b \sec \alpha + N' \tan \phi')$$

Thus
$$S_m = \frac{1}{F} \left[c' \, \Delta b \sec \alpha + \rho_s g D \, \Delta b \cos \alpha \left(1 - \frac{\rho_w}{\rho_s} \frac{D_w}{D} \right) \tan \phi' \right] \qquad (7.19)$$

Equating Eqs (7.19) and (7.18) we then obtain

$$F = \left[1 - \frac{\rho_w}{\rho_s} \frac{D_w}{D} \right] \frac{\tan \phi'}{\tan \alpha} + \frac{2c'}{\rho_s g D \sin 2\alpha} \qquad (7.20)$$

KNOW HOW TO DERIVE

Now for the case of *no seepage*, $D_w = 0$ and Eq. (7.20) becomes

$$F = \frac{\tan \phi'}{\tan \alpha} + \frac{2c'}{\rho_s g D \sin 2\alpha} \qquad (7.21)$$

Thus, if $c' > 0$ failure can only occur if $\alpha > \phi'$. The critical depth D_c at which instability will then occur is obtained by putting $F = 1$ in Eq. (7.21), whence we obtain

$$D_c = \frac{c'}{\rho_s g} \frac{\sec^2 \alpha}{(\tan \alpha - \tan \phi')} \qquad (7.22)$$

If $D < D_c$ then $F > 1$ and the slope is stable.

Similarly, for the case of *full seepage*, $D_w = D$ and Eq. (7.20) becomes

$$F = \frac{\rho'}{\rho_s} \frac{\tan \phi'}{\tan \alpha} + \frac{2c'}{\rho_s g D \sin 2\alpha} \qquad (7.23)$$

Thus if $c' > 0$ failure can only occur if $\alpha > \tan^{-1} \left(\frac{\rho'}{\rho_s} \tan \phi' \right)$ (i.e., α approximately greater than $\phi'/2$) and the critical depth D_c at which instability will occur is then given by

$$D_c = \frac{c'}{\rho_s g} \frac{\sec^2 \alpha}{\left(\tan \alpha - \dfrac{\rho'}{\rho_s} \tan \phi' \right)} \qquad (7.24)$$

If $D < D_c$ then $F > 1$ and the slope is stable.

From the above analyses we note two points of significant engineering importance:

1. For failure of clay slopes, the slip surface tends to be deep seated.
2. For slopes in sands, failure does not occur on a deep-seated slip plane but occurs by surface unravelling.

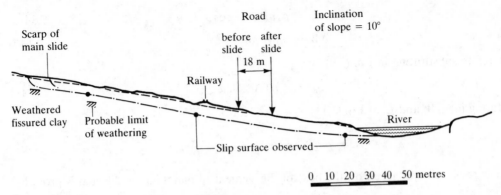

Figure 7.5 Example 7.1. (From Skempton, 1964.)

NB ⸺

Example 7.1 (from Skempton, 1964) Figure 7.5 shows the details of a landslide which occurred in 1952 at the village of Jackfield, Shropshire, England. The slide destroyed several houses and caused major dislocations in a railway and road.

The slide occurred in the zone of weathered fissured clay which extended to a depth of 6 m to 7.6 m below the surface. The slip surface ran parallel to the slope at an average depth of 5.49 m. The slope was inclined at an angle of 10° and the groundwater level was at an average depth of 0.61 m.

Drained shear box tests on samples taken from depths between 4.57 m and 5.79 m gave peak shear strength parameters of $c' = 10.5$ kN/m², $\phi' = 25°$, and residual strength parameters of $c'_r = 0$, $\phi'_r = 19°$.

ANALYSIS As all natural slopes occur in the long-term condition, we require an effective stress analysis. From the geometry of the problem we see that the stability of the slope may be analysed on an infinite basis. Thus from Eq. (7.20)

$$F = \left[1 - \frac{\rho_w}{\rho_s} \frac{D_w}{D} \right] \frac{\tan \phi'}{\tan \alpha} + \frac{2c'}{\rho_s gD \sin 2\alpha}$$

We have here $\alpha = 10°$, $D = 5.49$ m, $D_w = 5.49 - 0.61 = 4.88$ m, and ρ_s may be taken as 2.0 Mg/m³. The question that remains is what choice of effective stress parameters should the analysis be based upon? To answer this, two specific points are of particular importance. Firstly, since the clay is fissured the average value of ϕ' on the failure surface must be less than the peak value, since the value of ϕ' on a fissure plane will be close to the residual value. Secondly, the fissures act as stress concentrators causing the peak strength to be exceeded at specific points around the slip surface, whereupon the value of ϕ' at these points drops towards the residual. In so doing, stress is transferred onto neighbouring points causing the peak strength to be exceeded at these points also. In this way a *progressive failure* is initiated with the average value of ϕ' around the slip surface decreasing towards the residual value. Clearly, failure may occur before ϕ' becomes equal to ϕ'_r but as a basis for analysis it would be prudent here to assume the strength of the clay at the time of failure to have been determined by the residual strength parameters. Thus, with $c'_r = 0$ and $\phi'_r = 19°$ we obtain

NB
PROGRESSIVE
FAILURE

$$F = \left(1 - \frac{1}{2} \cdot \frac{4.88}{5.49} \right) \frac{\tan 19°}{\tan 10°} = \underline{1.08}$$

If the stability of the slope is analysed on the basis of the peak strength parameters $c' = 10.5$ kN/m² and $\phi' = 25°$, we obtain $F = 2.04$, a result which considerably overestimates the factor of safety since the actual value for F is 1.0.

STABILITY OF SLOPES **215**

7.3 STABILITY OF CUTTINGS

In practice, we are generally concerned with the stability of cuttings formed in clay soils where potential slip surfaces tend to be deep-seated. For homogeneous clay slopes, field observations tend to show that the failure surface is closely approximated by a circular arc, as indicated in Fig. 7.6a. As noted earlier, the statics of the whole failure mass must now be considered and the analyses are more involved than for infinite slopes.

When a cutting is made in a natural deposit of saturated clay, the change in porewater pressure at any point is given by Eq. (5.20):

$$\Delta u = \Delta\sigma_3 + A(\Delta\sigma_1 - \Delta\sigma_3)$$

which may be rearranged in the form

$$\Delta u = \tfrac{1}{2}(\Delta\sigma_1 + \Delta\sigma_3) + (A - \tfrac{1}{2})(\Delta\sigma_1 - \Delta\sigma_3) \tag{7.25}$$

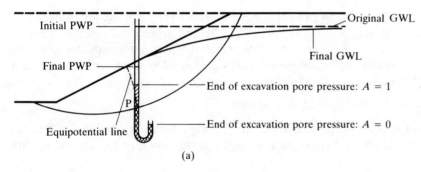

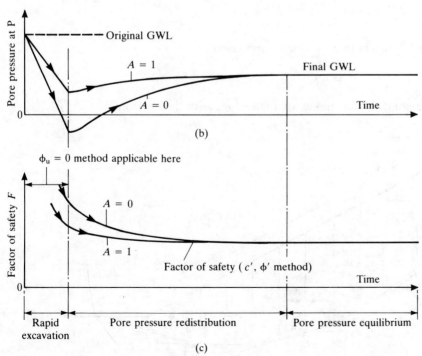

Figure 7.6 Changes in porewater pressure and factor of safety during and after construction of a cutting in clay. (From Bishop and Bjerrum, 1960.)

The reduction in the mean principal stress will thus lead to a decrease in the porewater pressure. This decrease will be enhanced or offset by the shear stress term, depending on whether the pore pressure parameter A is less than or greater than $\frac{1}{2}$. The actual changes in σ_1 and σ_3 can be estimated from either elastic theory or plastic theory, depending on the resulting state of the soil. Such calculations have been made by Bishop and Bjerrum (1960) and parts a and b of Fig. 7.6 show the typical decreases in porewater pressure at some point P on a potential slip surface.

In the course of time the porewater pressures through the clay gradually increase and adjust until they are everywhere in equilibrium with the long-term steady state seepage flow pattern. The effective stress at any point therefore decreases. In consequence, the shear strength and factor of safety decrease with time, as illustrated in Fig. 7.6c.

In practice then, we are concerned with both the short-term and long-term stability of a cutting in clay. We examine first the long-term stability. This is in terms of effective stress and as such allows the short-term factor of safety to be deduced directly.

Long-term Stability

Let c'_m and ϕ'_m denote the values of effective cohesion and effective angle of friction *mobilized* to prevent shear failure along a potential slip surface (Fig. 7.7). The problem involves a transition from active earth pressure at the crest through to passive earth pressure towards the toe of the slope. The boundary between the active and passive zones is denoted by some vertical plane such as CD. At the point C, continuity of the slip plane requires that

$$\theta'_a + \theta'_p = 90°$$

For this condition, an extension of the analysis of the slip path direction presented in Sec. 6.4 indicates that the mobilized effective stress shear strength parameters on CD, c'_{wm} and δ'_m, are defined by

$$\frac{c'_{wm}}{c'_m} = \frac{\delta'_m}{\phi'_m} = 1$$

for which state θ'_a and θ'_p are both a maximum and given by

$$\theta'_a = 45 - \frac{\phi'_m}{2} \qquad \theta'_p = 45 + \frac{\phi'_m}{2}$$

The slip plane at the point C thus makes an angle of ϕ'_m with the horizontal.

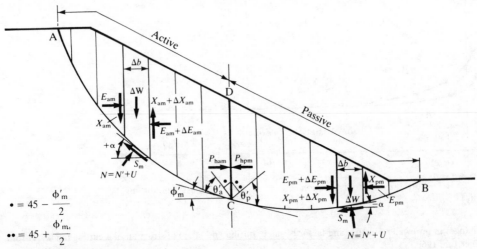

$\bullet = 45 - \dfrac{\phi'_m}{2}$

$\bullet\bullet = 45 + \dfrac{\phi'_{m_1}}{2}$

Figure 7.7 Potential slope failure. Forces on vertical slices of soil in the active and passive zones.

For equilibrium of the mass, the mobilized horizontal component of active thrust on the plane CD (P_{ham}) equals the mobilized horizontal component of passive resistance (P_{hpm}). Considering the slip surface to be a circular arc, an alternative procedure is to consider moment equilibrium about the potential centre of rotation wherein the disturbing moment arising from the weight of the soil mass is equated to the resisting moment from the shear strength of the soil mobilized along the potential slip surface.

DON'T NEED TO PROVE.

Horizontal force equilibrium The forces acting on an element of soil on the *active side* of CD are as shown in Fig. 7.7. The shear resistance mobilized on the base of the element is given by

$$S_m = c'_m \, \Delta b \sec \alpha + N' \tan \phi'_m \qquad (7.26)$$

where

$$c'_m = \frac{c'}{F} \quad \text{and} \quad \tan \phi'_m = \frac{\tan \phi'}{F} \qquad (7.27)$$

Thus resolving horizontally

$$\Delta E_{am} = N \sin \alpha - S_m \cos \alpha$$

Substituting for S_m from Eq. (7.26) and with $N = N' + U$ where $U = u \, \Delta b \sec \alpha$ in which u is the mean porewater pressure at the base of the element

$$\Delta E_{am} = (N' + u \, \Delta b \sec \alpha) \sin \alpha - (c'_m \, \Delta b \sec \alpha + N' \tan \phi'_m) \cos \alpha$$

$$\therefore \qquad \Delta E_{am} - u \, \Delta b \tan \alpha + c'_m \, \Delta b = N' \cos \alpha (\tan \alpha - \tan \phi'_m) \qquad (7.28)$$

Resolving vertically

$$\Delta W - \Delta X_{am} = N \cos \alpha + S_m \sin \alpha$$

$$\therefore \quad \Delta W - \Delta X_{am} = (N' + u \, \Delta b \sec \alpha) \cos \alpha + (c'_m \, \Delta b \sec \alpha + N' \tan \phi'_m) \sin \alpha$$

$$\therefore \quad \Delta W - \Delta X_{am} - u \, \Delta b - c'_m \, \Delta b \tan \alpha = N' \cos \alpha (1 + \tan \alpha \tan \phi'_m) \qquad (7.29)$$

Dividing Eq. (7.28) by (7.29)

$$\frac{\Delta E_{am} - u \, \Delta b \tan \alpha + c'_m \, \Delta b}{\Delta W - \Delta X_{am} - u \, \Delta b - c'_m \, \Delta b \tan \alpha} = \tan(\alpha - \phi'_m)$$

$$\therefore \quad \Delta E_{am} = \Delta W \tan (\alpha - \phi'_m) - \Delta X_{am} \tan (\alpha - \phi'_m) - u \, \Delta b [\tan (\alpha - \phi'_m) - \tan \alpha]$$

$$- c'_m \, \Delta b [\tan \alpha \tan (\alpha - \phi'_m) + 1] \qquad (7.30)$$

Thus

$$P_{\text{ham}} = \sum_A^C \Delta E_{am} = \sum_A^C \Delta W \tan (\alpha - \phi'_m) - \sum_A^C \Delta X_{am} \tan (\alpha - \phi'_m) - \sum_A^C u \, \Delta b [\tan (\alpha - \phi'_m) - \tan \alpha]$$

$$- \sum_A^C c'_m \, \Delta b [\tan \alpha \tan (\alpha - \phi'_m) + 1] \qquad (7.31)$$

We have established earlier that on the plane CD, $c'_{wm} = c'_m$ and $\delta'_m = \phi'_m$, whence

$$\text{the vertical shear force on CD} = c'_m h_{CD} + P'_{\text{ham}} \tan \phi'_m$$

$$\text{At A the vertical shear force} = 0$$

Assume all the shear change occurs at the plane CD, as this gives the most conservative estimate of the active thrust.† Thus $\Delta X_{am} = c'_m h_{CD} + P'_{\text{ham}} \tan \phi'_m$ at C, and thereafter through to the point

---

† This is compatible with the similar assumption made in the analysis of passive earth pressures against gravity walls, Sec. 6.4.

A the vertical shear force is zero. Thus in Eq. (7.31) the term

$$\sum_A^C \Delta X_{am} \tan(\alpha - \phi'_m) = (c'_m h_{CD} + P'_{ham} \tan \phi'_m) \tan(\alpha_C - \phi'_m) = 0 \text{ since } \alpha_C = \phi'_m$$

Eq. (7.31) then reduces to

$$P_{ham} = \sum_A^C \Delta W \tan(\alpha - \phi'_m) - \sum_A^C u\,\Delta b\,[\tan(\alpha - \phi'_m) - \tan \alpha]$$

$$- \sum_A^C c'_m \Delta b\,[\tan \alpha \tan(\alpha - \phi'_m) + 1] \tag{7.32}$$

The following relationships obtain:

$$\tan(\alpha - \phi'_m) = \tan \alpha - \frac{\tan \phi'_m \sec^2 \alpha}{1 + \tan \alpha \tan \phi'_m} \tag{7.33}$$

$$\tan(\alpha - \phi'_m) - \tan \alpha = -\frac{\tan \phi'_m \sec^2 \alpha}{1 + \tan \alpha \tan \phi'_m} \tag{7.34}$$

and
$$\tan \alpha \tan(\alpha - \phi'_m) + 1 = \frac{\sec^2 \alpha}{1 + \tan \alpha \tan \phi'_m} \tag{7.35}$$

Substituting these identities in Eq. (7.32) then gives

$$P_{ham} = \sum_A^C \Delta W \tan \alpha - \sum_A^C [(\Delta W - u\,\Delta b) \tan \phi'_m + c'_m \Delta b] \frac{\sec^2 \alpha}{1 + \tan \alpha \tan \phi'_m} \tag{7.36}$$

Considering now an element on the *passive side* of CD (Fig. 7.7) and adopting a common sign convention for α so that for the element shown α is negative, then in a similar manner to the above we obtain

$$P_{hpm} = -\sum_B^C \Delta W \tan \alpha + \sum_B^C [(\Delta W - u\,\Delta b) \tan \phi'_m + c'_m \Delta b] \frac{\sec^2 \alpha}{1 + \tan \alpha \tan \phi'_m} \tag{7.37}$$

it again being assumed that all the shear change occurs at the plane CD as this gives the most conservative estimate of the passive resistance.†
For horizontal equilibrium

$$P_{ham} = P_{hpm}$$

Thus equating Eqs (7.36) and (7.37) we obtain

$$\sum_A^B \Delta W \tan \alpha = \sum_A^B [(\Delta W - u\,\Delta b) \tan \phi'_m + c'_m \Delta b] \frac{\sec^2 \alpha}{1 + \tan \alpha \tan \phi'_m}$$

Noting that $c'_m = \dfrac{c'}{F}$ and $\tan \phi'_m = \dfrac{\tan \phi'}{F}$ [Eq. (7.27)], and considering the soil mass to be divided into *n* slices, we then obtain

$$F = \frac{\displaystyle\sum_1^n [(\Delta W - u\,\Delta b) \tan \phi' + c' \Delta b] \dfrac{\sec^2 \alpha}{1 + \dfrac{1}{F} \tan \alpha \tan \phi'}}{\displaystyle\sum_1^n \Delta W \tan \alpha} \tag{7.38}$$

DON'T NEED
TO REMEMBER
EQUATIONS.

† This is in keeping with the assumption made in the analysis of passive earth pressures against gravity walls, Sec. 6.4.

Moment equilibrium Assuming the failure surface to be a *circular arc* and considering moment equilibrium whereby the disturbing moment about the centre of rotation due to the weight of the slices is equated to the restoring moment arising from the shear resistance of the soil mobilized along the base of the slices, Bishop (1955) obtained

$$F = \frac{\sum_{1}^{n} [(\Delta W - \Delta X - u\,\Delta b)\tan\phi' + c'\,\Delta b]\dfrac{\sec\alpha}{1 + \dfrac{1}{F}\tan\alpha\tan\phi'}}{\sum_{1}^{n} \Delta W \sin\alpha}$$

To solve this equation it is necessary to know the distribution of vertical shear forces through the soil mass. However, considering various realistic distributions, it was found that the X forces could be neglected with little loss in accuracy. Thus neglecting ΔX

$$F = \frac{\sum_{1}^{n} [(\Delta W - u\,\Delta b)\tan\phi' + c'\,\Delta b]\dfrac{\sec\alpha}{1 + \dfrac{1}{F}\tan\alpha\tan\phi'}}{\sum_{1}^{n} \Delta W \sin\alpha} \tag{7.39}$$

Comparing Eqs (7.38) and (7.39) we note the similarity of the two expressions for F. There are, however, two very important differences. Firstly, the determination of Eq. (7.38) assumes that particular distribution for the vertical shear force through the soil mass maximizes the active thrust and minimizes the passive resistance, and therefore gives a conservative estimate for the factor of safety. Secondly, Eq. (7.38) does not invoke the equation of the slip surface and is therefore applicable to both circular and non-circular slip paths. In contrast, Bishop's equation [i.e., Eq. (7.39)] is strictly only valid for circular slip surfaces. However, rigorous analyses by Morgenstern and Price (1965) have shown that it may also be applied to non-circular slip surfaces with little loss in accuracy.

As the factor of safety occurs on both sides of Eqs (7.38) and (7.39), it can only be determined by an iterative procedure. Thus, to calculate F we assume a value on the right-hand side of say 1 and calculate the left-hand F; iteration proceeds until the two values of F agree to within 0.01. Convergence is generally very rapid and is usually obtained after only 2 to 3 iterations. We find that Eq. (7.38) gives a slightly more conservative estimate for the factor of safety than does Eq. (7.39).

Example 7.2 Figure 7.8 shows the cross-section through a cutting in boulder clay formed some 30 years ago but currently observed to be showing signs of instability. Support this observation by calculating the factor of safety for the potential slip surface shown, given that the steady state seepage flow net is as indicated and the effective stress shear strength parameters of the boulder clay are $c' = 8$ kN/m^2 and $\phi' = 32°$. The density of the clay $= 2.1$ Mg/m^3.

SOLUTION The analysis for the factor of safety is most conveniently carried out in tabular form. Assuming initially Bishop's equation [Eq. (7.39)], we obtain the results given in Table 7.1. Here h_s denotes the mean height of a particular slice and h_p the mean pressure head at the base, determined from the groundwater flow net. Thus, with $c' = 8$ kN/m^2, $\phi' = 32°$ and $\rho = 2.1$ Mg/m^3 we find $F = 1.09$.

Assuming Eq. (7.38) we obtain the results given in Table 7.2, from which we find $F = 1.04$.

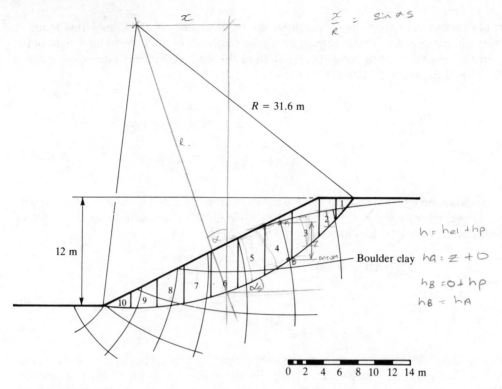

Figure 7.8 Example 7.2.

Clearly then, the cutting is close to limiting equilibrium. Possible remedial measures include reducing the slope angle and installing counterfort drains connected to a longitudinal toe drain.

For a stable slope the location of the most critical slip surface is not known. It is therefore necessary to carry out stability calculations for a large number of possible slip paths and hence predict the most critical slip path from that analysis which gives the lowest factor of safety. This is best done by establishing a grid system. For each grid position, a number of potential slip surfaces are analysed and the minimum factor of safety determined. Contour lines of equal values of F may then be drawn and hence the centre of the most critical slip surface and minimum factor of safety determined. Performed manually, the analysis of one slip surface may take an hour or more, so clearly this is a very lengthy and time-consuming operation. In such cases it is advantageous to use one of the readily available computer programs which will analyse any specified pattern of slip circles in a matter of a few seconds. This rapid analysis allows the engineer to readily investigate the effects of varying his assumptions about soil properties and porewater pressures, and if necessary to modify his design.

Short-term Stability

Generally, the excavation period will be short compared with the time for dissipation of excess porewater pressures so that the clay will be undrained at the end of construction. The short-term stability of the cutting may therefore be analysed in terms of total stress. The governing equation for the factor of safety can be obtained directly from the long-term effective stress equation by putting $c' = c_u$, $\phi' = \phi_u = 0$ (assuming the soil to be saturated) and disregarding the term in u since the porewater pressure does not appear explicitly in a total stress analysis. Thus: for

Table 7.1

Slice No.	Δb (m)	h_s (m)	$\Delta W = \rho g\,\Delta b\,h_s$ (kN/m)	α (°)	$\Delta W \sin\alpha$ (kN/m)	h_p (m)	$u\,\Delta b = \rho_w g h_p\,\Delta b$ (kN/m)	$(\Delta W - u\,\Delta b)\tan\phi' + c'\,\Delta b$ (kN/m)	$\dfrac{\sec\alpha}{1 + \frac{1}{F}\tan\alpha\tan\phi'}$			$[(\Delta W - u\,\Delta b)\tan\phi' + c'\,\Delta b] \times \dfrac{\sec\alpha}{1 + \frac{1}{F}\tan\alpha\tan\phi'}$ (kN/m)		
									$F = 1$	$F = 1.07$	$F = 1.09$	$F = 1$	$F = 1.07$	$F = 1.09$
1	1.90	1.33	52.1	49.5	39.6	0.40	7.5	43.1	0.889	0.914	0.921	38.3	39.4	39.7
2	1.90	3.20	125.3	44.7	88.1	1.60	29.8	74.9	0.869	0.892	0.898	65.1	66.8	67.3
3	3.10	4.62	295.0	38.2	182.4	3.20	97.3	148.3	0.853	0.872	0.877	126.5	129.3	130.1
4	3.10	5.28	337.2	31.4	175.7	4.48	136.2	150.4	0.848	0.864	0.868	127.5	129.9	130.5
5	3.10	5.40	344.9	25.0	145.8	4.90	149.0	147.2	0.854	0.867	0.871	125.7	127.6	128.2
6	3.10	5.10	325.7	18.8	105.0	5.00	152.1	133.3	0.871	0.881	0.884	116.1	117.4	117.8
7	3.10	4.60	293.8	13.1	66.6	4.74	144.1	118.3	0.896	0.904	0.906	106.0	106.9	107.2
8	3.10	3.60	229.9	7.3	29.2	4.04	122.9	91.7	0.933	0.938	0.939	85.6	86.0	86.1
9	3.10	2.40	153.3	1.6	4.3	2.80	85.2	67.4	0.983	0.984	0.985	66.3	66.3	66.4
10	3.10	0.84	53.6	−4.1	−3.8	1.20	36.5	35.5	1.050	1.046	1.046	37.3	37.1	37.1

$$\sum = 832.9$$

$$\sum = 894.4 \qquad 906.7 \qquad 910.4$$

$$F = \frac{894.4}{832.9} \qquad \frac{906.7}{832.9} \qquad \frac{910.4}{832.9}$$

$$= 1.07 \qquad 1.09 \qquad 1.09$$

Table 7.2

Slice No.	Δb (m)	h_s (m)	$\Delta W = \rho g\, \Delta b h_s$ (kN/m)	α (°)	$\Delta W \tan \alpha$ (kN/m)	h_p (m)	$u\,\Delta b =$ $\rho_w g h_p\, \Delta b$ (kN/m)	$(\Delta W - u\,\Delta b) \times$ $\tan \phi' + c'\,\Delta b$ (kN/m)	$\dfrac{\sec^2 \alpha}{1 + \frac{1}{F} \tan \alpha \tan \phi'}$			$\dfrac{[(\Delta W - u\,\Delta b)\tan \phi' + c'\,\Delta b] \times \sec^2 \alpha}{1 + \frac{1}{F}\tan \alpha \tan \phi'}$ (kN/m)		
									$F=1$	$F=1.03$	$F=1.04$	$F=1$	$F=1.03$	$F=1.04$
1	1.90	1.33	52.1	49.5	61.0	0.40	7.5	43.1	1.369	1.386	1.392	59.0	59.7	60.0
2	1.90	3.20	125.3	44.7	124.0	1.60	29.8	74.9	1.223	1.237	1.241	91.6	92.7	93.0
3	3.10	4.62	295.0	38.2	232.1	3.20	97.3	148.3	1.085	1.096	1.099	160.9	162.5	163.0
4	3.10	5.28	337.2	31.4	205.8	4.48	136.2	150.4	0.994	1.002	1.004	149.5	150.7	151.0
5	3.10	5.40	344.9	25.0	160.8	4.90	149.0	147.2	0.943	0.949	0.951	138.8	139.7	140.0
6	3.10	5.10	325.7	18.8	110.9	5.00	152.1	133.3	0.920	0.925	0.926	122.6	123.3	123.4
7	3.10	4.60	293.8	13.1	68.4	4.74	144.1	118.3	0.920	0.924	0.925	108.8	109.3	109.4
8	3.10	3.60	229.9	7.3	29.5	4.04	122.9	91.7	0.941	0.943	0.944	86.3	86.5	86.6
9	3.10	2.40	153.3	1.6	4.3	2.80	85.2	67.4	0.984	0.984	0.984	66.3	66.3	66.3
10	3.10	0.84	53.6	−4.1	−3.8	1.20	36.5	35.5	1.052	1.051	1.050	37.3	37.3	37.3

$\sum = 993.0$

$\sum = 1021.1 \qquad 1028.0 \qquad 1030.0$

$$F = \frac{1021.1}{993.0} \qquad \frac{1028.0}{993.0} \qquad \frac{1030.0}{993.0}$$

$$= 1.03 \qquad\qquad 1.04 \qquad\qquad 1.04$$

horizontal force equilibrium we obtain from Eq. (7.38)

$$F = \frac{\sum_{1}^{n} c_u \, \Delta b \sec^2 \alpha}{\sum_{1}^{n} \Delta W \tan \alpha} \tag{7.40}$$

and for moment equilibrium we obtain from Eq. (7.39)

$$F = \frac{\sum_{1}^{n} c_u \, \Delta b \sec \alpha}{\sum_{1}^{n} \Delta W \sin \alpha} \tag{7.41}$$

The short-term stability analysis is aided greatly by the use of a design chart prepared by Taylor (Fig. 7.9). This relates the slope angle i with the stability number $c_{um}/\rho_s gH$, wherein c_{um} is the value of undrained shear strength required to just maintain equilibrium along the most critical slip surface. The ratio c_u/c_{um} then defines the factor of safety against undrained shear failure. That is

$$F = \frac{c_u}{c_{um}} \tag{7.42}$$

For slope angles greater than 53°, the critical circle passes through the toe of the slope with the lowest point on the failure arc at the toe of the slope. For slope angles less than 53°, the critical circle passes below the toe and is tangent to the underlying firm base. In these cases the centre of the critical circle generally lies on a vertical line through the mid-point of the slope.

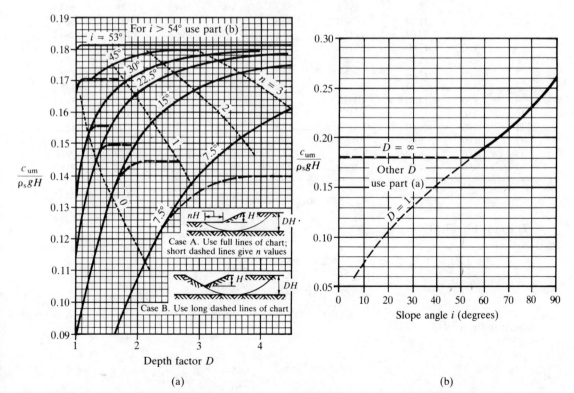

(a) (b)

Figure 7.9 Short-term stability of cuttings in saturated clay. Stability charts for $\phi_u = 0$ condition. (After Taylor, 1948. Reprinted with permission of Edith L. Nyman.)

Example 7.3 A temporary excavation is to be made to a depth of 8 m in a 20-m thick deposit of firm saturated clay overlying bedrock. Using Taylor's stability chart, calculate the required slope angle of the excavation if the short-term factor of safety is not to be less than 1.5 and the clay has an average undrained shear strength of 41.5 kN/m^2 and a density of 2.0 Mg/m^3. Check the short-term factor of safety for the slope using Eqs (7.40) and (7.41).

SOLUTION With reference to Fig. 7.9a we have

$$H = 8 \text{ m} \quad \text{and} \quad DH = 20 \text{ m} \quad \text{whence} \quad D = 2.5$$

Now

$$c_{um} = \frac{c_u}{F} = \frac{41.5}{1.5} = 27.\dot{6} \text{ kN/m}^2$$

Thus

$$\frac{c_{um}}{\rho_s g H} = \frac{27.\dot{6}}{2 \times 9.81 \times 8} = 0.176$$

From Fig. 7.9a we then obtain $i = 30°$.

For a slope angle of 30°, the critical circle is as shown in Fig. 7.10. Dividing the soil mass into vertical slices we obtain the following results:

Table 7.3

Slice No.	Δb (m)	h_s (m)	$\Delta W = \rho_s g \Delta b h_s$ (kN/m)	α (°)	$\Delta W \sin \alpha$ (kN/m)	$\Delta W \tan \alpha$ (kN/m)	$c_u \Delta b \sec \alpha$ (kN/m)	$c_u \Delta b \sec^2 \alpha$ (kN/m)
1	2.50	3.30	161.9	63.7	145.1	327.6	234.2	528.5
2	2.50	7.30	358.1	54.3	290.8	498.3	177.8	304.7
3	4.00	11.20	879.0	44.8	619.4	872.9	233.9	329.7
4	4.00	14.60	1145.8	34.8	653.9	796.4	202.2	246.2
5	4.00	17.00	1334.2	25.9	582.8	647.9	184.5	205.1
6	4.00	18.60	1459.7	17.8	446.2	468.7	174.3	183.1
7	3.50	18.40	1263.5	10.2	223.7	227.3	147.6	150.0
8	3.50	16.80	1153.7	3.4	68.4	68.5	145.5	145.8
9	3.50	14.70	1009.4	−3.4	−59.9	−60.0	145.5	145.8
10	3.50	12.20	837.8	−10.2	−148.4	−168.7	147.6	150.0
11	4.00	10.60	831.9	−17.8	−254.3	−267.1	174.3	183.1
12	4.00	9.00	706.3	−25.9	−308.5	−343.0	184.5	205.1
13	4.00	6.60	518.0	−34.8	−295.6	−360.0	202.2	246.2
14	4.90	2.80	269.2	−45.9	−193.3	−277.8	292.2	419.9
					$\sum = 1770.3$	2431.0	2646.3	3443.2

Thus for Eq. (7.40)

$$F = \frac{\sum_1^n c_u \Delta b \sec^2 \alpha}{\sum_1^n \Delta W \tan \alpha} = \frac{3443.2}{2431.0} = \underline{1.42}$$

and for Eq. (7.41)

$$F = \frac{\sum_1^n c_u \Delta b \sec \alpha}{\sum_1^n \Delta W \sin \alpha} = \frac{2646.3}{1770.3} = \underline{1.49}$$

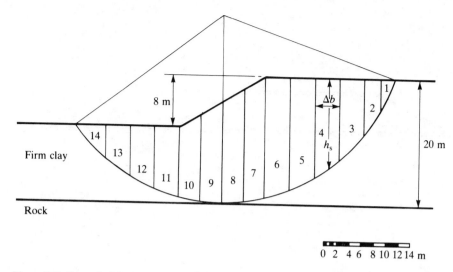

Figure 7.10 Example 7.3.

We see then that Eq. (7.40) gives a slightly lower estimate for the factor of safety than does Eq. (7.41). The value of $F = 1.49$ given by Eq. (7.41) is in very close agreement with the assumed design value of 1.5. The stability chart prepared by Taylor is in fact based on the ϕ circle method, and it was found that there was negligible difference between the stability numbers obtained by the ϕ circle method and those obtained by the slices method based on moment equilibrium.

If a clay deposit has a more permeable macrostructure, special care must be taken in the design of temporary excavations and cuts. The presence of such a structure allows a more rapid dissipation of excess porewater pressure and the long-term condition may be established in months rather than in years. A number of short-term failures attributable to this effect have been reported in the literature [see, for example, Rowe (1968a)]. In such cases, then, it would be wise to design temporary excavations and cuts on the basis that long-term conditions will apply.

7.4 STABILITY OF EMBANKMENTS

Embankments may be constructed for roads and dams. Consider first the case of a road embankment. With reference to Fig. 7.11a, we see that a failure may occur within the embankment itself or on a more deep-seated slip surface passing through the foundation soil. It is necessary therefore to ensure an adequate factor of safety against failure of the embankment and failure of the foundation. This latter aspect will be considered later. We confine our attention here to the stability of the embankment itself. With reference then to parts a, b and c of Fig. 7.11, the shear stress and porewater pressure at some particular point P on a potential slip surface increase under the weight of superimposed fill as construction proceeds. When construction is complete the shear stress at all points remains constant (Fig. 7.11b), whereas the porewater pressures decrease with time until they are everywhere zero (Fig. 7.11c). The effective stress at any point therefore increases, and in consequence the shear strength of the embankment material increases. The factor of safety of the embankment is thus a minimum at the end of construction and then increases with time as consolidation takes place (Fig. 7.11d). The factor of safety at the end of construction then represents the criterion for design.

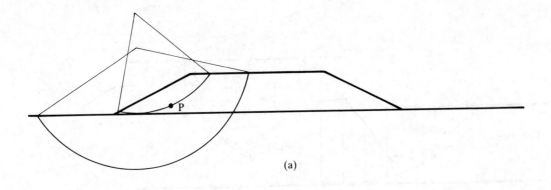

(a)

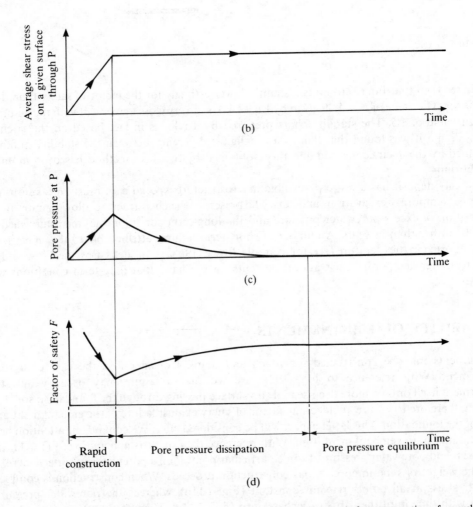

(b)

(c)

(d)

Figure 7.11 Changes in shear stress, pore pressure and factor of safety during and after construction of an embankment. (After Bishop and Bjerrum, 1960.)

If the height of the embankment is not too great and construction is relatively rapid, then in general there will have been insufficient time for any dissipation of excess porewater pressure to have occurred by the end of construction and a total stress analysis might be considered appropriate. However, as embankment materials tend to be partially saturated, $\phi_u \neq 0$. As we have seen earlier, values of c_u and ϕ_u then depend very much on the range of normal stress acting on the failure plane. Because c_u and ϕ_u are not unique, it is preferable to carry out the end-of-construction or short-term stability analysis in terms of effective stress using either Eq. (7.38) or (7.39) developed earlier. For this purpose we need to predict the distribution of porewater pressure around the slip surface.

For a change in total stress under undrained conditions, the change in porewater pressure is given by Eq. (5.19):

$$\Delta u = B[\Delta\sigma_3 + A(\Delta\sigma_1 - \Delta\sigma_3)]$$

This may be rearranged in the form

$$\frac{\Delta u}{\Delta\sigma_1} = \bar{B} \tag{7.43}$$

where

$$\bar{B} = B\left[1 - (1 - A)\left(1 - \frac{\Delta\sigma_3}{\Delta\sigma_1}\right)\right] \tag{7.44}$$

The pore pressure parameter $\bar{B}$ is determined from special triaxial tests in which the sample is subjected to stress changes corresponding to those expected in the field (see Bishop and Henkel, 1962). Considering, however, the factors that influence B, A and $\Delta\sigma_3/\Delta\sigma_1$, the accurate determination of $\bar{B}$ is not easy. Bishop and Henkel quote $\bar{B}$ values equal to 0.5 and 0.75 for two typical fill materials.

Because of the varying vertical shear forces across an embankment cross-section, the major and minor principal stresses σ_1 and σ_3 are not vertical and horizontal. However, the slopes of an embankment tend to be relatively flat, in which case the angular shift of the principal stresses is not too great and the change in major principal stress $\Delta\sigma_1$ may be taken equal to the change in vertical stress $\Delta\sigma_v$. Thus, Eq. (7.43) may be written as

$$\Delta u = \bar{B}\,\Delta\sigma_v \tag{7.45}$$

If u_o denotes the initial porewater pressure at any point, then the porewater pressure u subsequent on a change in total stress is given by

$$u = u_o + \Delta u$$

Thus

$$u = u_o + \bar{B}\,\Delta\sigma_v \tag{7.46}$$

In a natural deposit, u_o is defined by the depth of the point below the groundwater level. For a rolled fill, u_o is usually a suction and may reach quite a high negative value in clay soils placed at or below the optimum water content. For earth fills of low plasticity placed wet of the optimum (as is usual in many countries) u_o is small and may be neglected in initial design work, whence Eq. (7.46) becomes

$$u = \bar{B}\,\Delta\sigma_v \tag{7.47}$$

It should be remembered that Eqs (7.46) and (7.47) give the maximum porewater pressure under undrained loading conditions. If the rate of construction of the embankment is such that some consolidation will have occurred by the end of construction, then it will be necessary to estimate this from appropriate consolidation theory.

Because of the difficulties inherent in the accurate prediction of porewater pressures expected to arise in the field, instrumentation must be installed on any major project and the porewater pressures checked as construction proceeds. This allows the design to be modified if necessary.

If for a particular embankment design the factor of safety at the end of construction is not adequate (i.e., $F < 1.5$) then we may consider flattening the slopes and/or reducing the rate of construction. Both these factors, however, will increase the cost of the operation. If the slopes of the embankment cannot be altered and it is not desirable to reduce the rate of construction, then it will be necessary to accelerate the rate of consolidation of the embankment material. This is done by incorporating horizontal sand blankets in the embankment. The design of vertical spacing of sand blankets to achieve a specified factor of safety at the end of construction (normally 1.5) is illustrated in the following example.

Example 7.4 A rolled clay embankment is to be constructed on a firm base of bedrock. The embankment is to have side slopes of 18° and is to be built to a height of 13.2 m over a period of two seasons, each being from April to October inclusive. 5.5 m of fill are to be placed in the first season and 7.7 m in the second season. Analyse the stability of the embankment and incorporate any horizontal sand blankets as may be necessary in order to achieve a minimum factor of safety of 1.5 at the end of construction. The properties of the rolled clay fill are $\rho = 2.1 \text{ Mg/m}^3$, $c' = 7 \text{ kN/m}^2$, $\phi' = 31°$, $\bar{B} = 0.73$ and $c_v = 0.8 \text{ m}^2/\text{yr}$.

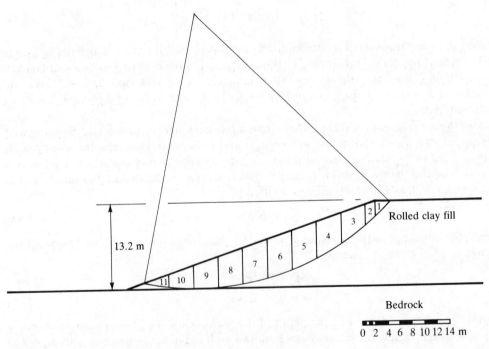

Figure 7.12 Example 7.4. Homogeneous clay fill embankment.

ANALYSIS Although the question implies that the embankment cannot be built without incorporating horizontal sand blankets to accelerate the rate of consolidation of the fill material, it is informative to consider first the stability of the embankment in its own right. A typical potential slip circle is as shown in Fig. 7.12. Assuming no dissipation of porewater pressure by the end of construction, the porewater pressure at the base of a particular slice is obtained from Eq. (7.47). With $\Delta\sigma_v = \rho g h_s$ this gives

$$u = \bar{B}\rho g h_s$$

Thus

$$u \, \Delta b = \bar{B}\rho g h_s \, \Delta b = \bar{B} \, \Delta W$$

Table 7.4

Slice No.	Δb (m)	h_s (m)	$\Delta W = \rho g\,\Delta b h_s$ (kN/m)	α (°)	$\Delta W \sin\alpha$ (kN/m)	$\Delta W(1-\bar{B})\tan\phi' + c'\Delta b$ (kN/m)	$\dfrac{\sec\alpha}{1+\frac{1}{F}\tan\alpha\tan\phi'}$			$\left[\Delta W(1-\bar{B})\tan\phi' + c'\Delta b\right]\times\dfrac{\sec\alpha}{1+\frac{1}{F}\tan\alpha\tan\phi'}$ (kN/m)		
							$F=1$	$F=0.80$	$F=0.78$	$F=1$	$F=0.80$	$F=0.78$
1	2.40	1.40	69.2	43.3	47.5	28.0	0.877	0.805	0.796	24.6	22.5	22.3
2	1.60	2.80	92.3	39.7	59.0	26.2	0.867	0.801	0.793	22.7	21.0	20.8
3	4.00	4.00	329.6	35.0	189.1	81.5	0.859	0.800	0.793	70.0	65.2	64.6
4	4.00	5.20	428.5	28.6	205.1	97.5	0.858	0.808	0.802	83.7	78.8	78.2
5	4.00	5.90	486.2	23.0	190.0	106.9	0.866	0.824	0.819	92.6	88.1	87.6
6	4.00	6.00	494.4	17.4	147.8	108.2	0.882	0.848	0.844	95.4	91.8	91.3
7	4.00	5.80	477.9	11.9	98.5	105.5	0.907	0.882	0.879	95.7	93.1	92.7
8	4.00	5.20	428.5	6.5	48.5	97.5	0.942	0.927	0.925	91.8	90.4	90.2
9	4.00	4.20	346.1	1.2	7.2	84.1	0.988	0.985	0.984	83.1	82.8	82.8
10	4.00	2.80	230.7	−4.1	−16.5	65.4	1.048	1.060	1.061	68.5	69.3	69.4
11	4.00	1.00	82.4	−9.4	−13.5	41.4	1.126	1.158	1.162	46.6	47.9	48.1

(Handwritten annotations: "width of each slice scaled from diagram" over Δb; "mean height of slice" over h_s; "measuring wrt protractor" over α; slices 10 and 11 marked "positive region".)

$$\sum = 962.7$$

$$\sum = 774.7 \qquad 750.9 \qquad 748.0$$

$$F = \frac{774.7}{962.7} \qquad \frac{750.9}{962.7} \qquad \frac{748.0}{962.7}$$

$$= 0.80 \qquad\quad = 0.78 \qquad\quad 0.78$$

Check this!

see notes in file

Table 7.5

Slice No.	Season	Mean height constructed Δh_s (m)	Max. undrained pore pressure $u = \bar{B}\rho g\,\Delta h_s$ (kN/m²)	Max. undrained pressure head $u/\rho_w g$ (m)	Average time t to end of construction (yr)	Time Factor $T_v = \dfrac{c_v t}{H^2}$	Mid-plane degree of consol'n U_v	Residual pore pressure $u(1 - U_v)$ (kN/m²)	Residual pressure head $u(1 - U_v)/\rho_w g$ (m)
14	1	0.96	14.44	1.47	1.342	0.477	0.61	5.63	0.57
13	1	2.51	37.75	3.85	1.259	0.448	0.58	15.86	1.62
12	1	3.70	55.64	5.67	1.196	0.425	0.555	24.76	2.52
11	1	3.70	55.64	5.67	1.196	0.425	0.555	24.76	2.52
	2	1.18	17.75	1.81	0.539	0.192	0.21	14.02	1.43
		4.88	73.39	7.48				38.78	3.95
10	1	3.70	55.64	5.67	1.196	0.425	0.555	24.76	2.52
	2	2.37	35.64	3.63	0.494	0.176	0.18	29.22	2.98
		6.07	91.28	9.30				53.98	5.50
9	1	3.70	55.64	5.67	1.196	0.425	0.555	24.76	2.52
	2	3.55	53.39	5.44	0.449	0.160	0.155	45.11	4.60
		7.25	109.03	11.11				69.87	7.12

(handwritten annotations in Time Factor column: "sand blanket5 dist between"; "see notes" → Fig. 9.6)

230

8	1	3.70	55.64	5.67	1.196	0.425	0.555	24.76	2.52
	2	4.74	71.28	7.27	0.404	0.144	0.13	62.01	6.32
		8.44	126.92	12.94				86.77	8.84
7	1	3.50	52.64	5.37	1.186	0.422	0.55	23.69	2.41
	2	5.93	89.18	9.09	0.359	0.128	0.10	80.26	8.18
		9.43	141.82	14.46				103.95	10.59
6	1	3.20	48.12	4.91			0	48.12	4.91
	2	7.00	105.27	10.73			0	105.27	10.73
		10.20	153.39	15.64				153.39	15.64
5	1	2.20	33.09	3.37			0	33.09	3.37
	2	7.70	115.80	11.80			0	115.80	11.80
		9.90	148.89	15.17				148.89	15.17
4	1	1.00	15.04	1.53			0	15.04	1.53
	2	7.70	115.80	11.80			0	115.80	11.80
		8.70	130.84	13.33				130.84	13.33
3	2	7.00	105.27	10.73			0	105.27	10.73
2	2	4.80	72.19	7.36			0	72.19	7.36
1	2	1.90	28.57	2.91			0	28.57	2.91

Substituting in Eqs (7.38) and (7.39) then gives particular forms of the general effective stress stability equations. Considering initially Bishop's equation (7.39), this becomes

$$F = \frac{\sum_{1}^{n} [\Delta W(1 - \bar{B}) \tan \phi' + c' \Delta b] \dfrac{\sec \alpha}{1 + \dfrac{1}{F} \tan \alpha \tan \phi'}}{\sum_{1}^{n} \Delta W \sin \alpha} \qquad (7.48)$$

We thus obtain the results given in Table 7.4 from which we find $F = 0.78$.†

Even with a drainage blanket at the bottom of the embankment, resulting in zero porewater pressure at the base of slices 9 and 10 and essentially 8 and 11, the factor of safety only rises to approximately 1.3 and is still less than the required value of 1.5. But even for this situation there are still other potential slip surfaces with $F < 1.0$. Thus, we may conclude that the embankment cannot be built without using horizontal sand blankets to accelerate the rate of consolidation of the fill material.

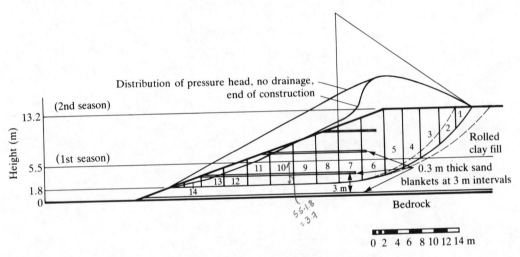

Figure 7.13 Example 7.4. Clay fill embankment incorporating horizontal sand blankets.

Consider then the arrangement shown in Fig. 7.13. At any given time the porewater pressure will be a maximum and correspondingly the shear resistance a minimum at the mid-points between the sand blankets. The most dangerous slip surface will thus be along the mid-plane between the first two blankets. Although the potential slip surface is now non-circular we may still apply Bishop's equation, as explained earlier. However, we need to calculate first the degree of consolidation and resulting distribution of porewater pressure around the slip surface at the end of construction. Soil elements at the base of slices 7 to 14 will undergo vertical consolidation and hence the (mid-plane) degrees of consolidation may be reasonably predicted from simple Terzaghi theory. Soil elements at the base of slices 1 to 6 will, in general, involve three-dimensional flow and an estimate of the corresponding degrees of consolidation cannot easily be made. However, for the geometry and consolidation parameters of this particular problem, it is reasonable (and conservative) to assume zero degree of consolidation at the base of slices 1 to 6. The calculations are illustrated in Table 7.5.

† Equation (7.38) gives $F = 0.73$.

The distribution of pressure head around the potential slip surface at the end of construction is then as shown in Fig. 7.13. Also shown is the undrained distribution, assuming no consolidation to have occurred. Considering the areas under the piezometric lines, the corresponding degree of consolidation U along the slip surface is equal to 0.213. An effective stress stability analysis using Bishop's equation [namely, Eq. (7.39)] then gives the results in Table 7.6, from which we find $F = 1.62$.

Two other potential slip surfaces immediately to the left and right (Fig. 7.13) give $F = 1.63$ and $F = 1.66$. We may therefore conclude that the surface analysed above is, for all practical purposes, the most critical one. The factor of safety at the end of construction is thus 1.62. As the minimum required value for F is 1.5, the assumed design can be considered satisfactory. We could in fact slightly increase the vertical spacing of the sand blankets.

As the porewater pressures within the embankment continue to dissipate, the factor of safety against slip will continue to increase. For a given slip surface, it is informative to examine the relationship between F and the degree of pore pressure dissipation around the surface. Thus, for the slip surface analysed above we examine the two limiting values for F corresponding to the undrained and fully drained conditions. For *undrained* conditions we may use Bishop's equation in the form of Eq. (7.48). Analysis then gives $F = 1.10$. For the *fully drained* condition $u = 0$ at all points in the embankment. Using the general form of Bishop's equation [i.e., Eq. (7.39)] with $u = 0$, we then obtain $F = 3.53$. We therefore have

$$
\begin{aligned}
&F \text{ undrained } (U = 0) &&= 1.10 \\
&F \text{ end-of-construction } (U = 0.213) &&= 1.62 \\
\text{and} \quad &F \text{ drained } (U = 1) &&= 3.53
\end{aligned}
$$

If we plot the values of F against the corresponding degrees of consolidation around the slip surface (Fig. 7.14) we see in fact that F increases linearly with U.

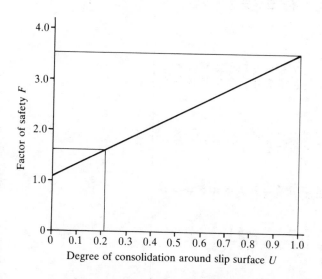

Figure 7.14 Example 7.4. Variation of factor of safety with degree of consolidation around the slip surface.

Using Eq. (7.38), the most critical slip surface at the end of construction gives $F = 1.32$. On this basis the sand blankets need to be placed closer together. We leave this as an exercise to the reader.

It is a matter of engineering judgement as to which analysis to favour. In the circumstances it would not seem unreasonable to consider the average safety factor for the two analyses. This is equal to 1.47 which is very close to the required value of 1.5. This, together with the long-standing use of Bishop's equation, favours the proposed design.

Table 7.6

weight of slice

Slice No.	Δb (m)	h_s (from Col. 3 Table 7.5) (m)	$\Delta W = \rho g\, \Delta b\, h_s$ (kN/m)	α (°)	$\Delta W \sin\alpha$ (kN/m)	u (from Col. 9 Table 7.5) (kN/m²)	$(\Delta W - u\,\Delta b)\tan\phi' + c'\,\Delta b$ (kN/m)	$\dfrac{\sec\alpha}{1+\frac{1}{F}\tan\alpha\tan\phi'}$ $F=1$	$F=1.58$	$F=1.62$	$\left[(\Delta W - u\,\Delta b)\tan\phi' + c'\,\Delta b\right] \times \dfrac{\sec\alpha}{1+\frac{1}{F}\tan\alpha\tan\phi'}$ (kN/m) $F=1$	$F=1.58$	$F=1.62$
1	2.93	1.90	114.7	50.0	87.9	28.57	39.1	0.907	1.071	1.079	35.5	41.9	42.2
2	2.93	4.80	289.7	41.1	190.4	72.19	67.5	0.871	0.996	1.003	58.8	67.2	67.7
3	2.93	7.00	422.5	33.5	233.2	105.27	89.0	0.858	0.958	0.963	76.4	85.3	85.7
4	2.93	8.70	525.1	26.0	230.2	130.84	105.7	0.860	0.939	0.942	90.9	99.3	99.6
5	2.93	9.90	597.6	19.3	197.5	148.89	117.5	0.875	0.935	0.938	102.8	109.9	110.2
6	2.93	10.20	767.0	11.9	158.2	153.39	150.0	0.907	0.946	0.948	136.1	141.9	142.2
7	3.65	9.43	709.1	3.8	47.0	103.95	223.6	0.964	0.978	0.978	215.6	218.7	218.7
8	3.65	8.44	634.6	0	0	86.77	216.6	1.000	1.000	1.000	216.6	216.6	216.6
9	3.65	7.25	545.2	0	0	69.87	199.9	1.000	1.000	1.000	199.9	199.9	199.9
10	3.65	6.07	456.4	0	0	53.98	181.4	1.000	1.000	1.000	181.4	181.4	181.4
11	3.65	4.88	366.9	0	0	38.78	161.0	1.000	1.000	1.000	161.0	161.0	161.0
12	3.65	3.70	278.2	0	0	24.76	138.4	1.000	1.000	1.000	138.4	138.4	138.4
13	3.65	2.51	188.7	0	0	15.86	104.1	1.000	1.000	1.000	104.1	104.1	104.1
14	5.90	0.96	116.7	0	0	5.63	91.5	1.000	1.000	1.000	91.5	91.5	91.5

$\sum = 1144.4$

$\sum = 1809.0 \qquad 1857.1 \qquad 1859.2$

$$F = \frac{1809.0}{1144.4} \qquad \frac{1857.1}{1144.4} \qquad \frac{1859.2}{1144.4}$$

$$= 1.58 \qquad\qquad 1.62 \qquad\qquad 1.62$$

If the embankment is to be founded on a clay deposit, then overall stability against failure on a more deep-seated slip surface passing through the foundation soil must always be checked. This is illustrated in the following example.

Example 7.5 Figure 7.15 shows the details of a proposed embankment which is to be built to a height of 12 m on a 16-m thick deposit of clay overlying bedrock. The water table is at a depth of 1 m below ground level. The embankment is to be composed of a compacted granular fill and will be built rapidly. Assuming no dissipation of excess porewater pressure in the clay foundation soil by the end of construction, calculate the immediate factor of safety for the potential slip surface indicated. The properties of the compacted granular fill are $\rho = 1.80$ Mg/m³, $\phi' = 37°$ and $\bar{B} = 0$, and for the clay foundation soil are $\rho_s = 2.0$ Mg/m³, $c' = 20$ kN/m², $\phi' = 24°$ and $\bar{B} = 0.8$.

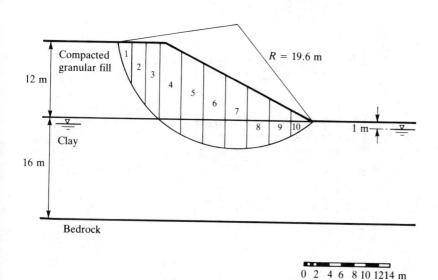

Figure 7.15 Example 7.5.

ANALYSIS The potential failure mass is divided into a number of vertical slices, as shown in Fig. 7.15. The important point here is to have a vertical section at the point where the slip surface passes from the fill into the foundation soil. The base of the soil element immediately to the left is then wholly in the fill, and the base of the soil element immediately to the right is wholly in the foundation soil. Along the bases of slices 1 to 3 we then have $\phi' = 37°$ and along the bases of slices 4 to 10 we have $c' = 20$ kN/m², $\phi' = 24°$. The porewater pressure at the base of slices 1 to 3 will be zero (as indeed it will be at all points in the granular fill). Assuming no dissipation of excess porewater pressure in the clay foundation soil by the end of construction, the porewater pressure u at the base of slices 4 to 10 is given by

$$u = u_o + \bar{B}\,\Delta\sigma_v \qquad (7.46 \text{ bis})$$

wherein u_o is the *in situ* hydrostatic pressure and $\bar{B}\,\Delta\sigma_v$ is the excess pore pressure set up due to the placement of fill. If for a particular slice h_{s1} denotes the mean height of fill and h_{s2} the mean height of foundation soil, then with the water table at a depth of 1 m below ground level we obtain

$$u = 1 \times 9.81(h_{s2} - 1) + 0.8 \times 1.80 \times 9.81 \times h_{s1}$$

$$= 9.81(h_{s2} - 1) + 14.13h_{s1} \text{ kN/m}^2$$

Table 7.7

Slice No.	Δb (m)	h_{s1} (m)	h_{s2} (m)	ΔW (kN/m)	α (°)	$\Delta W \sin \alpha$ (kN/m)	u (kN/m²)	$(\Delta W - u\,\Delta b)\tan\phi' + c'\,\Delta b$ (kN/m)	$\dfrac{\sec\alpha}{1+\frac{1}{F}\tan\alpha\tan\phi'}$ $F=1$	$F=1.45$	$F=1.52$	$\left[(\Delta W - u\,\Delta b)\tan\phi' + c'\,\Delta b\right] \times \dfrac{\sec\alpha}{1+\frac{1}{F}\tan\alpha\tan\phi'}$ (kN/m) $F=1$	$F=1.45$	$F=1.52$
1	2.27	4.10	0	164.3	68.3	152.7	0	123.8	0.935	1.173	1.204	115.8	145.2	149.1
2	2.27	8.32	0	333.5	54.6	271.8	0	251.3	0.838	0.997	1.017	210.6	250.5	255.6
3	2.27	11.00	0	440.9	43.9	305.7	0	332.2	0.804	0.925	0.940	267.1	307.3	312.3
4	3.54	11.60	1.40	822.3	32.7	444.2	167.8	172.4	0.924	0.993	1.000	159.3	171.2	172.4
5	3.54	9.84	3.10	830.4	21.4	303.0	159.6	189.0	0.914	0.959	0.963	172.7	181.3	182.0
6	3.54	8.00	4.10	784.8	10.3	140.3	143.5	194.0	0.940	0.963	0.965	182.4	186.8	187.2
7	3.54	6.30	4.42	700.8	0	0	122.6	189.6	1.000	1.000	1.000	189.6	189.6	189.6
8	3.54	4.40	4.20	566.8	−10.3	−101.3	93.6	175.6	1.106	1.076	1.074	194.2	188.9	188.6
9	3.54	2.70	3.16	388.3	−21.4	−141.7	59.3	150.2	1.301	1.221	1.213	195.4	183.4	182.2
10	3.54	1.00	1.30	152.8	−32.7	−82.5	17.1	111.9	1.664	1.480	1.464	186.2	165.6	163.8

$$\sum = 1292.2$$

$$\sum = 1873.3 \qquad 1969.8 \qquad 1982.8$$

$$F = \frac{1873.3}{1292.2} \qquad \frac{1969.8}{1292.2} \qquad \frac{1982.8}{1292.2}$$

$$= 1.45 \qquad 1.52 \qquad 1.53$$

Table 7.8

Slice No.	Δb (m)	h_{s1} (m)	h_{s2} (m)	ΔW (kN/m)	α (°)	$\Delta W \tan \alpha$ (kN/m)	u (kN/m²)	$(\Delta W - u\,\Delta b) \times \tan \phi' + c'\,\Delta b$ (kN/m)	$\dfrac{\sec^2 \alpha}{1 + \frac{1}{F}\tan\alpha\tan\phi'}$ $F=1$	$F=1.24$	$F=1.30$	$\dfrac{[(\Delta W - u\,\Delta b)\tan\phi' + c'\,\Delta b]\times \sec^2\alpha}{1 + \frac{1}{F}\tan\alpha\tan\phi'}$ (kN/m) $F=1$	$F=1.24$	$F=1.30$
1	2.27	4.10	0	164.3	68.3	412.9	0	123.8	2.528	2.894	2.978	313.0	358.3	368.7
2	2.27	8.32	0	333.5	54.6	469.3	0	251.3	1.446	1.606	1.641	363.4	403.6	412.4
3	2.27	11.00	0	440.9	43.9	424.3	0	332.2	1.116	1.215	1.236	370.7	403.6	410.6
4	3.54	11.60	1.40	822.3	32.7	527.9	167.8	172.4	1.098	1.148	1.158	189.3	197.9	199.6
5	3.54	9.84	3.10	830.4	21.4	325.4	159.6	189.0	0.982	1.011	1.017	185.6	191.1	192.2
6	3.54	8.00	4.10	784.8	10.3	142.6	143.5	194.0	0.956	0.970	0.972	185.5	188.2	188.6
7	3.54	6.30	4.42	700.8	0	0	122.6	189.6	1.000	1.000	1.000	189.6	189.6	189.6
8	3.54	4.40	4.20	566.8	-10.3	-103.0	93.6	175.6	1.124	1.105	1.102	197.4	194.0	193.5
9	3.54	2.70	3.16	388.3	-21.4	-152.2	59.3	150.2	1.397	1.342	1.332	209.8	201.6	200.1
10	3.54	1.00	1.30	152.8	-32.7	-98.1	17.1	111.9	1.977	1.835	1.810	221.2	205.3	202.5

$\sum = 1949.1$

$\sum = 2425.5 \qquad 2533.2 \qquad 2557.8$

$$F = \frac{2425.5}{1949.1} \qquad \frac{2533.2}{1949.1} \qquad \frac{2557.8}{1949.1}$$

$$= 1.24 \qquad 1.30 \qquad 1.31$$

Using Bishop's equation [i.e., Eq. (7.39)], we then obtain the results given in Table 7.7 from which we find $F = 1.53$.

Using Eq. (7.38) we obtain the results given in Table 7.8, where we now find $F = 1.31$.

We see again then the difference in predicted value for F between Eqs (7.39) and (7.38). This difference is greatest in the case of deep-seated slip surfaces, as herein.

Generally the factor of safety for the design of cuttings and embankments should not be less than 1.3, and for earth dams not less than 1.5. The slip surface analysed is in fact the most critical one and therefore by both analyses the proposed construction is satisfactory. If, however, the short-term undrained factor of safety had been less than 1.3 then, without altering the design of the embankment or the rate of construction, it would be necessary to install vertical sand drains in the clay foundation soil to accelerate the rate of consolidation. To determine the required average degree of consolidation $\bar{U}$, we proceed by calculating the fully drained factor of safety F_d corresponding to $\bar{U} = 1$. For a specified F at the end of construction, we then read off from the linear F vs $\bar{U}$ line the required value of $\bar{U}$. The problem is then one of designing a vertical sand drain system to give this average degree of consolidation (see earlier worked examples in Chapter 4).

7.5 STABILITY OF EARTH DAMS

Figure 7.16 shows the changes in shear stress, porewater pressure and factor of safety within an earth dam arising during construction and subsequent operation of the reservoir.

During construction the shear stress and porewater pressure at some particular point P on a potential slip surface increase under the weight of superimposed fill (parts b and c of Fig. 7.16). When construction is complete, the porewater pressures begin to decrease initially but then increase again as the reservoir is impounded. The restraining influence of water pressure on the upstream face of the dam causes a reduction in shear stress within the upstream slope. This increases again on rapid drawdown of the reservoir.

We see then from Fig. 7.16d that the critical times for the upstream slope are at the end of construction and during rapid drawdown, whereas the critical times for the downstream slope are at the end of construction and steady seepage under full reservoir.

Where the dam is founded on a clay deposit it will also be necessary to consider overall stability against failure on a deep-seated slip surface passing through the foundation soil, as discussed earlier. In this section, attention will be limited to the fill and the essential steps involved in the design are illustrated in the following example.

Example 7.6 Assess the proposed design for the rolled clay fill dam shown in Fig. 7.17, given that the properties of the clay fill are $\rho = 2.32 \text{ Mg/m}^3$, $c' = 17 \text{ kN/m}^2$, $\phi' = 37.5°$ and $\bar{B} = 0.4$.

ANALYSIS
1. *Stability of upstream and downstream slopes at end of construction*
A potential slip circle is as shown in Fig. 7.18. Assuming no dissipation of porewater pressure by the end of construction, we may use Bishop's equation in the form of Eq. (7.48). We then obtain the results given in Table 7.9 from which we find $F = 1.55$.

Further analyses give $F \geqslant 1.55$ and hence we may conclude that the slip circle shown is, for all practical purposes, the most critical one. Therefore, based on Bishop's equation, the factor of safety of the upstream slope at the end of construction is 1.55. This is also the factor of safety for the downstream slope since the two gradients are to be the same. On this analysis the immediate stability of the dam is satisfactory.

The immediate stability is also found to be satisfactory using Eq. (7.38) where for the most critical slip circle we obtain $F = 1.47$.

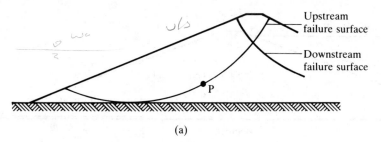

(a)

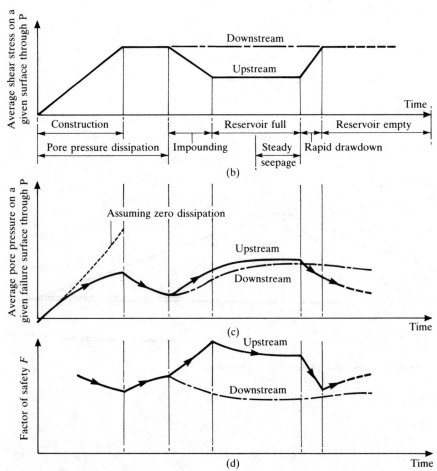

Figure 7.16 Changes in shear stress, pore pressure and factor of safety during and after construction of an earth dam. (From Lambe and Whitman, 1979; after Bishop and Bjerrum, 1960.)

2. Stability of downstream slope under full reservoir

The steady state seepage flow net is as shown in Fig. 7.19. For the potential slip circle indicated, an effective stress analysis using Bishop's equation gives the results in Table 7.10 from which we find $F = 2.72$.

Further analyses for deeper slip surfaces give $F > 2.72$, whereas for the second potential slip circle shown $F = 2.60$. For all practical purposes this is the most critical one.

Clearly then, the stability of the downstream slope under steady seepage is perfectly satisfactory.

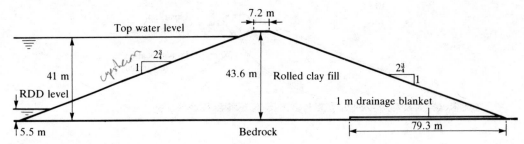

Figure 7.17 Example 7.6. (Adapted from Bishop, 1955.)

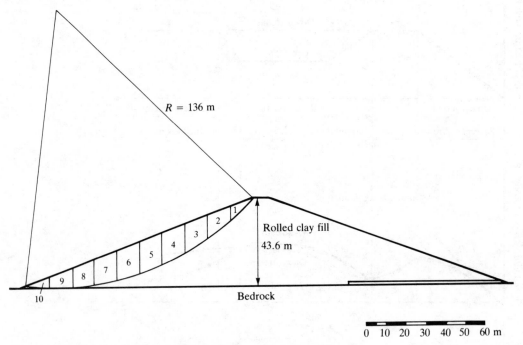

Figure 7.18 Example 7.6. Stability of upstream slope at end of construction.

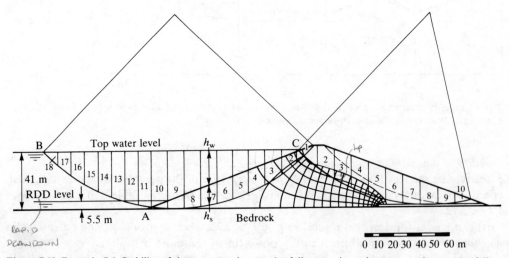

Figure 7.19 Example 7.6. Stability of downstream slope under full reservoir, and upstream slope under full reservoir and rapid drawdown.

Table 7.9

Slice No.	Δb (m)	h_s (m)	α (°)	ΔW (kN/m)	$\Delta W \sin \alpha$ (kN/m)	$\Delta W(1-\bar{B})\tan\phi' + c'\,\Delta b$ (kN/m)	$\dfrac{\sec \alpha}{1 + \frac{1}{F}\tan\alpha\tan\phi'}$			$\dfrac{[\Delta W(1-\bar{B})\tan\phi' + c'\,\Delta b]\times \sec\alpha}{1 + \frac{1}{F}\tan\alpha\tan\phi'}$ (kN/m)		
							$F=1$	$F=1.45$	$F=1.54$	$F=1$	$F=1.45$	$F=1.54$
1	11.65	4.0	43.0	1060.6	723.3	686.3	0.797	0.916	0.934	547.0	628.7	641.0
2	11.65	9.5	36.8	2518.3	1508.9	1357.7	0.793	0.895	0.910	1076.7	1215.1	1235.5
3	11.65	13.0	30.9	3446.9	1770.1	1785.0	0.799	0.885	0.898	1426.2	1579.7	1602.9
4	11.65	15.0	25.4	3977.2	1706.0	2029.1	0.811	0.885	0.895	1645.6	1795.8	1816.0
5	11.65	15.75	20.1	4176.0	1435.1	2120.7	0.831	0.892	0.901	1762.3	1891.7	1910.8
6	11.65	15.4	14.9	4083.2	1049.9	2077.9	0.859	0.907	0.914	1784.9	1884.7	1899.2
7	11.65	13.75	10.0	3645.7	633.1	1876.5	0.894	0.929	0.933	1677.6	1743.3	1750.8
8	11.65	11.0	5.1	2916.6	259.3	1540.8	0.940	0.959	0.961	1448.4	1477.6	1480.7
9	11.65	7.5	0.3	1988.6	10.4	113.6	0.996	0.997	0.997	1109.1	1110.3	1110.3
10	11.65	3.0	-4.7	795.4	-65.2	564.2	1.071	1.049	1.046	604.3	591.8	590.2

(handwritten note over α / ΔW columns: "inclination of slip plane at base of each slice")

$\sum = 9030.9$

$\sum = 13082.1 \qquad 13918.7 \qquad 14037.4$

$$F = \frac{13082.1}{9030.9} \qquad \frac{13918.7}{9030.9} \qquad \frac{14037.4}{9030.9}$$

$$= 1.45 \qquad 1.54 \qquad 1.55$$

241

Table 7.10

Slice No.	Δb (m)	h_s (m)	ΔW (kN/m)	α (°)	$\Delta W \sin \alpha$ (kN/m)	h_p (m)	$u = \rho_w g h_p$ (kN/m²)	$(\Delta W - u\,\Delta b)\tan\phi' + c'\,\Delta b$ (kN/m)	$\dfrac{\sec\alpha}{1 + \frac{1}{F}\tan\alpha\tan\phi'}$			$\left[(\Delta W - u\,\Delta b)\tan\phi' + c'\,\Delta b\right] \times \dfrac{\sec\alpha}{1 + \frac{1}{F}\tan\alpha\tan\phi'}$ (kN/m)		
									$F = 1$	$F = 2.42$	$F = 2.69$	$F = 1$	$F = 2.42$	$F = 2.69$
1	12.35	9.0	2529.7	40.6	1646.3	0	0	2151.1	0.795	1.036	1.058	1710.1	2228.5	2275.9
2	12.35	18.5	5199.9	34.1	2915.3	3.0	29.43	3921.1	0.795	0.994	1.012	3117.3	3897.6	3968.2
3	12.35	21.25	5972.9	27.9	2794.9	5.5	53.96	4281.8	0.805	0.969	0.983	3446.8	4149.1	4209.0
4	12.35	22.5	6324.2	22.2	2389.5	5.5	53.96	4551.3	0.823	0.956	0.967	3745.7	4351.0	4401.1
5	12.35	22.25	6253.9	16.6	1786.7	1.8	17.66	4841.4	0.849	0.953	0.962	4110.3	4613.9	4657.4
6	12.35	20.75	5832.3	11.2	1132.8	0	0	4685.2	0.885	0.959	0.965	4146.4	4493.1	4521.2
7	12.35	18.5	5199.9	6.0	543.5	0	0	4200.0	0.930	0.973	0.976	3906.0	4086.6	4099.2
8	12.35	14.75	4145.9	0.8	57.9	0	0	3391.2	0.989	0.996	0.996	3353.9	3377.6	3377.6
9	12.35	9.75	2740.5	−4.5	−215.0	0	0	2312.8	1.068	1.029	1.026	2470.1	2379.9	2372.9
10	12.35	3.75	1054.0	−9.6	−175.8	0	0	1018.7	1.165	1.072	1.066	1186.8	1092.0	1085.9
					$\sum = 12876.1$							$\sum = 31193.4$	34669.3	34968.4

$$F = \frac{31193.4}{12876.1} \qquad \frac{34669.3}{12876.1} \qquad \frac{34968.4}{12876.1}$$

$$= 2.42 \qquad\qquad 2.69 \qquad\qquad 2.72$$

Table 7.11

Slice No.	Δb (m)	h_w (m)	h_s (m)	ΔW (kN/m)	α (°)	$\Delta W \sin\alpha$ (kN/m)	h_p (m)	u (kN/m²)	$(\Delta W - u\,\Delta b)\times\tan\phi' + c'\,\Delta b$ (kN/m)	$\dfrac{\sec\alpha}{1+\frac{1}{F}\tan\alpha\tan\phi'}$ $F=1$	$F=2.73$	$F=3.14$	$[(\Delta W - u\,\Delta b)\tan\phi' + c'\,\Delta b]\dfrac{\sec\alpha}{1+\frac{1}{F}\tan\alpha\tan\phi'}$ (kN/m) $F=1$	$F=2.73$	$F=3.14$
1	11.65	0	4.0	1060.6	43.0	723.3	1.25	12.26	902.3	0.797	1.083	1.114	719.1	977.2	1005.2
2	11.65	3.0	9.5	2861.7	36.8	1714.2	9.0	88.29	1604.7	0.793	1.032	1.056	1272.5	1656.1	1694.6
3	11.65	7.25	13.0	4275.5	30.9	2195.6	17.0	166.77	1987.9	0.799	0.998	1.017	1588.3	1983.9	2021.7
4	11.65	11.75	15.0	5320.0	25.4	2281.9	25.0	245.25	2087.9	0.811	0.977	0.992	1693.3	2039.9	2071.2
5	11.65	16.0	15.75	6004.6	20.1	2063.5	30.2	296.26	2157.2	0.831	0.966	0.977	1792.6	2083.9	2107.6
6	11.65	20.3	15.4	6403.2	14.9	1646.5	34.3	336.48	2103.5	0.859	0.963	0.972	1806.9	2025.7	2044.6
7	11.65	24.75	13.75	6474.3	10.0	1124.3	37.25	365.42	1899.3	0.894	0.967	0.973	1698.0	1836.6	1848.0
8	11.65	28.75	11.0	6202.3	5.1	551.3	39.2	384.55	1519.6	0.940	0.979	0.983	1428.4	1487.7	1493.8
9	11.65	33.5	7.5	5817.2	0.3	30.5	40.6	398.29	1101.3	0.996	0.999	0.999	1096.9	1100.2	1100.2
10	11.65	37.5	3.0	5081.2	-4.7	-416.3	39.7	389.46	615.5	1.071	1.027	1.024	659.2	632.1	630.3
11	10.0	38.5	0	3776.9	-9.5	-623.4			0				0	0	0
12	10.0	36.5	0	3580.7	-13.8	-854.1			0				0	0	0
13	10.0	33.5	0	3286.4	-18.1	-1021.0			0				0	0	0
14	10.0	30.0	0	2943.0	-22.8	-1140.5			0				0	0	0
15	10.0	25.5	0	2501.6	-27.2	-1143.5			0				0	0	0
16	10.0	19.75	0	1937.5	-32.0	-1026.7			0				0	0	0
17	10.0	13.0	0	1275.3	-37.1	-769.3			0				0	0	0
18	10.0	4.5	0	441.5	-42.6	-298.8			0				0	0	0
						$\sum = 5037.5$							$\sum = 13755.2$	$\sum = 15823.3$	$\sum = 16017.2$

$$F = \frac{13755.2}{5037.5} = 2.73 \qquad F = \frac{15823.3}{5037.5} = 3.14 \qquad F = \frac{16017.2}{5037.5} = 3.18$$

Table 7.12

Slice No.	Δb (m)	h_w (m)	h_s (m)	ΔW (kN/m)	α (°)	$\Delta W \sin\alpha$ (kN/m)	u_o (as Col. 9, Table 7.11) (kN/m²)	Δh_w (m)	$\Delta u = \rho_w g\,\Delta h_w$ (kN/m²)	$u = u_o + \Delta u$ (kN/m²)	$(\Delta W - u\,\Delta b)\tan\phi' + c'\,\Delta b \times$ (kN/m)	$\dfrac{\sec\alpha}{1+\frac{1}{F}\tan\alpha\tan\phi'}$ $F=1$	$F=1.54$	$F=1.66$	$[(\Delta W - u\,\Delta b)\tan\phi' + c'\,\Delta b]\times\dfrac{\sec\alpha}{1+\frac{1}{F}\tan\alpha\tan\phi'}$ (kN/m) $F=1$	$F=1.54$	$F=1.66$
1	11.65	0	4.0	1060.6	43.0	723.3	12.3	0	0	12.3	901.9	0.797	0.934	0.955	718.8	842.4	861.3
2	11.65	0	9.5	2518.9	36.8	1508.9	88.3	−3.0	−29.4	58.9	1604.3	0.793	0.910	0.928	1272.2	1459.9	1488.8
3	11.65	0	13.0	3446.9	30.9	1770.1	166.8	−7.25	−71.1	95.7	1987.5	0.799	0.898	0.913	1588.0	1784.8	1814.6
4	11.65	0	15.0	3977.2	25.4	1706.0	245.3	−11.75	−115.3	130.0	2087.7	0.811	0.895	0.908	1693.1	1868.5	1895.6
5	11.65	0	15.75	4176.0	20.1	1435.1	296.3	−16.0	−157.0	139.3	2157.2	0.831	0.901	0.911	1792.6	1943.6	1965.2
6	11.65	0	15.4	4083.2	14.9	1049.9	336.5	−20.3	−199.1	137.4	2102.9	0.859	0.914	0.921	1806.4	1922.1	1936.8
7	11.65	0	13.75	3645.7	10.0	633.1	365.4	−24.75	−242.8	122.6	1899.5	0.894	0.933	0.939	1698.2	1772.2	1783.6
8	11.65	0	11.0	2916.6	5.1	259.3	384.6	−28.75	−282.0	102.6	1518.9	0.940	0.961	0.964	1427.8	1459.7	1464.2
9	11.65	0	7.5	1988.6	0.3	10.4	398.3	−33.5	−328.6	69.7	1100.9	0.996	0.997	0.998	1096.5	1097.6	1098.7
10	11.65	2.3	3.0	1058.3	−4.7	−86.7	389.5	−35.2	−345.3	44.2	615.0	1.071	1.046	1.043	658.7	643.3	641.4
11	10.0	3.5	0	343.4	−9.5	−56.7					0				0	0	0
12	10.0	1.75	0	171.7	−13.8	−41.0					0				0	0	0

$$\Sigma = 8911.7$$

$$\Sigma = 13752.3 \qquad 14794.1 \qquad 14950.2$$

$$F = \frac{13752.3}{8911.7} \qquad \frac{14794.1}{8911.7} \qquad \frac{14950.2}{8911.7}$$

$$= 1.54 \qquad 1.66 \qquad 1.68$$

3. Stability of upstream slope under full reservoir

Although stability of the upstream slope under full reservoir will not be critical, it is nevertheless informative to consider this case, as we may then compare the factor of safety with the more critical value that obtains on rapid drawdown.

For the potential slip surface shown in Fig. 7.19, the failure mass includes the area ABC which is within the water. Therefore the weight of water above line AC must be included in the weight of slices 2 to 10 inclusive. Slices 11 to 18 have a $\Delta W \sin \alpha$ component which acts in an anti-clockwise sense (i.e., negative α values) to give appreciable aid to the stability. However, there is no shearing resistance along the base of these slices. Thus, for an effective stress analysis using Bishop's equation we obtain the results given in Table 7.11 where we now find $F = 3.18$. The slip circle analysed is in fact the most critical one and therefore the factor of safety of the upstream slope under full reservoir is 3.18.

4. Stability of upstream slope under rapid drawdown (RDD)

For an effective stress stability analysis of the upstream slope under conditions of rapid drawdown, we require to calculate the resulting distribution of porewater pressure around the potential slip surface. With reference then to Fig. 7.19, the change in porewater pressure at any point consequent on a change in total stress is given by

$$\Delta u = \bar{B} \, \Delta \sigma_\text{v} \qquad\qquad (7.45 \text{ bis})$$

It is conservative here to take $\bar{B} = 1$, as the fill material will tend to become saturated under prolonged steady seepage. Also in the present problem the change in total vertical stress $\Delta \sigma_\text{v}$ at any point results solely from the change in vertical height of water Δh_w above the point. Thus, $\Delta \sigma_\text{v} = \rho_\text{w} g \, \Delta h_\text{w}$ and therefore we obtain

$$\Delta u = \rho_\text{w} g \, \Delta h_\text{w}$$

If u_o denotes the initial porewater pressure at any point under full reservoir, then the porewater pressure u at any point after rapid drawdown is given by

$$u = u_\text{o} + \Delta u$$

Thus
$$u = u_\text{o} + \rho_\text{w} g \, \Delta h_\text{w}$$

As the slip surface to be analysed is the same as that analysed above under conditions of full reservoir, then the values of u_o herein are the same as those evaluated earlier and as given in column 9, Table 7.11. Thus, for the potential slip circle shown in Fig. 7.19 we obtain the results given in Table 7.12 from which we find $F = 1.68$.

Using Eq. (7.38) we obtain $F = 1.60$. Therefore, by both analyses the stability of the upstream slope on rapid drawdown is quite satisfactory.

The assumption that $\bar{B} = 1$ implies that there is no immediate change in effective stress at any point on rapid drawdown since Eq. (7.45) then gives $\Delta u = \Delta \sigma_\text{v}$. Thus, there is no change in the shear resistance of the soil along a potential slip surface. The shear stresses, however, are approximately doubled on rapid drawdown because of the removal of the restraining water pressures on the upstream face. Hence there is a marked reduction in the factor of safety.

From the foregoing analyses we may conclude that the proposed earth dam design is satisfactory.

PROBLEMS

7.1 Figure P7.1 shows a natural slope inclined at an angle of 14° and composed of weathered clay. A bed of shale runs parallel to the surface at a depth of 4 m. As part of a road construction scheme, it is proposed to excavate over AB and place fill over BC. Assess the feasibility of this proposal given that the properties of the weathered clay are $\rho_\text{s} = 2.0 \text{ Mg/m}^3$, $c' = 8 \text{ kN/m}^2$ and $\phi' = 20°$.

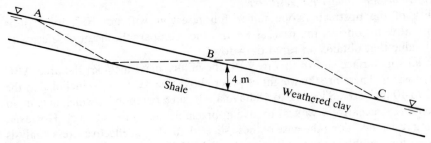

Fig. P7.1

Ans.   The natural slope is close to limiting equilibrium ($F = 1.16$) and therefore it would be prudent not to proceed with the proposed scheme

7.2 Figure P7.2 shows the details of Chingford reservoir which failed during construction when the embankment had reached a height of 7.92 m, approximately 2.5 m short of the proposed height. Calculate the factor of safety for the slip surface indicated given that the properties of the various soils are:

Clay fill: $\rho = 1.84$ Mg/m^3, $c_u = 21$ kN/m^2
Select fill: $\rho = 1.60$ Mg/m^3, $c_u = 21$ kN/m^2
Puddle clay: $\rho = 1.76$ Mg/m^3, $c_u = 10$ kN/m^2
Yellow clay: $\rho = 1.52$ Mg/m^3, $c_u = 12$ kN/m^2
[Ans.   1.00 (using Eq. (7.40)),   1.09 (using Eq. (7.41))]

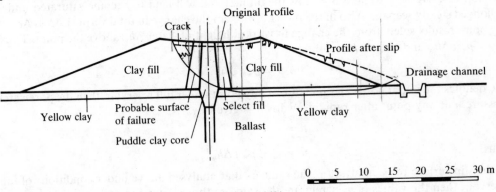

Figure P7.2 Chingford dam. (From Cooling and Golder, 1942.)

7.3 Figure P7.3 shows the expected distribution of pressure head around a potential slip surface in a clay fill embankment if it is built rapidly to its proposed height of 20 m. For these conditions show that the stability of the embankment is questionable given that the properties of the clay fill are $\rho = 2.10$ Mg/m^3, $c' = 25$ kN/m^2 and $\phi' = 32°$. What measures might be incorporated in the design to ensure that the short-term stability does not become critical?
[Ans. $F = 1.04$ (using Eq. (7.38)), $F = 1.14$ (using Eq. (7.39))]

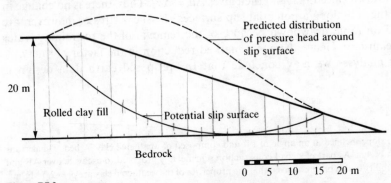

Figure P7.3

7.4 Figure P7.4 shows the downstream slope of a rolled clay fill earth dam subject to steady seepage flow, the position of the top flow line being as indicated. Calculate the factor of safety for the potential slip surface shown given that the properties of the clay fill are $\rho = 2.0$ Mg/m^3, $c' = 15$ kN/m^2 and $\phi' = 32°$.
[Ans. $F = 1.63$ (using Eq. (7.38)), $F = 1.79$ (using Eq. (7.39))]

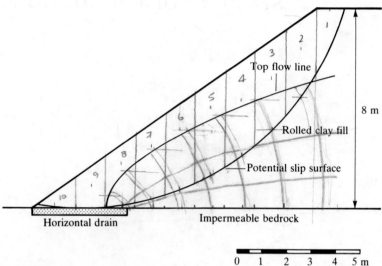

Figure P7.4

STABILITY OF FOUNDATIONS

8.1 INTRODUCTION

All civil engineering structures impose a loading on the underlying soil or rock. That part of the structure, usually lying below ground level, which transmits the load to the supporting strata is referred to as the *foundation*. In the case of earth or rockfill structures the interface between the structure and the foundation may not be clearly defined. However, with structures built of steel, brick or concrete, the foundation is usually a readily identifiable component and will generally be one of the following common types.

A *pad footing* or *individual column footing* (Fig. 8.1a), which may be constructed of plain or reinforced concrete, can be used, for example, to support the load from a single column. Pad footings may be square, rectangular or circular in shape.

A *strip footing* or *continuous footing* (Fig. 8.1b) is usually constructed of reinforced concrete and can be used, for example, to support a load-bearing wall or a row of columns. A strip footing generally has a length many times greater than its width.

A *raft foundation* or *mat foundation* (Fig. 8.1c) is usually a large rigidly reinforced concrete slab which covers the entire area beneath the structure while supporting all the columns and walls. Raft foundations are used principally in soils of low bearing capacity or where there is a particular requirement to restrict differential settlements. To provide the necessary rigidity, the raft may be a stiffened beam-and-slab structure, or may be of cellular or rigid-frame construction.

Pile foundations. Piles are used to transmit structural loads through soil strata of low bearing capacity into suitable strata usually at some considerable depth below foundation level, and are normally slender vertical or slightly raked structural members of reinforced concrete or steel having a relatively small cross-sectional area in relation to their depth. Piles are commonly used in groups and structural loads are transmitted through a foundation slab or cap cast over the top of the piles (Fig. 8.1d).

Pier foundations. A pier foundation is a heavy underground structural member which acts as a massive strut, and thus behaves in a similar manner to a pile under compression. Although there is no clear division between the two, pier foundations are traditionally thought of as having a rather larger cross-sectional area and shorter length than piles. Concrete piers may be constructed in holes drilled using a large-diameter auger or within a temporary cofferdam.

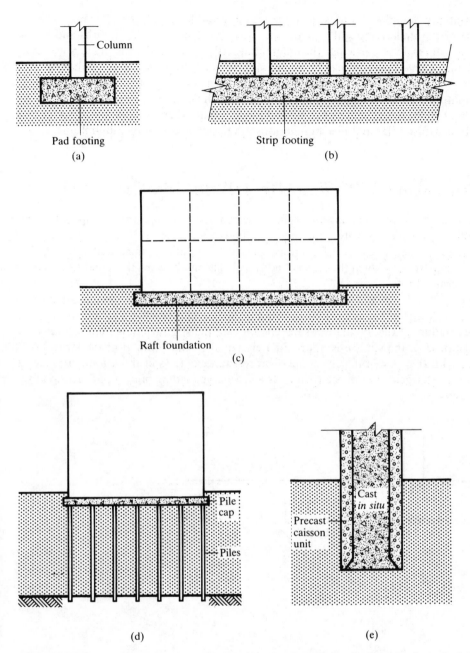

Figure 8.1 (a) Pad or individual column footing, (b) strip or continuous footing, (c) raft or mat foundation, (d) pile foundation, (e) pier foundation.

Alternatively, construction may be carried out using a *caisson* which sinks through the ground under its own weight during excavation and on reaching the required foundation level becomes an integral part of the permanent foundation (Fig. 8.1e).

The term 'pier' is also used to describe the structural component which supports the superstructure of a bridge, and in this context may be founded directly on a firm bearing stratum or may be supported on piles.

To ensure stability, foundations must provide an adequate factor of safety against shear or bearing failure of the underlying soil and the structure must be capable of withstanding the settlements that will result, in particular the differential settlements. In the vast majority of cases the choice of foundation is governed by the second of these two factors, thus in general the need to limit settlements of the structure will control the design of its foundation.

In general, footing and raft foundations are constructed at a depth below ground level which is less than or about equal to the width of the foundation, and are therefore designated as *shallow* foundations. In contrast, piles and pier foundations are designated as *deep* foundations.

8.2 BEARING CAPACITY OF SHALLOW FOUNDATIONS ON CLAY

We are concerned here with a loading problem. Excess porewater pressures set up in the clay foundation soil will dissipate slowly with time, leading to an increase in effective stress and therefore an increase in shear strength. The critical period for stability of the foundation will thus be at the end of construction when the clay is undrained. The analysis for this condition may be carried out in terms of total stress.

Consider then a strip footing of width B founded at a shallow depth D ($D \leqslant B$) in a deposit of saturated clay, as shown in Fig. 8.2a. Let q_{ult} denote the *ultimate bearing pressure* to cause an undrained shear failure of the foundation soil. The form of the slip surface is then as indicated, wherein the depth H of the surface is approximately equal to the width B of the strip. For a shallow footing with $D \leqslant B$, we can neglect the shear resistance of the soil above foundation level. The depth D of overburden can thus be treated as a surcharge loading of $q_s = \rho g D$ acting at the level of the foundation.

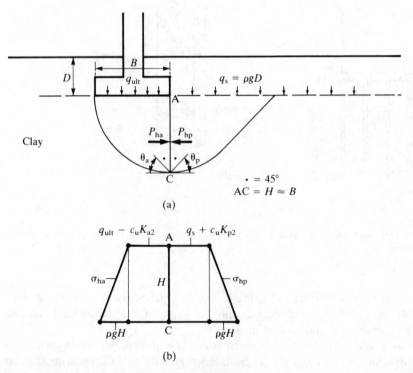

Figure 8.2 Bearing capacity of a strip footing in clay.

The failure mass involves a transition from active earth pressure under the footing through to passive earth pressure in the surrounding soil. The vertical plane AC defines the boundary between the active and passive zones. At the point C, continuity of the slip plane requires that

$$\theta_a + \theta_p = 90°$$

For this condition, an analysis of the stress conditions at the point C indicates full mobilization of shear on AC, the adhesion c_w being defined by

$$\frac{c_w}{c_u} = 1$$

for which state θ_a and θ_p are both a maximum and equal to 45°. The slip surface at the point C is thus horizontal, as shown.

For equilibrium, the horizontal component of active thrust on the plane AC (P_{ha}) equals the horizontal component of passive resistance (P_{hp}).

The distribution of passive pressure on AC is given by

$$\sigma_{hp} = \sigma_v + c_u K_{p2} \qquad (6.52 \text{ bis})$$

For a curved failure surface and assuming the vertical shear on AC to be dissipated through the mass,† the passive pressure coefficient K_{p2} is given by Eq. (6.51). With $c_w/c_u = 1$ on AC and $\theta_p = 45°$, this gives $K_{p2} = 2\sqrt{2}$.

Considering the curved failure surface on the active side of AC, a similar analysis to the determination of the passive pressure gives the active pressure distribution on AC as

$$\sigma_{ha} = \sigma_v - c_u K_{a2}$$

where for $c_w/c_u = 1$ on AC and again assuming the vertical shear on AC to be dissipated through the mass we also find $K_{a2} = 2\sqrt{2}$.

Considering then the *active* side of AC we have $\sigma_{ha} = \sigma_v - c_u K_{a2}$

At A: $\qquad\qquad \sigma_v = q_{ult}, \qquad\qquad \sigma_{ha} = q_{ult} - c_u K_{a2}$

At C: $\qquad\qquad \sigma_v = q_{ult} + \rho g H, \qquad \sigma_{ha} = q_{ult} + \rho g H - c_u K_{a2}$

For the *passive* side of AC we obtain $\sigma_{hp} = \sigma_v + c_u K_{p2}$

At A: $\qquad\qquad \sigma_v = q_s, \qquad\qquad \sigma_{hp} = q_s + c_u K_{p2}$

At C: $\qquad\qquad \sigma_v = q_s + \rho g H, \qquad \sigma_{hp} = q_s + \rho g H + c_u K_{p2}$

The distributions of σ_{ha} and σ_{hp} on AC are then as shown in Fig. 8.2b. For limiting equilibrium

$$P_{ha} = P_{hp}$$

Since the rate of increase of active and passive pressures are the same this implies that

$$q_{ult} - c_u K_{a2} = q_s + c_u K_{p2}$$

Thus

$$q_{ult} = c_u(K_{a2} + K_{p2}) + \rho g D$$

This may be written as

$$q_{ult} = c_u N_c + \rho g D \qquad (8.1)$$

where N_c is a *bearing capacity factor* defined herein by

$$N_c = K_{a2} + K_{p2} \qquad (8.2)$$

† This assumption raises the value of K_{p2} by approximately 20 per cent (see Table 6.4) and gives a more realistic estimate of the passive resistance (Sec. 6.4).

Thus, with $K_{a2} = K_{p2} = 2\sqrt{2}$ we have

$$N_c = 4\sqrt{2} = 5.66 \tag{8.3}$$

The problem of a shallow strip footing on clay has been investigated by a number of workers using different methods of analysis. These all yield the same form of bearing capacity equation as Eq. (8.1) but slightly different numerical values for N_c. For example, Prandtl (1921) obtained $N_c = 5.14$ and Terzaghi (1943) found $N_c = 5.70$. We see then that the value of $N_c = 5.66$ obtained herein is in close agreement with these values.

When the depth D of the foundation is greater than the width B, the contribution of the shear resistance of the overburden to the bearing capacity of the footing becomes more important. The bearing capacity is also enhanced if the footing is of finite length L. On the basis of model tests, field observations and theoretical considerations, Skempton (1951) proposed the following empirical equation for N_c

$$N_c = 5\left(1 + 0.2\frac{D}{B}\right)\left(1 + 0.2\frac{B}{L}\right) \quad \text{\scriptsize KNOW} \tag{8.4}$$

where

$$\frac{D}{B} \leqslant 2.5$$

The term inside the first brackets reflects the strength of the overburden and the term inside the second brackets reflects the shape of the loaded area. For a given value of B/L, N_c does not increase indefinitely with depth D but reaches a maximum value when $D/B = 2.5$. Thus, if for a particular geometry $D/B > 2.5$ we substitute $D/B = 2.5$.

Equation (8.4) gives a general expression for N_c which can be applied to all foundations in clay, whether strip, spread or raft foundations and whether they are located at ground level or at some depth D. Having obtained the value of N_c from Eq. (8.4), the ultimate bearing capacity of the foundation is determined from Eq. (8.1).

For a foundation located at depth D below ground level, it is only when the bearing pressure from the foundation exceeds the original overburden pressure $\rho g D$ that there is any nett increase in stress in the clay under the foundation and hence any possibility of a shear failure. From Eq. (8.1), the *nett ultimate bearing pressure* $q_{n(ult)}$ at which undrained bearing capacity failure occurs is given by

$$q_{n(ult)} = c_u N_c \tag{8.5}$$

If $q_{n(app)}$ denotes the *nett applied foundation pressure*, then the *factor of safety against undrained bearing capacity failure* F_{bu} is defined by

$$F_{bu} = \frac{q_{n(ult)}}{q_{n(app)}} \tag{8.6}$$

For a stable foundation, only part of the undrained shear strength of the clay foundation soil will be mobilized to maintain equilibrium. Thus, if c_{um} denotes the *mobilized* undrained shear strength, then the *factor of safety against undrained shear failure* F_{su} is given by

$$F_{su} = \frac{c_u}{c_{um}} = \frac{c_u N_c}{c_{um} N_c} = \frac{q_{n(ult)}}{q_{n(app)}} \tag{8.7}$$

We see then that the factor of safety against undrained bearing capacity failure and undrained shear failure are the same.

In practice, the factor of safety (whether with respect to undrained bearing failure or undrained shear failure) is generally specified as at least 3. This is usually sufficient to limit the settlement of the foundation to an acceptable value.

Example 8.1 A load-bearing wall is to be founded on a strip footing located 0.5 m below ground level in a deposit of saturated clay having an undrained shear strength of 70 kN/m². It is estimated that the wall load, including self-weight above ground level, will be 125 kN per metre run of the wall. Neglecting the difference in density between the soil and the footing, calculate the required width of the strip to give a factor of safety of 3 against a shear failure of the foundation clay immediately after construction.

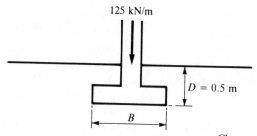

125 kN/m

$D = 0.5$ m

B

Clay   **Figure 8.3** Example 8.1.

SOLUTION The problem is illustrated in Fig. 8.3. The nett ultimate bearing pressure for the footing is given by Eq. (8.5), namely

$$q_{n(ult)} = c_u N_c$$

For a strip foundation $N_c = 5.66$ [Eq. (8.3)] and with $c_u = 70$ kN/m² we obtain

$$q_{n(ult)} = 70 \times 5.66 = 396.20 \text{ kN/m}^2$$

Neglecting the difference in density between the soil and the footing, the nett applied pressure is given by

$$q_{n(app)} = \frac{125}{B} \text{ kN/m}^2$$

From Eq. (8.7)

$$F_{su} = \frac{q_{n(ult)}}{q_{n(app)}}$$

Therefore for a factor of safety of 3 against undrained shear failure we obtain

$$3 = \frac{396.2}{\dfrac{125}{B}}$$

whence

$$B = 0.946 \text{ m}$$

Considering N_c to be given by Skempton's equation, namely Eq. (8.4), we have

$$N_c = 5\left(1 + 0.2\frac{D}{B}\right)\left(1 + 0.2\frac{B}{L}\right)$$

With $D = 0.5$ m and $L = \infty$ for a strip

$$N_c = 5\left(1 + 0.2\frac{0.5}{B}\right)$$

whence

$$q_{n(ult)} = c_u N_c = 70 \times 5\left(1 + \frac{0.1}{B}\right)$$

Therefore for a factor of safety of 3 against undrained shear failure

$$3 = \frac{70 \times 5\left(1 + \dfrac{0.1}{B}\right)}{\dfrac{125}{B}}$$

from which $\qquad\qquad B = 0.971 \text{ m}$

Example 8.2 A vertical concrete column is to carry a total load of 520 kN, inclusive of self-weight above ground level. The column is to be supported by a square concrete footing founded at a depth of 1.5 m in a 14-m thick deposit of firm boulder clay. The clay is fully saturated and overlies Bunter sandstone. Neglecting the difference in density between the concrete and the clay, calculate the size of footing required to provide a factor of safety of 3 against an undrained shear failure of the foundation soil. Calculate also the total settlement of the footing and comment on the value obtained. The properties of the clay are $c_u = 56 \text{ kN/m}^2$, $m_v = 0.00012 \text{ m}^2/\text{kN}$, $E = 10\,500 \text{ kN/m}^2$ and $A = 0.4$.

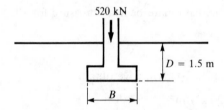

520 kN

$D = 1.5$ m

B

Firm boulder clay

Figure 8.4 Example 8.2.

SOLUTION The problem is illustrated in Fig. 8.4. The nett ultimate bearing pressure for the footing is given by

$$q_{n(ult)} = c_u N_c \quad \text{wherein} \quad N_c = 5\left(1 + 0.2\frac{D}{B}\right)\left(1 + 0.2\frac{B}{L}\right)$$

Thus $\qquad q_{n(ult)} = 56 \times 5\left(1 + 0.2\frac{1.5}{B}\right)\left(1 + 0.2 \times 1\right) = 336\left(1 + \frac{0.3}{B}\right)$

Neglecting the difference in density between the soil and the footing, the nett applied pressure is given by

$$q_{n(app)} = \frac{520}{B^2}$$

For a specified factor of safety of 3 against undrained shear failure

$$3 = \frac{336\left(1 + \dfrac{0.3}{B}\right)}{\dfrac{520}{B^2}}$$

from which $\qquad\qquad B^2 + 0.3B - 4.643 = 0$

whence $\qquad\qquad B = 2.010 \text{ m}$

The settlement analysis for this problem has been presented earlier in Example 4.4, whence we obtained $S = 27 \text{ mm}$. This should be acceptable.

8.3 BEARING CAPACITY OF SHALLOW FOUNDATIONS ON SAND

For foundations on sand, excess porewater pressures set up in the foundation soil will dissipate rapidly and the sand will be essentially fully drained by the end of construction. There will thus be no difference between the short-term and long-term stability. The stability analysis must be in terms of effective stress.

Consider then a strip footing of width B founded at a shallow depth D $(D \leqslant B)$ in a deposit of sand, as shown in Fig. 8.5a. Let q_{ult} denote the ultimate bearing pressure to cause a shear failure of the foundation soil. The form of the slip surface is then as indicated, wherein the depth H of the surface is approximately equal to the width B of the strip. Let the water table be located within the zone of influence at depth ηH below the base of the strip. The depth D of overburden is treated as a surcharge loading of $q_s = \rho g D$ acting at the level of the foundation.

The failure mass involves a transition from active earth pressure under the footing through to passive earth pressure in the surrounding soil. The vertical plane AC defines the boundary between the active and passive zones. At the point C, continuity of the slip plane requires that

$$\theta'_a + \theta'_p = 90°$$

This in turn implies full mobilization of shear on AC, the effective angle of friction δ' being defined by

$$\frac{\delta'}{\phi'} = 1$$

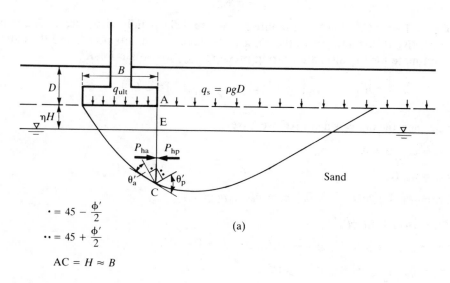

$$\bullet = 45 - \frac{\phi'}{2}$$

$$\bullet\bullet = 45 + \frac{\phi'}{2}$$

$$AC = H \approx B$$

(a)

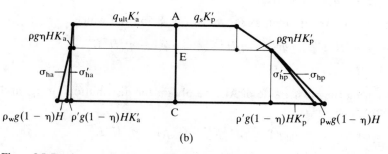

(b)

Figure 8.5 Bearing capacity of a strip footing in sand.

For this condition, θ_a' and θ_p' are both a maximum and given respectively by

$$\theta_a' = 45 - \frac{\phi'}{2} \qquad \theta_p' = 45 + \frac{\phi'}{2}$$

The slip surface at the point C thus makes an angle of ϕ' with the horizontal.

For equilibrium, the horizontal component of active thrust P_{ha} on the plane AC equals the horizontal component of passive resistance P_{hp}.

The distribution of effective passive earth pressure on AC is given by

$$\sigma_{hp}' = \sigma_v' K_p' \qquad (6.46 \text{ bis})$$

We assume that the vertical shear on AC is fully dissipated at AC (rather than through the failure mass) as this gives the minimum estimate for the passive resistance. The value of K_p' is then given by Eq. (6.45). With $\delta'/\phi' = 1$ on AC and assuming a log spiral for the shape of the failure surface, integration then gives

$$K_p' = 2 \exp\left[(\tfrac{1}{2}\pi + \phi') \tan \phi'\right] \sin^2\left(45 + \frac{\phi'}{2}\right) \qquad (8.8)$$

Considering the curved failure surface on the active side of AC, a similar analysis to the determination of the passive pressure gives the distribution of effective active earth pressure on AC as

$$\sigma_{ha}' = \sigma_v' K_a'$$

where for $\delta'/\phi' = 1$ on AC, a log spiral failure surface, and shear fully dissipated at AC (which maximizes the active thrust, minimizes the passive resistance as already noted, and thus gives a conservative estimate for the ultimate bearing pressure q_{ult}) we obtain for K_a'

$$K_a' = 2 \exp\left[(\phi' - \tfrac{1}{2}\pi) \tan \phi'\right] \sin^2\left(45 - \frac{\phi'}{2}\right) \qquad (8.9)$$

Considering then the *active* side of AC we have

At A: $\sigma_v = q_{ult}, u = 0, \sigma_v' = q_{ult}$

$\qquad \sigma_{ha}' = q_{ult} K_a'$

At E: $\sigma_v = q_{ult} + \rho g \eta H, \quad u = 0, \quad \sigma_v' = q_{ult} + \rho g \eta H,$

$\qquad \sigma_{ha}' = [q_{ult} + \rho g \eta H] K_a'$

At C: $\sigma_v = q_{ult} + \rho g \eta H + \rho_s g (1 - \eta) H, \quad u = \rho_w g (1 - \eta) H$

$\qquad \sigma_v' = q_{ult} + \rho g \eta H + \rho' g (1 - \eta) H,$

$\qquad \sigma_{ha}' = [q_{ult} + \rho g \eta H + \rho' g (1 - \eta) H] K_a'$

The distribution of σ_{ha}' and σ_{ha} on AC are then as shown in Fig. 8.5b from which

$$P_{ha}' = q_{ult} H K_a' + \tfrac{1}{2}\rho g \eta^2 H^2 K_a' + \rho g \eta (1 - \eta) H^2 K_a' + \tfrac{1}{2}\rho' g (1 - \eta)^2 H^2 K_a' \qquad (8.10)$$

and $P_{hw} = \tfrac{1}{2}\rho_w g (1 - \eta)^2 H^2$

In a similar manner, considering the *passive* side of AC, we obtain the distribution for σ_{hp}' and σ_{hp} shown in Fig. 8.5b from which

$$P_{hp}' = q_s H K_p' + \tfrac{1}{2}\rho g \eta^2 H^2 K_p' + \rho g \eta (1 - \eta) H^2 K_p' + \tfrac{1}{2}\rho' g (1 - \eta)^2 H^2 K_p' \qquad (8.11)$$

and $P_{hw} = \tfrac{1}{2}\rho_w g (1 - \eta)^2 H^2$

For limiting equilibrium

$$P_{ha} = P_{hp}$$

As the water thrusts P_{hw} on the active and passive sides of AC are equal then

$$P'_{ha} = P'_{hp}$$

Thus, equating Eqs (8.10) and (8.11) and taking the depth H of the slip surface to be equal to the width B of the footing, we obtain

$$q_{ult} = q_s \frac{K'_p}{K'_a} + \frac{1}{2} \rho g B \left[1 - (1 - \eta)^2 \left(1 - \frac{\rho'}{\rho} \right) \right] \left[\frac{K'_p}{K'_a} - 1 \right] \tag{8.12}$$

where

$$0 \leqslant \eta \leqslant 1$$

Equation (8.12) may be written in the form

$$q_{ult} = \rho g D N_q + \frac{1}{2} \rho g B \left[1 - (1 - \eta)^2 \left(1 - \frac{\rho'}{\rho} \right) \right] N_\gamma \tag{8.13}$$

where $\rho g D = q_s$ and N_q and N_γ are *bearing capacity factors* defined herein by

$$N_q = \frac{K'_p}{K'_a} \tag{8.14}$$

and

$$N_\gamma = \frac{K'_p}{K'_a} - 1 = N_q - 1 \tag{8.15}$$

Thus, with K'_p and K'_a defined by Eqs (8.8) and (8.9) we obtain

$$N_q = \frac{2 \exp\left[(\frac{1}{2}\pi + \phi') \tan \phi' \right] \sin^2 \left(45 + \frac{\phi'}{2} \right)}{2 \exp\left[(\phi' - \frac{1}{2}\pi) \tan \phi' \right] \sin^2 \left(45 - \frac{\phi'}{2} \right)} = \exp\left[\pi \tan \phi' \right] \tan^2 \left(45 + \frac{\phi'}{2} \right) \tag{8.16}$$

and

$$N_\gamma = N_q - 1 = \exp\left[\pi \tan \phi' \right] \tan^2 \left(45 + \frac{\phi'}{2} \right) - 1 \tag{8.17}$$

The relationship between N_γ and ϕ' is shown in Figs 8.6 and 8.8.

The problem of a shallow strip footing on sand was first investigated by Terzaghi and later by Meyerhof and others. The same form of bearing capacity equation as Eq. (8.13) is obtained but with different expressions for N_q and N_γ. A comparison of the bearing capacity factors is given in Table 8.1 and, in general, these correlate reasonably well. The apparent large discrepancies for a very dense sand with $\phi' = 40°$ are in fact relatively unimportant since as a result of progressive failure the greater values predicted by Terzaghi and others are unlikely to be achieved in practice.

Table 8.1 Values of bearing capacity factors N_q and N_γ

ϕ' (°)	N_q Eq. (8.16)	N_γ Eq. (8.17)	N_q (after Terzaghi, 1943)	N_γ
25	10.7	9.7	12.7	9.7
30	18.4	17.4	22.5	19.7
35	33.3	32.3	41.4	42.4
40	64.2	63.2	81.3	130

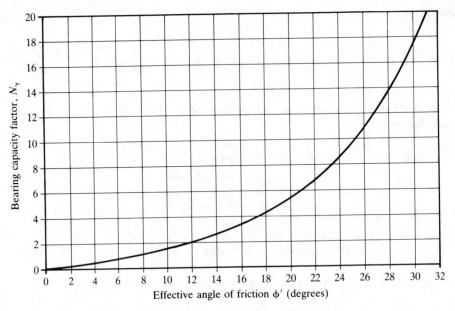

Figure 8.6 Relationship between bearing capacity factor N_γ and effective angle of friction ϕ' for a shallow foundation. (Eq. 8.17.)

Noting from Eq. (8.15) that $N_q = N_\gamma + 1$, Eq. (8.13) may be written as

$$q_{ult} = \left\{ \rho g D + \frac{1}{2} \rho g B \left[1 - (1-\eta)^2 \left(1 - \frac{\rho'}{\rho} \right) \right] \right\} N_\gamma + \rho g D \qquad (8.18)$$

For $\eta = 0$ with the water table at the underside of the footing, the expression inside the braces { } in Eq. (8.18) becomes $\rho g D + \frac{1}{2} \rho' g B$ which is the initial effective overburden pressure at a depth of $D + \frac{1}{2}B$, denoted herein by $\sigma'_{vo[D+(1/2)B]}$. This is also the result when $\eta = 1$ with the water table at a depth B (or greater) below the footing. For intermediate values of η the term inside the braces is approximately equal to $\sigma'_{vo[D+(1/2)B]}$, the maximum error being of the order of 7 per cent. Thus, for all practical purposes Eq. (8.18) is closely approximated by

$$q_{ult} = N_\gamma \sigma'_{vo[D+(1/2)B]} + q_s \qquad (8.19)$$

This same equation also obtains if the water table is located between the ground surface and the base of the footing. Thus, Eq. (8.19) is of general application. Since Eq. (8.17) gives a conservative estimate for N_γ, Eq. (8.19) may also be applied to spread and raft foundations. It also follows from Eq. (8.19) that

$$q_{n(ult)} = N_\gamma \sigma'_{vo[D+(1/2)B]} \qquad (8.20)$$

The associated *factor of safety against a drained bearing capacity failure* F_{bd} is given by

$$F_{bd} = \frac{q_{n(ult)}}{q_{n(app)}} \qquad (8.21)$$

For a stable foundation only part of the drained shear strength of the sand will be mobilized to maintain equilibrium. Thus, if ϕ'_m denotes the *mobilized* effective angle of friction of the sand, then it follows from Eq. (8.20) that the associated value of the *mobilized* bearing capacity factor $N_{\gamma m}$ is defined by

$$N_{\gamma m} = \frac{q_{n(app)}}{\sigma'_{vo[D + (1/2)B]}}$$

The value of ϕ'_m is then obtained from Fig. 8.6 and the *factor of safety against drained shear failure* F_{sd} calculated from

$$F_{sd} = \frac{\tan \phi'}{\tan \phi'_m} \tag{8.22}$$

A study of Eq. (8.20) indicates a number of important points:

1. For a given geometry of problem, the greater the value of ϕ' (that is, the greater the relative density) the greater the value of N_γ and therefore the greater the nett ultimate bearing pressure.
2. For a foundation of given width B, the nett ultimate bearing pressure increases as the depth D increases.
3. For a foundation at a given depth D, the nett ultimate bearing pressure increases as the width B increases.
4. If the water table is originally at a depth B (or greater) below the foundation and subsequently rises to ground level, then $\sigma'_{vo[D + (1/2)B]}$ is approximately halved (since $\rho' \approx \frac{1}{2}\rho$) and consequently the nett ultimate bearing pressure is approximately halved.

8.4 *IN SITU* PENETRATION AND PLATE LOAD TESTS

Because of the difficulty in obtaining undisturbed samples of sand for laboratory shear strength testing, the value of ϕ' (and therefore the value of N_γ) is usually assessed from field tests, generally carried out as *in situ* penetration tests or plate load tests.

The Standard Penetration Test (SPT)

This is probably the most common of the field tests and measures the resistance of the soil to dynamic penetration by a 50-mm diameter split-barrel sampler of the type shown in Fig. 8.7a which is driven into the soil at the base of a cased borehole. The sampler is attached to drill rods and the dynamic driving force is a 65-kg mass falling through a free height of 760 mm onto the top of the rods. The sampler is driven a total distance of 450 mm and the number of blows required to drive the final 300 mm is termed the *standard penetration value*, denoted by N. Full details of the test procedure are given in BS 1377: 1975, Test 19, and ASTM D–1586–67.

The more dense the sand, the greater will be the value of N and the higher will be the value of ϕ'. A correlation between relative density, N and ϕ' has been produced by Peck *et al.* (1974) and is shown here in Fig. 8.8. Also shown plotted in Fig. 8.8 are the associated values of N_γ as defined by Eq. (8.17).

The Cone Penetrometer Test (CPT)

This is a static penetration test developed originally at Delft Soil Mechanics Laboratory in the Netherlands in the thirties but now widely used in many parts of the world. A full description of the test is given in BS 5930: 1981, Sec. 23.3, and ASTM D–3441–79.

One form of the penetrometer, shown in Fig. 8.7b, has a 60° cone with a base diameter of 35.7 mm and a cross-sectional area of 10 cm^2, and a friction jacket of similar diameter and a surface area of 150 cm^2. The principal feature of the penetrometer is that the end resistance to

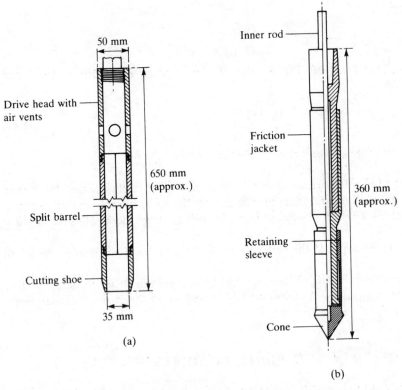

Figure 8.7 (a) Split-barrel sampler used for SPT, (b) cone penetrometer.

penetration by the cone and the frictional resistance acting on the friction jacket can be assessed separately. To carry out a test the penetrometer is driven to the required depth, the cone section only is pushed down at a constant rate of 20 mm/s by means of the inner rod until the retaining sleeve engages with the friction jacket, after which both cone and jacket penetrate together. Recording the load during both phases of the test gives the end resistance directly and the frictional resistance by difference. An electrical form of the penetrometer is also available in which the forces on the cone section and the friction jacket are measured independently by strain gauges.

To provide the necessary reaction for penetration, the equipment may be lorry mounted or may be jacked against kentledge, screw pickets or ground anchors.

The end resistance of the cone is called the *cone penetration resistance*, denoted by q_c, and is defined as the force required to advance the cone divided by the end area. A correlation between q_c and ϕ' has been proposed by Meyerhof (1976) and is shown here in Fig. 8.9. A state-of-the-art review of cone penetrometer testing has been presented by De Ruiter (1982).

The Plate Load Test

In this test a gradually increasing static load is applied to the soil through a steel plate, and readings of the settlement and applied load are recorded, from which a relationship between bearing pressure and deformation for the soil can be obtained. The test may be carried out at ground level, in the base of a trial pit or excavation, or at the bottom of a borehole. In the latter case, unless the borehole is of sufficient diameter to permit a man to enter, cleaning of the bottom of the hole and bedding of the plate have to be done from the surface and there is then no

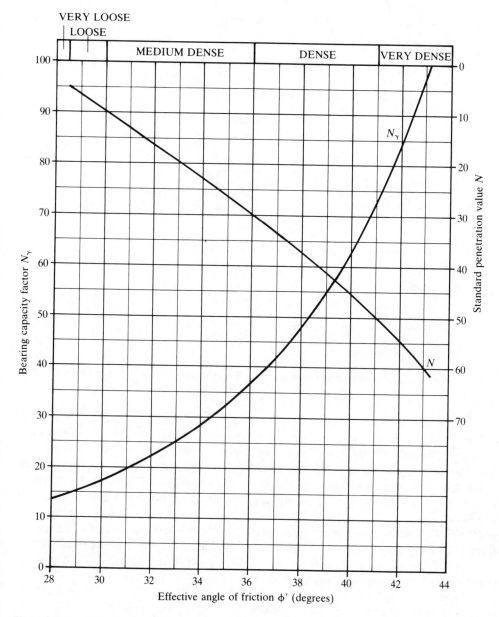

Figure 8.8 Correlation between relative density, standard penetration value N, bearing capacity factor N_γ and effective angle of friction ϕ'. (Adapted from Peck, Hanson and Thornburn, 1974.)

guarantee that the plate is founded evenly on undisturbed soil. Normal practice is to use square or circular plates having a width or diameter in the range 300–1000 mm, with the load being applied either as a series of step increments or at a constant rate of deformation. A full description of the test procedure is given in BS 5930: 1981, Sec. 29.1, and ASTM D–1194–72.

It has to be appreciated that the extent of the stressed zone under the plate is a function of the size of the plate, with the stress increase being less than 5 per cent of the applied load at a depth equivalent to about three times the width or diameter. Thus, a plate load test will not adequately reflect the bearing capacity or deformation characteristics of any weak compressible layers that

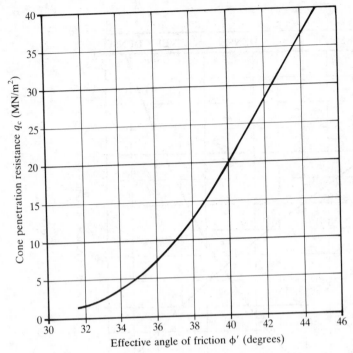

Figure 8.9 Correlation between cone penetration resistance q_c and effective angle of friction ϕ'. (From Meyerhof, 1976.)

may lie below the zone of influence of the plate but within that of the full-size foundation. To be as representative as possible, a series of plate load tests should be carried out at different depths and preferably using plates of different sizes, but for reasons of economy this is seldom done.

The plate load test is in effect a model footing test. Therefore with the ultimate bearing capacity q_{ult} of the plate being obtained from the bearing pressure–deformation relationship, a value of N_γ for the soil can be inferred from Eq. (8.19), and if required the corresponding value of ϕ' may be found from Fig. 8.8.

A variation of the plate load test is the screw-plate test (Janbu and Senneset, 1973; Kay and Parry, 1982) in which a screw-plate is augered into the soil until the required depth is reached, thus by-passing any disturbed soil at the base of the hole and dispensing with the need to prepare the base of the hole for the conventional steel plate.

8.5 DESIGN PROCEDURE FOR SHALLOW FOUNDATIONS ON SAND

In the design of footings on sand it is necessary to ensure that there is an adequate factor of safety against a bearing capacity failure and that the resulting settlements are acceptable. Generally, F_{bd} should not be less than 2 and S should not exceed 25 mm.

A study of the load–settlement relationships for footings of different widths on sand shows that in general for $B < 1$ m bearing capacity considerations tend to control design. For footings greater than 1 m in width the ultimate bearing pressures become so large that the resulting settlements become excessive long before a shear failure is induced. Thus, in the majority of practical cases settlement considerations control design of the footing.

Now the bearing pressure which produces any given settlement on a loose sand will obviously be smaller than that which produces the same settlement in a dense sand. Hence in some rough way there should exist a relationship between the bearing pressure which produces a given settlement and the N values obtained from the Standard Penetration Test. Such a correlation has been given by Peck *et al.* (1974), where for a foundation on a sand with the water table at a depth B or greater below the base of the footing it is suggested that for an allowable settlement of 25 mm, the *nett allowable bearing pressure* $q_{n(all)}$ is given by

$$q_{n(all)} = 11N \text{ kN/m}^2 \qquad (8.23)$$

If the water table rises from a depth B or greater below the base of the footing up to the ground surface, the effective pressures within the sand are reduced to approximately half their original values. Correspondingly, the stiffness of the sand is reduced. Hence the bearing pressure required to produce a settlement of 25 mm, if the water table is at the ground surface, is about half that required to produce a 25-mm settlement if the water table is at a depth of B or more below the base of the footing. Thus, for the water table at ground level

$$q_{n(all)} = 0.5 \times 11N = 5.5N \text{ kN/m}^2 \qquad (8.24)$$

In general, then, for a water table at a depth D_w below ground level wherein $0 \leqslant D_w \leqslant D + B$

$$q_{n(all)} = 11N \left[0.5 + 0.5 \frac{D_w}{D + B} \right] \text{kN/m}^2 \qquad (8.25)$$

The limit of 25 mm total settlement for footings is assumed in order to restrict differential settlements between any two footings supporting a structure to not more than 20 mm. For an adequately reinforced raft foundation the differential settlements are less than those for a footing foundation designed for the same bearing pressure. Therefore it is reasonable to permit larger allowable bearing pressures under raft foundations, and consequently larger total settlements. Experience has shown that differential settlements are unlikely to exceed 20 mm if the total settlement of the raft is restricted to 50 mm, and the conventional design approach is to take the nett allowable bearing pressure as twice that given by Eq. (8.25).

Alternatively, there are methods of predicting settlements for foundations on sand which make use of values of the cone penetration resistance q_c. The Buisman–De Beer method, for example, relates the value of q_c to a constant of compressibility C of the soil (De Beer and Martens, 1957) and calculates the settlement of the foundation as the summation of the settlements of a number of incremental sublayers of thickness Δz from:

$$S = \sum \frac{\Delta z}{C} \ln \frac{\sigma'_{vf}}{\sigma'_{vo}} \qquad (8.26)$$

where σ'_{vo} and σ'_{vf} are the initial and final values of vertical effective stress in the sublayer.

However, it has been found that in its original form the method generally overestimates the actual settlement (Meyerhof, 1965), and it has become common practice to modify the original De Beer relationship between q_c and compressibility to a less conservative form given by

$$C = \frac{1.9 \, q_c}{\sigma'_{vo}} \qquad (8.27)$$

The method is strictly applicable only to normally consolidated sands, and in the case of overconsolidated sands will therefore overestimate the likely settlements.

Another method, proposed by Schmertmann (1970) and modified by Schmertmann *et al.* (1978), uses a semi-empirical strain influence factor I_z to represent the distribution of vertical strain with depth under shallow foundations, and calculates the settlement of the foundation from

$$S = C_1 C_2 q_{n(app)} \sum \frac{I_z}{E} \Delta z \qquad (8.28)$$

where C_1 = a factor which takes into account the depth of the foundation

C_2 = a factor which accounts for creep of the soil

and E = Young's modulus for the soil.

Over the zone of influence of the foundation the soil is divided into a number of incremental sublayers of thickness Δz and the total settlement is obtained by summation. Distributions of I_z are presented by Schmertmann *et al.* for square and strip foundations, and values of E for each sublayer are inferred from cone penetration resistances using

$$E = 2.5q_c \quad \text{for square foundations}$$

and $$E = 3.5q_c \quad \text{for strip foundations}$$

There have been a number of attempts to establish a correlation between the N values obtained from the SPT and values of the cone penetration resistance q_c. However, no consistently reliable relationship has yet emerged (Sutherland, 1963; Rodin *et al.*, 1974).

Despite the limitations of the plate load test, the likely settlements of foundations on sand are often assessed by extrapolating the results of such tests. The extrapolation is generally based on an empirical relationship proposed originally by Terzaghi and Peck in 1948 and which in dimensionless form is closely approximated by the expression

$$\frac{S_f}{S_p} = \frac{4}{(1 + B_p/B_f)^2} \tag{8.29}$$

where S_p = settlement of a plate of width B_p

S_f = settlement of a foundation of width B_f

and where *the bearing pressure is the same for both plate and foundation.* However, there is considerable evidence that the correlation between foundation settlement and foundation size is not as simple as that suggested by Eq. (8.29) (Bjerrum and Eggestad, 1963; D'Appolonia *et al.*, 1968). This evidence taken together with the doubts expressed earlier on the truly representative nature of plate load tests suggests that predictions of foundation settlement based simply on Eq. (8.29) must be treated with considerable caution.

Example 8.3 A vertical concrete column is to carry a total load of 2200 kN, inclusive of self-weight above ground level. The column is to be supported by a square concrete footing founded at a depth of 2 m below ground level in a thick deposit of sand. A site investigation revealed that the water table was static at a depth of 2 m, and Standard Penetration Tests in the sand gave N values in the range 30–34. The sand was found to have a bulk density above the water table of 1.60 Mg/m^3 and a saturated density of 1.90 Mg/m^3. If the total settlement is not to exceed 25 mm and the factor of safety against a drained bearing capacity failure is not to be less than 2, calculate a suitable size for the square footing. Neglect the difference in density between the concrete foundation and the sand.

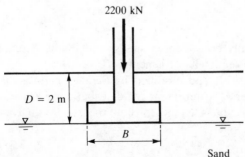

Sand   **Figure 8.10** Example 8.3.

SOLUTION The problem is illustrated in Fig. 8.10. Assuming settlement controls design, Eq. (8.25) gives

$$q_{n(all)} = 11 \times 30\left(0.5 + 0.5\frac{2}{2+B}\right) = 165 + \frac{330}{2+B} \text{ kN/m}^2$$

$$q_{n(app)} = \frac{2200}{B^2} \text{ kN/m}^2$$

Equating $q_{n(app)}$ and $q_{n(all)}$

$$\frac{2200}{B^2} = 165 + \frac{330}{2+B}$$

from which $\qquad B^3 + 4B^2 - 13.3B - 26.\dot{6} = 0$

By trial $\qquad\qquad\qquad\qquad\qquad\qquad B = \underline{3.094 \text{ m}}$

Check factor of safety against drained bearing capacity failure. From Eq. (8.20)

$$q_{n(ult)} = N_\gamma \sigma'_{vo[D+(1/2)B]}$$

From Fig. 8.8 for $N = 30$, $N_\gamma = 36.75$

$$D + \tfrac{1}{2}B = 2 + \tfrac{1}{2} \times 3.094 = 3.547 \text{ m}$$

Thus $\qquad \sigma'_{vo[D+(1/2)B]} = 1.60 \times 9.81 \times 2 + 0.9 \times 9.81 \times 1.547 = 45.0\overset{5}{4} \text{ kN/m}^2$

Hence $\qquad q_{n(ult)} = 36.75 \times 45.05 = 1655.6 \text{ kN/m}^2$

$$q_{n(app)} = \frac{2200}{3.094^2} = 229.8 \text{ kN/m}^2$$

Thus $\qquad\qquad F_{bd} = \frac{1655.6}{229.8} = 7.20$

This is greater than the minimum specified value of $F_{bd} = 2$. Therefore settlement considerations control design and we require to use a 3.094-m square footing.

Example 8.4 Figure 8.11 shows the details of a bridge pier which is to be founded on the bed of a river on a deposit of sand having a density of 2.0 Mg/m³ and an effective angle of friction of 35°. The depth of the river is 4 m and the base of the pier is to be located 2.5 m below the river bed. The pier is 3 m wide and the total load including the weight of the structure and foundation is 1500 kN/m run. Calculate the factor of safety against drained bearing capacity failure and the factor of safety on shear strength.

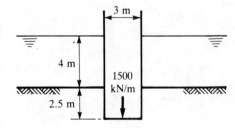

Sand   **Figure 8.11** Example 8.4.

SOLUTION The problem is illustrated in Fig. 8.11.

$$q_{n(ult)} = N_\gamma \sigma'_{vo[D+(1/2)B]}$$

From Fig. 8.8 for $\phi' = 35°$, $N_\gamma = 32.3$

$$D + \tfrac{1}{2}B = 2.5 + \tfrac{1}{2} \times 3 = 4 \text{ m}$$

Thus
$$\sigma_{vo[D+(1/2)B]} = 1 \times 9.81 \times 4 + 2 \times 9.81 \times 4 = 117.72 \text{ kN/m}^2$$

$$u_{o[D+(1/2)B]} = 1 \times 9.81 \times 8 = 78.48 \text{ kN/m}^2$$

and
$$\sigma'_{vo[D+(1/2)B]} = 117.72 - 78.48 = 39.24 \text{ kN/m}^2$$

Alternatively
$$\sigma'_{vo[D+(1/2)B]} = 1 \times 9.81 \times 4 = 39.24 \text{ kN/m}^2$$

Hence
$$q_{n(ult)} = 32.3 \times 39.24 = 1267.45 \text{ kN/m}^2$$

$$q_{n(app)} = \frac{1500}{3 \times 1} - (1 \times 9.81 \times 4 + 2 \times 9.81 \times 2.5) = 411.71 \text{ kN/m}^2$$

Therefore
$$F_{bd} = \frac{q_{n(ult)}}{q_{n(app)}} = \frac{1267.45}{411.71} = \underline{3.08}$$

For a stable foundation

$$q_{n(app)} = N_{\gamma m} \sigma'_{vo[D+(1/2)B]}$$

$$\therefore \qquad N_{\gamma m} = \frac{q_{n(app)}}{\sigma'_{vo[D+(1/2)B]}} = \frac{411.71}{39.24} = 10.49$$

whence from Fig. 8.6, $\phi'_m = 25.7°$

Thus
$$F_{sd} = \frac{\tan \phi'}{\tan \phi'_m} = \frac{\tan 35°}{\tan 25.7°} = \underline{1.45}$$

failure tends to be block failure

8.6 BEARING CAPACITY OF PILES IN CLAY

The critical period for the stability of a pile or group of piles in clay will be at the end of construction while the clay is undrained. The analysis for this condition may be carried out in terms of total stress.

Single Pile in Clay

With reference to Fig. 8.12 let:

D = embedded length of the pile
B = diameter of the pile
A_s = shaft area of the pile
A_b = base area of the pile
ρ_p = density of the pile
W = weight of the pile = $\rho_p g D A_b$
c_w = undrained adhesion between the pile shaft and the clay
c_u = undrained shear strength of the clay
$\alpha = c_w/c_u$, the *shaft adhesion factor*
and Q_{ult} = ultimate load *on* the pile to cause an undrained shear failure of the clay

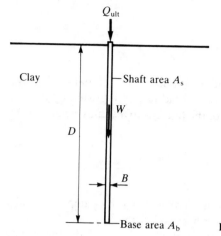

Figure 8.12 Single pile in clay.

We have then:

Ultimate load for the pile = Ultimate end bearing load + Ultimate shaft adhesion load

Thus
$$Q_{ult} + W = (c_u N_c + \rho g D) A_b + c_w A_s$$

$\therefore$
$$Q_{ult} = c_u N_c A_b + \alpha c_u A_s + (\rho - \rho_p) g D A_b$$

Neglecting the difference in density between the pile and the clay we obtain

$$Q_{ult} = c_u N_c A_b + \alpha c_u A_s \qquad \alpha = \frac{c_w}{c_u} \qquad (8.30)$$

The bearing capacity factor N_c is given by Eq. (8.4), namely

$$N_c = 5\left(1 + 0.2\,\frac{D}{B}\right)\left(1 + 0.2\,\frac{B}{L}\right)$$

wherein $D/B \leqslant 2.5$. With $B/L = 1$ for a pile having a circular or square cross-section and with $D/B \gg 2.5$, this gives

$$N_c = 5(1 + 0.2 \times 2.5)(1 + 0.2 \times 1) = 9 \qquad (8.31)$$

Values of the shaft adhesion factor α vary from approximately 0.95 for soft clays to 0.55 or so for stiff clays.

Pile Groups in Clay

When piles are arranged in a closely spaced group they act together as a single unit, and if failure occurs it occurs as a block failure. In consequence, the ultimate load of a pile group is not necessarily that of a single pile times the number of piles in the group. We define the *efficiency E* of a pile group then as

$$E = \frac{\text{Average load per pile in the group at failure}}{\text{Ultimate load for a single pile}} \qquad (8.32)$$

Various empirical formulae have been proposed for the efficiency of pile groups. One of the most widely used of these is the Converse–Labarre formula:

$$E = 1 - \left[\tan^{-1}\frac{B}{s}\right]^{\circ}\left[\frac{m(n-1) + n(m-1)}{90mn}\right] \qquad (8.33)$$

angle in degrees

where B = diameter of the piles
 s = centre-to-centre spacing of the piles
 m = number of rows of piles in the group
and n = number of columns of piles in the group

It follows from Eq. (8.32) that the immediate ultimate load for a pile group is equal to $Q_{ult}EN_p$, where N_p is the number of piles in the group. If Q_g denotes the load to be supported by the pile group, then the factor of safety for the immediate stability of the pile group, F_u, may be defined as

$$F_u = \frac{Q_{ult}EN_p}{Q_g} \tag{8.34}$$

Example 8.5 An investigation at a proposed construction site revealed a thick deposit of fully saturated clay having an average undrained shear strength of $50\,\text{kN/m}^2$.
(a) If a 0.5-m diameter pile is driven into the clay to a depth of 20 m, calculate the immediate ultimate load that can be carried by the pile. Take the shaft adhesion factor α to be 0.82 and neglect the difference in density between the pile and the clay.
(b) If a 12×10 rectangular group of such piles is arranged at a constant centre-to-centre spacing of 2.5 m, calculate the immediate allowable load that can be carried by the pile group for a specified load factor of 3.

SOLUTION (a) The immediate ultimate load that can be carried by a single pile in clay is given by

$$Q_{ult} = c_u N_c A_b + \alpha c_u A_s \tag{8.30 bis}$$

$$= 50 \times 9 \times \frac{\pi}{4}(0.5)^2 + 0.82 \times 50 \times \pi(0.5) \times 20$$

$$= 88.36 + 1288.05 = \underline{1376.4\,\text{kN}}$$

(b) From Eq. (8.33), the efficiency of a pile group is given by

$$E = 1 - \left[\tan^{-1}\frac{B}{s}\right]^\circ \left[\frac{m(n-1) + n(m-1)}{90mn}\right]$$

$$= 1 - \left[\tan^{-1}\frac{0.5}{2.5}\right]^\circ \left[\frac{12 \times 9 + 10 \times 11}{90 \times 12 \times 10}\right] = 0.772$$

Therefore immediate ultimate load that can be carried by the pile group

$$= 1376.4 \times 0.772 \times 12 \times 10 = \underline{127\,509.7\,\text{kN}}$$

Thus, for a load factor of 3, the immediate allowable load that can be carried by the pile group

$$= \frac{127\,509.7}{3} = \underline{42\,503\,\text{kN}}$$

Example 8.6 A bridge pier, 4 m × 3 m, is to be founded at a depth of 2 m below ground level at a site where the soil conditions consist of 2 m of silt overlying 15 m of normally consolidated clay resting on bedrock. The water table is at a depth of 4 m, and the total pier load including the weight of the structure and foundation is 2500 kN. Design a suitable piled foundation for the pier assuming a load factor of 3 on the immediate ultimate load for the pile group. Calculate

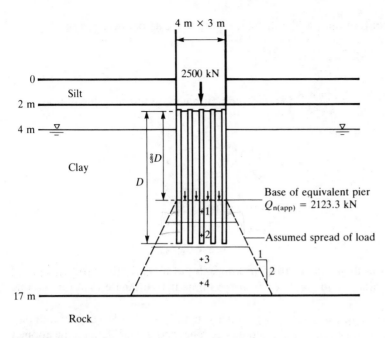

Figure 8.13 Example 8.6.

also the order of expected settlement for the pier. The properties of the clay are $\rho = 1.92 \text{ Mg/m}^3$, $c_u = 55 \text{ kN/m}^2$, $e_o = 0.80$, $C_c = 0.25$, and for the silt $\rho = 1.60 \text{ Mg/m}^3$. Neglect the difference in density between the piles and the clay, and take the shaft adhesion factor α to be 0.8.

SOLUTION The problem is illustrated in Fig. 8.13.

Weight of excavated silt $= 1.60 \times 9.81 \times 4 \times 3 \times 2 = 376.70 \text{ kN}$

Therefore load to be supported by pile group,

$$Q_g = 2500 - 376.7 = 2123.3 \text{ kN}$$

Now the immediate ultimate load that can be carried by a single pile is given by

$$Q_{ult} = c_u N_c A_b + \alpha c_u A_s \tag{8.30 bis}$$

Consider 0.3-m diameter piles. Then

$$Q_{ult} = 55 \times 9 \times \frac{\pi}{4} (0.3)^2 + 0.8 \times 55 \times \pi (0.3) D$$

$$= 35.15 + 41.45 D \text{ kN}$$

To minimize the settlement of the pier, the piles need to be long compared with the size of the foundation. Thus, if $D = 10 \text{ m}$ then $Q_{ult} = 449.65 \text{ kN}$. As a typical value of efficiency for a pile group is 0.7, then with a specified value for F_u of 3 it follows from Eq. (8.34) that the required number of piles, N_p, is given by

$$N_p = \frac{Q_g F_u}{Q_{ult} E} = \frac{2123.3 \times 3}{449.65 \times 0.7} \approx 20$$

Thus, consider a 5 × 4 group of piles at 0.9-m centres (i.e., 3 × pile diameter). Then

$$E = 1 - \left[\tan^{-1}\frac{B}{s}\right]^{\circ}\left[\frac{m(n-1)+n(m-1)}{90mn}\right]$$

$$= 1 - \left[\tan^{-1}\frac{0.3}{0.9}\right]\left[\frac{5\times3+4\times4}{90\times5\times4}\right] = 0.68 \text{ (compare with assumed value of 0.7)}$$

Invoking Eq. (8.34) again

$$F_u = \frac{Q_{ult}EN_p}{Q_g}$$

We thus have

$$3 = \frac{(35.15 + 41.45D)\times0.68\times20}{2123.3}$$

whence $D = \underline{10.45 \text{ m}}$

Thus a 5 × 4 group of 0.3-m diameter by 10.45-m long piles at a centre-to-centre spacing of 0.9 m may be used to provide a load factor of 3 on the immediate ultimate load for the pile group.

For the purpose of a settlement analysis, a pile group is generally assumed to behave as a pier with its base at a depth of two-thirds the length of the piles. The load is considered to be applied to the soil at this level and then spread with increasing depth at an angle of 2 vertical to 1 horizontal (Fig. 8.13). This results in a reasonable approximation to the average increase in pressure at any level under the pile group. Allowing then a thickness of 0.5 m for the pile cap, the depth of the base of the equivalent pier below ground level $= 2 + 0.5 + \frac{2}{3}\times10.45 = 9.47$ m. Therefore the depth of clay below the pier $= 17 - 9.47 = 7.53$ m, and the resulting consolidation settlement is computed from

$$S = \sum \frac{C_c \Delta D \log\frac{\sigma'_{vf}}{\sigma'_{vo}}}{1 + e_o}$$

As the base area of the foundation is 4 m × 3 m, we require a thickness of sublayer $\Delta D \approx 2$ m. Thus, consider 4 sublayers with $\Delta D = 7.53/4 = 1.88$ m. We thus obtain at the centre of layer 1:

$$\sigma'_{vo} = 1.60\times9.81\times2 + 1.92\times9.81\times8.41 - 1\times9.81\times6.41 = 126.91 \text{ kN/m}^2$$

$$\Delta\sigma_v = \frac{2123.3}{(4+0.94)(3+0.94)} = 109.09 \text{ kN/m}^2$$

Thus $\sigma'_{vf} = \sigma'_{vo} + \Delta\sigma_v = 126.91 + 109.09 = 236.0$ kN/m^2

In a similar manner we find

At the centre of layer 2: $\sigma'_{vo} = 143.88$ kN/m^2, $\sigma'_{vf} = 197.37$ kN/m^2
At the centre of layer 3: $\sigma'_{vo} = 160.85$ kN/m^2, $\sigma'_{vf} = 192.55$ kN/m^2
At the centre of layer 4: $\sigma'_{vo} = 177.82$ kN/m^2, $\sigma'_{vf} = 198.77$ kN/m^2

Thus $$S = \frac{0.25\times1.88}{1+0.80}\left[\log\frac{236.00}{126.91} + \log\frac{197.37}{143.88} + \log\frac{192.55}{160.85} + \log\frac{198.77}{177.82}\right]$$

$$= \underline{0.139 \text{ m}}$$

This order of expected settlement for the pier is such that it may be necessary to consider alternative foundation designs, such as driving the piles down to the bedrock.

8.7 BEARING CAPACITY OF PILES IN SAND   Not on Exam.

For a pile or group of piles in sand there will be no difference between the short-term and long-term condition, the sand being drained throughout. The analysis must then be in terms of effective stress.

Single Pile in Sand

With reference to Fig. 8.14 let:

D = embedded length of the pile
B = diameter of the pile
ρ_p = density of the pile
W = weight of the pile
δ' = effective angle of friction between the pile shaft and the sand
K' = effective coefficient of earth pressure of the sand against the pile shaft
ϕ' = effective angle of friction of the sand
βD = depth of the water table below ground level wherein $0 \leqslant \beta \leqslant 1$

and Q_{ult} = ultimate load *on* the pile to cause a drained shear failure of the sand

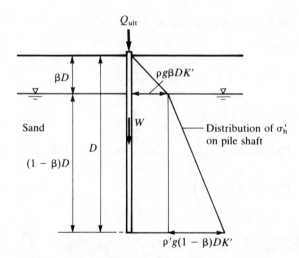

Figure 8.14 Single pile in sand.

The ultimate load for the pile will be the sum of the ultimate load in end bearing and the ultimate load in skin friction developed between the pile shaft and the sand.

Ultimate end bearing load for the pile The ultimate end bearing pressure is of the form derived earlier for a shallow foundation [Eq. (8.19)]. Noting from Eq. (8.15) that $N_\gamma = N_q - 1$ we have then

$$\text{Ultimate end bearing pressure} = (N_q - 1)\sigma'_{vo[D + (1/2)B]} + q_s$$

We note of course that Eq. (8.16) for the bearing capacity factor N_q is not relevant here, as this applies only to shallow foundations where $D \leqslant B$. The analysis of deep foundations taking account of the depth factor has been carried out by a number of research workers, notably Meyerhof (see, for example, Meyerhof 1976).

Since for a pile $B \ll D$ then

$$\sigma'_{vo[D + (1/2)B]} \approx \sigma'_{vo(D)} = \rho g \beta D + \rho' g (1 - \beta) D$$

Also q_s = total overburden pressure at the base of the pile = $\rho g \beta D + \rho_s g (1 - \beta) D$. We thus obtain:

Ultimate end bearing load

$$= [\rho g \beta D + \rho' g (1 - \beta) D][N_q - 1] \frac{\pi B^2}{4} + [\rho g \beta D + \rho_s g (1 - \beta) D] \frac{\pi B^2}{4} \quad (8.35)$$

$\underset{\text{area}}{\text{base}}$

Ultimate skin friction load for the pile At any depth down the shaft of the pile the horizontal effective earth pressure acting on the pile is given by

$$\sigma'_h = \sigma'_v K' \quad \text{where} \quad K'_a < K' < K'_p$$

The value of the effective earth pressure coefficient K' will vary, depending on the properties of the sand in which the pile is installed. Meyerhof has suggested that, in general, for loose sands $K' = 0.5$ and for dense sands $K' = 1.0$. Thus

At the soil surface: $\sigma'_v = 0$, $\sigma'_h = 0$
At the level of the water table: $\sigma'_v = \rho g \beta D$, $\sigma'_h = \rho g \beta D K'$
At the base of the pile: $\sigma'_v = \rho g \beta D + \rho' g (1 - \beta) D$, $\sigma'_h = [\rho g \beta D + \rho' g (1 - \beta) D] K'$

The distribution of σ'_h along the pile shaft is then as shown in Fig. 8.14 from which:

Horizontal effective force acting on the pile shaft

$$= [\tfrac{1}{2} \rho g \beta^2 D^2 K' + \rho g \beta (1 - \beta) D^2 K' + \tfrac{1}{2} \rho' g (1 - \beta)^2 D^2 K'] \pi B$$

$$= \tfrac{1}{2} \rho g D^2 K' \pi B \left[1 - (1 - \beta)^2 \left(1 - \frac{\rho'}{\rho} \right) \right]$$

Thus, upward vertical shear force acting on the pile shaft (i.e., supporting skin friction force)

$$= \tfrac{1}{2} \rho g D^2 K' \pi B \left[1 - (1 - \beta)^2 \left(1 - \frac{\rho'}{\rho} \right) \right] \tan \delta' \quad (8.36)$$

Ultimate load for the pile Adding Eqs (8.35) and (8.36)

Ultimate load for the pile

$$= [\rho g \beta D + \rho' g (1 - \beta) D][N_q - 1] \frac{\pi B^2}{4} + [\rho g \beta D + \rho_s g (1 - \beta) D] \frac{\pi B^2}{4}$$

$$+ \tfrac{1}{2} \rho g D^2 K' \pi B \left[1 - (1 - \beta)^2 \left(1 - \frac{\rho'}{\rho} \right) \right] \tan \delta' \quad (8.37)$$

Since ultimate load for the pile = Ultimate load on the pile + Weight of the pile

$$= Q_{ult} + \rho_p g D \frac{\pi B^2}{4}$$

$$= Q_{ult} + \rho_p g [\beta D + (1 - \beta) D] \frac{\pi B^2}{4} \quad (8.38)$$

then equating Eqs (8.38) and (8.37) and neglecting the difference in density between the pile and

the sand, we obtain

$$Q_{ult} = [\rho g \beta D + \rho' g (1 - \beta) D][N_q - 1] \frac{\pi B^2}{4}$$

$$+ \tfrac{1}{2}\rho g D^2 K' \pi B \left[1 - (1 - \beta)^2 \left(1 - \frac{\rho'}{\rho} \right) \right] \tan \delta' \qquad (8.39)$$

Pile Groups in Sand

The action of driving piles in sand leads to a change in the relative density and hence a change in the shear strength of the sand within and around the group of piles. With loose sands, pile driving will tend to cause compaction and the shear strength of the sand will increase. Consequently, the efficiency of a group of piles will generally exceed 1.0 and in certain conditions may reach 3.0 or even higher. With very dense sands, pile driving will cause loosening and therefore a decrease in shear strength. Consequently, an efficiency less than 1.0 may result.

The ultimate load for a pile group is thus equal to $Q_{ult}EN_p$ where N_p is the number of piles in the group and the efficiency E may be less than or greater than unity. If Q_g denotes the load to be supported by the pile group, then the factor of safety for stability of the pile group, F_d, may be defined as

$$F_d = \frac{Q_{ult}EN_p}{Q_g} \qquad (8.40)$$

PROBLEMS

8.1 A load-bearing wall is to be founded on a concrete strip footing located at a depth of 1.5 m below ground level in a deep deposit of saturated clay having an average undrained shear strength of 75 kN/m². It is estimated that the wall load, including self-weight above ground level, will be 250 kN per metre run of the wall. Calculate the required width of the strip to give a factor of safety of 3 against a shear failure of the foundation clay immediately after construction. Neglect the difference in density between the soil and the footing, and assume Skempton's equation for the bearing capacity factor N_c.
[Ans. 1.70 m]

8.2 A rectangular water storage tank is to be founded at a depth of 3 m below the surface of a thick deposit of saturated clay having a density of 1.80 Mg/m³ and an average undrained shear strength of 35 kN/m². The tank is 6 m wide by 12 m long and the total weight when full will be 8900 kN. Calculate the factor of safety against an undrained bearing capacity failure of the foundation soil.
[Ans. 3.00]

8.3 A vertical concrete column is to carry a total load of 3300 kN, inclusive of self-weight above ground level. The column is to be supported by a rectangular footing having a length 1.5 times the breadth and is to be founded at a depth of 2 m below ground level in a thick deposit of sand. A site investigation revealed that the water table was static at a depth of 3 m and Standard Penetration Tests in the sand gave N values in the range 30–34. The sand was found to have a bulk density above the water table of 1.60 Mg/m³ and a saturated density of 1.90 Mg/m³. If the total settlement is not to exceed 25 mm and the factor of safety against a drained bearing capacity failure is not to be less than 2, calculate the suitable size for the footing. Neglect the difference in density between the concrete foundation and the sand.
[Ans. 2.873 m wide by 4.310 m long]

8.4 A building for part of a new power station is to be constructed on a piled foundation at the surface of a thick deposit of saturated clay having an average undrained shear strength of 70 kN/m². It is proposed that the building has a plan area of 40 m by 20 m, and preliminary estimates suggest that the total weight of the building will be in the order of 150 MN. For this proposal, design a suitable piled foundation assuming a load factor of 3 on the immediate ultimate load for the pile group. Neglect the difference in density between the piles and the clay and take the shaft adhesion factor α to be 0.7.
[Ans. A 23 × 12 group of 0.5-m diameter piles at 1.75 m centres and 30 m long would be suitable]

8.5 A bridge pier is to be located at the site of a disused sand quarry which has recently been filled in under a land reclamation scheme. Borings at the site now show the soil profile to consist of 5 m of loose granular fill overlying 4 m of soft alluvial clay resting on an extensive thickness of stiff glacial clay, the equilibrium groundwater level at the site being

1 m below the surface of the fill. The pier is to have a base area of 16 m by 4 m and it is estimated that the total load from the pier inclusive of self-weight will be 19 500 kN.

In view of the excessive settlement likely to occur if the pier is founded directly in the loose fill, one proposal being considered is a piled foundation which has a 12 × 4 group of 0.5 m-diameter piles at a centre-to-centre spacing of 1.5 m together with a pile cap in the form of a rectangular slab 17.5 m by 5.5 m in plan and 1.2 m in thickness cast over the top of the piles, the base of the slab being located 1 m below the surface of the fill.

Based on a site investigation report, the following soil parameters are recommended for design.

Ganular fill: $\rho = 1.60$ Mg/m^3, $\rho_s = 1.87$ Mg/m^3, $N = 10$
Alluvial clay: $\rho_s = 1.83$ Mg/m^3, $c_u = 36$ kN/m^2, $\alpha = 0.9$
Glacial clay: $\rho_s = 2.10$ Mg/m^3, $c_u = 160$ kN/m^2, $\alpha = 0.5$

On the basis of the information given and taking the efficiency of the pile group to be 66 per cent, make a reasoned estimate of the length of piles required to provide adequate support for the pier.

[Ans.   24 m]

NINE

GROUND INVESTIGATION AND METHODS OF GROUND IMPROVEMENT

Prior to the construction of any civil engineering works, it is necessary to investigate conditions at the proposed site in order to evaluate its general suitability and the capacity of the ground to support the proposed structure without undue stress or deformation. In the case of earthworks, it is also necessary to verify the suitability of any proposed fill material and to select an appropriate method of construction.

Where ground conditions over part or all of a site are found to be inadequate, say with respect to strength, compressibility or permeability, it may be possible to achieve some improvement in one or more of these properties in the field through certain geotechnical processes.

Thus, the first section of Chapter 9 describes the steps involved in the ground investigation stage of an overall site investigation, while the remainder describes techniques for ground improvement, including surface and deep compaction, chemical stabilization and grouting, and the use of geotextiles. The use of preloading as a technique for minimizing the post-construction settlement of highly compressible clays and peats has already been described in Chapter 4.

9.1 GROUND INVESTIGATION

A ground investigation forms one stage of the general site investigation carried out to assess the overall suitability of a site for any proposed civil engineering works and to enable an adequate and economic design of the works to be prepared. Details of the procedures for a full site investigation are presented in BS 5930: 1981, ASTM D–420–69, Joyce (1982), and Weltman and Head (1983).

The ground investigation is usually conducted after initially studying any relevant records or documented information available about the area and following a preliminary reconnaissance of the site. In certain cases it is carried out in conjunction with aerial photography and geophysical surveying. It is also likely that a ground investigation will be required when the safety of an existing civil engineering works is to be assessed, or when an actual failure has occurred.

The principal aims of the investigation are:

(a) to establish the soil profile across the site by determining the sequence of strata with depth, the vertical thickness and lateral continuity of each stratum and, if appropriate, the depth to bedrock,
(b) to obtain information on groundwater conditions at the site,
(c) to determine the properties relevant to an identification, description and classification of the various strata, and where appropriate to obtain parameters for use in design.

Thus, the ground investigation usually includes a programme of subsurface exploration, groundwater observations, the recovery of samples for examination and laboratory testing, and in some cases a series of *in situ* field tests.

On certain projects, monitoring of the ground conditions at the site continues during and after construction with the installation of field instrumentation equipment to enable pressure changes and displacements in the ground to be recorded.

Subsurface Exploration

Subsurface exploration is usually done by means of *trial pits* and *boreholes*. The location and spacing of trial pits and boreholes should be selected in order to highlight conditions at points of particular engineering difficulty or importance, while yielding general information about conditions over the site as a whole. This may involve phasing or modifying the exploration programme in the light of what the initial borings reveal, or may involve some continuous sampling in order to reveal where the major exploration should be concentrated. The depth of exploration is influenced by the size and type of the proposed engineering works but, as a general rule, exploration should be carried out to below the depth where stress increases cease to be significant and through any compressible soils likely to contribute significantly to settlement of the proposed works. If rock is encountered, a penetration of at least 3 m in more than one borehole may be required in order to establish that it is true bedrock and not just a large boulder.

Trial pits These are usually dug using a back-acting excavator. They permit the *in situ* condition of the ground to be examined both vertically and laterally, and also provide access for sampling and/or *in situ* testing. However, the cost of providing support for the sides of the excavation and installing a de-watering system if the excavation is taken below groundwater level in free-draining strata limits the economic depth of trial pits to generally not more than about 5 m.

Boreholes These may be formed by a variety of boring or drilling techniques, depending upon the required borehole diameter, the depth of exploration and the location of the site.
(a) *Hand augers* are light, portable boring tools available with various cutting shoes up to 200 mm in diameter, and can be used to a depth of about 5 m in self-supporting strata which are free of coarse gravel or larger particles. They are frequently used during the preliminary stages of a site investigation. The most common types are the post-hole auger and small helical auger shown in Fig. 9.1.
(b) *Light cable percussion boring*, or *shell and auger* as it is usually known, is a common method used in Britain for routine exploration to depths in excess of 3 m. The typical percussion rig consists of a tripod frame and a powered winch connected to a light steel cable which passes over a pulley at the apex of the tripod, as shown in Fig. 9.2a. Most rigs have running wheels permanently attached and can fold down to form a simple trailer for easy transportation.

The borehole is formed by the percussive action of repeatedly raising and dropping a cutting tool attached to drill rods suspended from the end of the steel cable. The most commonly used tools are the clay cutter, the shell and the chisel. The *clay cutter*, Fig. 9.2b, is used in cohesive soils

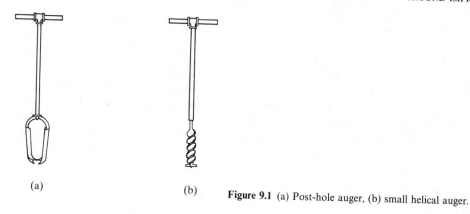

Figure 9.1 (a) Post-hole auger, (b) small helical auger.

and consists of an open-ended steel tube with a cutting edge at its lower end which when dropped over a distance of 1–2 m cuts a plug of clay. After a number of strokes, the cutter is withdrawn from the borehole and emptied. The *shell* or *bailer*, Fig. 9.2c, is an open-ended steel tube with a flap valve located above the cutting edge and is used in cohesionless soils. When below the water table in free-draining strata, the borehole is partly filled with natural groundwater, and as the shell is moved up and down at the base of the hole the loose fragmented material is carried into the shell in the water and retained by the flap valve. When the shell contains a reasonable amount of material, it is raised to the surface and emptied. When operating above groundwater level, water may need to be added to the borehole. The flat *chisel*, Fig. 9.2d, is a heavy solid tool with a hardened cutting edge used for breaking up dense or hard soil strata or soft rock, the fragments of which can then be removed using the shell.

Boreholes in cohesionless soils and soft cohesive soils usually require casing for support. The casing is advanced with the borehole, as shown in Fig. 9.2a, the steel sections of casing being screwed together as required.

The light cable percussion rig is suitable for boring through most soils and weak rocks, and can produce cased boreholes with diameters of 150–300 mm over depths in excess of 50 m. The rig can be fitted with attachments for undisturbed sampling and *in situ* testing, and in some cases may be

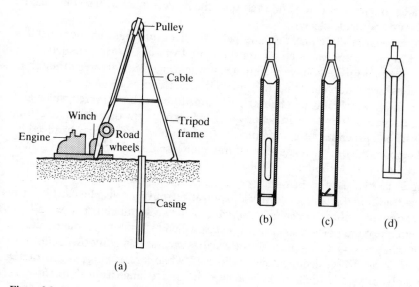

Figure 9.2 (a) Percussion boring rig (shell and auger), (b) clay cutter, (c) shell, (d) chisel.

provided with a hydraulic power take-off to drive mechanical power augers and light rotary core-drilling equipment.

(c) *Mechanical power augers* generally consist of a continuous helical blade on a central shaft which is rotated into the ground and removes material by displacing it upwards along the blade. *Continuous flight augers*, Fig. 9.3a, often have a hollow shaft which is closed off at the lower end while boring is in progress. At any required depth of penetration the centre rods can be removed to permit access through the stem for undisturbed sampling, *in situ* testing or core drilling with no need to remove the auger from the hole. This is of particular advantage when boring through soils which would otherwise require casing for support.

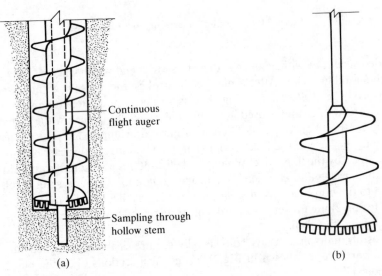

(a)   (b)

Figure 9.3 (a) Continuous flight auger, (b) short-flight auger.

In stiff clays a solid stem auger can be used, as the clay will stand unsupported when the auger is withdrawn to permit sampling or *in situ* testing. Alternatively, a *short-flight auger*, Fig. 9.3b, may be used. This has a fixed length of blade and each time the helix is filled with soil it must be removed from the hole and the blade cleared.

Power augers may come as an attachment to the percussion boring rig, but more usually require greater mechanical power and weight, and are therefore lorry or tractor mounted. They can reach depths of 30–50 m and usually have a diameter in the range 75–300 mm, although in suitable ground conditions inspection shafts up to 1 m in diameter can be formed.

(d) *Wash boring* is a technique which utilizes a light tripod frame fitted with a powered winch and a water pump. The pump forces a high-pressure jet of water through hollow drill rods and out of holes in the end of a chisel bit suspended by cable from the tripod frame. The hole is advanced by raising, rotating and dropping the bit, the loosened and fragmented material being carried to the surface in suspension in the water. Although well suited to rapid boring through sands, silts and soft clays, wash boring is seldom used in Britain.

(e) *Rotary drilling* is the traditional technique for rock exploration, but may also be used in hard clays and marls. It is carried out either as *open-hole drilling* in which a cutting bit removes all the material within the diameter of the hole, or as *core drilling* in which an annular coring bit cuts a continuous core of material which is brought to the surface for examination and possible testing. In weak or fragmented rock, open-hole drilling is generally used, while core drilling is appropriate for intact rock and possibly for very hard clays. Typical core diameters range from 17 to 165 mm, with the commonest sizes being 54 mm and 76 mm.

A drilling fluid pumped down through hollow drill rods serves to lubricate and cool the bit and also flushes the drill debris up the borehole. Water is usually employed as the drilling fluid, although drilling mud in the form of a clay or bentonite slurry may be used, particularly if some support for the sides of the hole is required.

Determination of Groundwater Conditions

An important aspect of any ground investigation is the determination of the groundwater conditions at the site. This is not always a simple matter since the piezometric levels for all strata will not necessarily be the same, particularly when a layer of free-draining material occurs between two relatively impermeable layers. Indeed some strata may exist under artesian conditions (see Example 3.1). Moreover, groundwater conditions may fluctuate with time owing, for instance, to seasonal or tidal variations, and it will be necessary to make observations over an extended period if such fluctuations are to be measured.

The traditional method of determining groundwater levels is to measure the depth to the water surface in a borehole. However, the time required for the water to reach an equilibrium level depends on the permeability of the soil, and in free-draining materials may be only a few hours but in low permeability soils may be days or even weeks. Moreover, even in a cased borehole it may not always be obvious from which soil stratum the water is actually entering—it is possible for groundwater from an upper stratum to seep down the outside of the casing and enter the borehole at a lower level, or even for surface water to run off into the hole during heavy rainfall. For an accurate assessment of the groundwater conditions it is therefore preferable to use some form of *piezometer* installed at the appropriate depth.

All piezometers require some finite flow of water in or out in order to record the true porewater pressure. The time taken for the piezometer to adjust to the true pressure is known as the response time, and this depends on the quantity of flow required to operate the piezometer and the permeability of the soil in which it is placed. For efficient and reliable measurements of porewater pressure, a piezometer should operate with the minimum of flow and should have the shortest possible response time.

The simplest form is the *standpipe piezometer* consisting simply of a pipe with a perforated end section, or alternatively a tube connected to a porous element. The end section or porous element is embedded in a pocket of sand or fine gravel and sealed into the borehole at the appropriate level. The top of the standpipe must be accessible if the water level is to be established by plumbing, and if capped it must be vented to allow equilization of pressure. A Casagrande-type standpipe piezometer is shown in Fig. 9.8a.

The main disadvantage of the standpipe piezometer is in soils of relatively low permeability where its response time is rather slow. In such materials it is preferable to use a *hydraulic piezometer* in which the porewater pressure is sensed by a small porous element and conducted through fine-bore tubes to a mercury manometer or Bourdon gauge. The use of fine-bore tubes and a closed pressure system enables the piezometer to operate effectively with only a small flow through the porous element. However, a rapid response time also requires that the system remains free of air, and therefore most hydraulic piezometers are of the twin-tube type in which the porous element is connected to the measuring point by two tubes which enable de-aired water to be circulated through the system periodically to flush out any air. A typical hydraulic piezometer suitable for borehole use is shown in Fig. 9.8b.

Soil Sampling Techniques

The method used to obtain samples of a soil stratum depends upon the required quality of the samples and the type of soil to be sampled. Sample quality falls broadly into one of two

Table 9.1 Classification for soil samples (BS 5930: 1981)

Sample quality	Soil properties that can reliably be determined
Class 1	Classification; water content; density; strength; deformation and consolidation parameters
Class 2	Classification; water content; density
Class 3	Classification; water content
Class 4	Classification
Class 5	Strata identification only

categories: disturbed and undisturbed. However BS 5930: 1981 recognizes five classes of sample quality based largely on their suitability for reliably determining particular soil properties, as outlined in Table 9.1. Class 1 and 2 samples are commonly regarded as 'undisturbed' and Class 3, 4 and 5 samples as 'disturbed'.

A *disturbed* sample is one in which the macrostructure or fabric of the soil mass has been seriously distorted or even totally destroyed, but whose particle size distribution remains representative of the soil *in situ*. Disturbed samples are used mainly for strata identification and soil classification tests, and are obtained by excavating in trial pits, sampling in boreholes, or even from the clay cutter and augering tools used during test boring. The material recovered from the shell in percussion boring will not, however, satisfy the requirements of a disturbed sample as it may contain broken fragments and will be deficient of the fines left in suspension in the water in the borehole.

In order to obtain consolidation and shear strength parameters for use in settlement and stability analyses, high-quality *undisturbed* samples are required. These must preserve the natural macrostructure and must have the same density and water content as the soil mass *in situ*. In addition to quality, these undisturbed samples must be *representative* of the soil mass in the field. Thus, in soils which possess an obvious fabric of laminations, fissuring, small inclusions or discontinuities, the sample must be large enough to encompass a representative pattern of this fabric (Rowe, 1972b). In such soils this may require the undisturbed samples to be as large as 250 mm in diameter.

Of course, it is impossible to obtain samples that are completely undisturbed. Despite efforts to eliminate physical disturbance, the mere act of removing the sample from the ground will subject it to stress relief and consequently a change in pore pressure. Realistically, therefore, the aim must be to reduce disturbance to a minimum. However, all soils are not equally susceptible to sampling disturbance. Soft clays are particularly sensitive and great care must be exercised during sampling. Moreover, if they possess a permeable macrostructure it is recommended that sampling is carried out with a water level in the borehole to balance the pressure head in the clay, otherwise rapid softening and loss of strength is likely to occur in the clay at the bottom of the hole. On the other hand, stiff clays are generally believed to be less sensitive to disturbance and consequently less elaborate sampling techniques may suffice. The data obtained from laboratory tests on undisturbed samples of clay soils may be supplemented by *in situ* tests carried out in the field.

In the case of non-cohesive soils the lack of stiction makes it virtually impossible to recover undisturbed samples, particularly from below the water table, unless special techniques are employed (e.g., Bishop, 1948; Serota and Jennings, 1958). Consequently, the compressibility and shear strength properties of granular soils are often assessed on the basis of data obtained from *in situ* tests carried out in trial pits or boreholes.

Undisturbed samples may be cut by hand from the base or sides of a trial pit, but are more usually obtained by pushing or driving a sampling tube into the soil at the base of a borehole using the equipment and techniques described below.

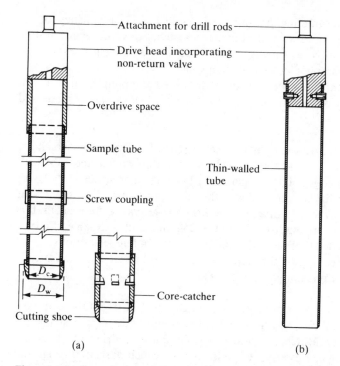

Figure 9.4 (a) General-purpose U 100 open-tube sampler, (b) thin-walled open-tube sampler.

(a) **General-purpose open-tube sampler (U 100)** As shown in Fig. 9.4a, this consists essentially of a steel tube with a screw thread at each end. A cutting shoe is fitted to the lower end, and the upper end screws into a drive head which can be attached to the drill rods of a boring rig. The head has an overdrive space and incorporates a non-return valve to permit the escape of air or water as the sample enters the tube.

The *area ratio* of the sampler, defined as

$$A_r = \frac{D_w^2 - D_c^2}{D_c^2} \times 100 \text{ per cent} \tag{9.1}$$

gives a measure of the mechanical disturbance of the sample, being the ratio of the volume of soil displaced by the sampling tube to the volume of the sample. In order to minimize sampling disturbance, this ratio should be as low as possible consistent with the strength requirements of the tube.

The general-purpose open-tube sampler has an internal diameter of 100 mm and an area ratio in the order of 25–30 per cent, and is often referred to as the U 100 sampler. In practice, two sampling tubes are often coupled together forming a sampler about 1 m in length. This has the advantage that the additional length helps to penetrate well past the zone of disturbed material likely to be encountered at the base of the borehole, but has the disadvantage that the side friction on the sample from the inside of the tube may increase to the point where the sample suffers excessive compression and disturbance.

Before attempting to sample, the bottom of the borehole (or the base of the trial pit) should be cleared of loose or fragmented material. The sampler is then driven into the soil either by dynamic means using a drop hammer or by a continuous static thrust from a hydraulic jack. There is some suggestion that static driving may induce less disturbance and may be less likely to result in overdriving of the sampler. On withdrawal of the sampler, the non-return valve assists in retaining the sample in the tube. When sampling in non-cohesive soils there is a tendency for the sample to drop out of the tube as it is withdrawn. Fitting a core-catcher (a short length of tube with spring-loaded flaps to grip the sample, as shown in Fig. 9.4a) between the cutting shoe and the sampling tube helps to improve sample recovery in such soils.

The general-purpose open-tube sampler is suitable for undisturbed sampling in firm to stiff clays, but is also used to obtain partly disturbed samples of soft or hard clays, clayey sands and silts, and soft rocks.

(b) **Thin-walled open-tube sampler** Thin-walled samplers are designed for use in soils which are particularly sensitive to disturbance. The open-tube type consists of a thin-walled steel tube with the lower end shaped to form a cutting edge and the upper end attached to a drive head fitted with a non-return valve, as shown in Fig. 9.4b. The reduced wall thickness gives an area ratio of about 10 per cent, but restricts the use of this type of sampler to soft–firm fine-grained cohesive soils. It is available in various internal diameters ranging from 75 mm to 250 mm, and is capable of giving top quality undisturbed samples provided that the soil at the base of the borehole has not suffered serious disturbance by the action of boring or through stress relief. When such disturbance is suspected, the use of a thin-walled piston sampler is preferable.

(c) **Stationary piston sampler** Piston samplers are formed from thin-walled steel tube and have an area ratio of about 10 per cent. As shown in Fig. 9.5a, the lower end of the tube is shaped to form a cutting edge and the upper end is attached to a drive head and hollow drill rods. The tube contains a close-fitting sliding piston which is attached to inner rods which pass up through the

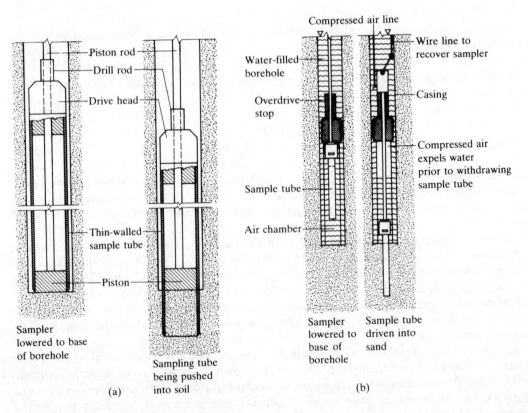

Figure 9.5 (a) Stationary piston sampler, (b) Bishop sand sampler.

hollow drill rods. Initially, the piston is locked in position at the lower end of the sampling tube while it is lowered to the bottom of the borehole. If necessary, the whole assembly can be jacked through any disturbed material at the base of the borehole until the required sample level is reached, typically a distance of about 0.5 m. The piston is then unlocked and held stationary at this level while the sampling tube is pushed down into the soil under a static thrust until the drive head encounters the upper face of the piston. The piston is then clamped at the upper end of the tube as the sampler is extracted. Any tendency for the sample to slip out at this stage creates a vacuum between it and the piston which helps to retain the sample in the tube.

Piston samplers are available in diameters of 75 mm, 100 mm and 250 mm, and are used principally in low-strength fine-grained soils, including sensitive clays, in which they are capable of giving top-quality undisturbed samples.

(d) **The Bishop sand sampler** Recovery of tube samples from non-cohesive silt or sand deposits below the water table presents special difficulties which may be overcome to some degree by use of the Bishop compressed air sampler (Bishop, 1948), shown in Fig. 9.5b. This comprises a sampling tube located within an air chamber supplied by a compressed air line. The assembly is lowered to the base of a water-filled borehole, the sampling tube is pushed out of the air chamber and into the soil, and the water in the chamber is expelled by compressed air. During withdrawal the sample remains isolated from the water in the borehole, and the apparent stiction generated by the negative pore pressures within the sample assists in retaining the soil in the tube.

(e) **Block samples** In some fissured clays, marls or weak rocks, the disturbance produced by tube sampling may be unacceptable. Alternatively, it may be that a specially orientated sample is required, or a particularly large sample to ensure that the natural macrofabric of the material is adequately represented.

In such cases, block samples may be cut by hand from material exposed in trial pits, inspection shafts or excavations. A bench is usually formed and material removed from around the sides of a cube to give access for final trimming. A box is eased down over the sample as trimming is carried out, and any gaps are filled with paraffin wax. With the box in place the base is finally cut, the sample is removed and the exposed face waxed and sealed. It is important that the exact location and orientation of the sample is clearly and indelibly marked on the box before or immediately after the sample is cut.

(f) **Continuous soil sampling** At an early stage in the ground investigation, it may be advisable or even necessary to examine and record the soil fabric over the proposed depth of exploration before deciding at what precise location and depth undisturbed samples should be taken. This is particularly important in soft laminated clay deposits where thin bands of silt, sand or peat may abound, and it can best be achieved by continuous sampling using specialist equipment to overcome the problem of excessive side friction associated with very long sampling tubes.

One such system is the *Swedish foil sampler* (Kjellman *et al.*, 1950) which is capable of producing a 68-mm diameter continuous core sample over depths in the order of 25 m. As the tube is being driven, steel foil strips are fed from magazines in the sampler head to encase the soil sample and reduce the effects of side friction. Lengths of sampling tube are attached as required to the upper end of the sampler. On withdrawal the lengths of tube are uncoupled and the continuous core encased in foil is cut into suitable lengths for transportation to the laboratory.

An alternative is the *Delft system* in which a core sample is continuously fed into a nylon stockinette sleeve which has been impregnated with a vulcanizing fluid to make it impervious. The sample within the sleeve is supported by a bentonite–barytes fluid of comparable density to the surrounding ground. This system offers a choice of two diameters, 29 mm and 66 mm, and normally has a maximum penetration of 18 m, although in certain cases depths up to 30 m can be achieved. During recovery, the continuous core is cut into lengths of about 1 m.

In the laboratory the sections of continuous core can be laid out, carefully split by pulling apart along their length, inspected, logged and allowed to dry. Often the natural fabric will be revealed clearly only as the drying process takes place since any bands of sand dry out first, followed by the silt and finally the clay. During this stage the samples may be photographed to provide a permanent record.

Laboratory and *in situ* Testing of Soils

The soil samples obtained during the ground investigation are subjected to laboratory testing in order to determine the properties relevant to a classification and description of the soil, and to obtain parameters for use in design calculations. The most important of these tests are described elsewhere in the text: soil classification tests in Chapter 1, consolidation and permeability tests in Chapter 4, shear strength tests in Chapter 5, and compaction tests later in this Chapter.

However, under certain circumstances the strength, compressibility or permeability parameters required for design calculations can more reliably be determined from *in situ* tests carried out in trial pits or boreholes rather than from laboratory tests. This is particularly true in the case of cohesionless soils and very sensitive clay soils where the recovery of undisturbed samples is very difficult, or in the case of soils having a highly defined macrostructure in which it may be difficult to obtain undisturbed samples large enough to be representative.

The *standard penetration test, cone penetrometer test* and *plate load test* are among the commonest *in situ* tests carried out to determine strength and compressibility characteristics, and have already been discussed in Sec. 8.4.

The *vane shear test* (BS 1377: 1975, Test 18; ASTM D–2573–72) is carried out to determine the *in situ* undrained shear strength of fully saturated intact clays by measuring the torque necessary to rotate a cruciform-shaped vane similar to that shown in Fig. 9.6a which has been pushed into the undisturbed soil below the base of a borehole. The vane is rotated at some 6–12° per minute and produces a cylindrical surface of shear which closely approximates to the surface prescribed by the blades of the vane.

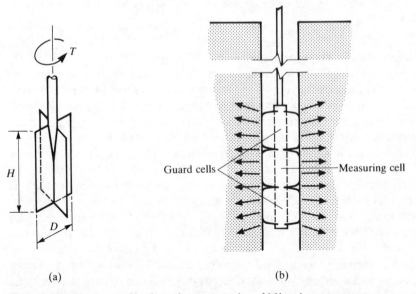

(a)   (b)

Figure 9.6 (a) Shear vane, (b) schematic representation of Ménard pressuremeter.

The relationship between the torque at failure, T, and the undrained shear strength, c_u, is given by

$$T = \pi c_u \left(\frac{D^2 H}{2} + \frac{D^3}{6} \right) \tag{9.2}$$

where D and H are respectively the overall width and height of the vane blades.

After determining the undisturbed strength, measurement of the remoulded strength can be achieved by rapidly rotating the vane through 6 complete turns, waiting for 5 minutes and then re-testing in the normal way.

The vane test is usually carried out in clays with an undrained shear strength not exceeding about 100 kN/m^2. For soils having $c_u < 50 \text{ kN/m}^2$, a vane with blades about 150 mm in height and 75 mm in width would usually be used, and for soils having a higher strength a vane with blades about 100 mm × 50 mm would be more suitable.

The *pressuremeter test* (BS 5930: 1981, Sec. 21.7) employs a cylindrical probe which is inserted to the required depth in an appropriately sized borehole and using compressed air or gas is expanded laterally as a means of stressing the ground radially. Measurements of the applied pressure and the resulting deformation enable the strength and deformation characteristics of the ground to be investigated.

The concept of the borehole pressuremeter was pioneered by Ménard in the fifties and the *Ménard pressuremeter*, shown schematically in Fig. 9.6b, is the probe in most common use (Ménard, 1965). It consists of three separate pressurizing cells, although only the water-filled central cell is used for measurement. The pressure applied to the water can be continuously monitored while the volume of water entering the central cell is measured to yield the volume change in the ground. The guard cells top and bottom are similarly pressurized in an effort to eliminate end effects and ensure a plane strain condition in the ground adjacent to the measuring cell. The probe comes in a number of sizes up to 75 mm in diameter and can be used in soil and weak rock. A gas-expandable pressuremeter with a 150-mm diameter probe in which the deformation over the central portion is recorded directly by potentiometers was developed by McKinlay and Anderson (1975) for use primarily in glacial tills.

A *self-boring pressuremeter* referred to as the Camkometer (Cambridge K_0 meter) was developed in an attempt to minimize disturbance of the soil during boring (Wroth and Hughes, 1973; Windle and Wroth, 1977). The device is jacked slowly into the ground while the soil is broken up by a rotating cutting head at the lower end, the cuttings being flushed out in water or drilling mud circulated through the cutting head from the surface. During the test an inflatable rubber membrane is expanded using gas pressure, the expansion being monitored electrically by three feelers within the probe. A total pressure cell and a pore pressure cell are also incorporated within the membrane. In addition to minimizing disturbance, the self-boring pressuremeter has the advantage over borehole-type probes that it can be used below the water table in soft clays or loose granular soils which would be liable to collapse in an unsupported borehole.

An interesting discussion of the interpretation and use of *in situ* test results has been presented by Wroth (1984).

Field pumping tests (BS 5930: 1981, Secs 25 and 26) may be carried out to determine the mass permeability of free-draining soil deposits. The usual practice is to pump water out of a borehole or pumping well until steady state conditions are reached, and then observe the drawdown in piezometric level in observation wells set at different radial distances from the pumping well. The interpretation of pumping test results has been considered in Chapter 3.

Field Instrumentation

It is important to appreciate that in the design of soil structures the ground engineer has to cope with many uncertainties: the enormous variability of many soil deposits, the problems of recovering representative undisturbed samples for laboratory testing, and the limitations of many of the *in situ* tests. Thus, despite elaborate testing techniques and elegant analytical methods for predicting stresses and deformations, the engineer can never really be sure how a particular soil structure will actually behave in practice.

For this reason, in recent years it has become increasingly common on many major projects to install field instrumentation during the construction stage to monitor behaviour during construction and subsequently under operating conditions. This gives the engineer scope to modify the existing design if the behaviour observed during construction deviates significantly from that assumed in the design. Moreover, instrumentation provides invaluable information on soil/structure interaction which should be a benefit in the future design of similar structures.

Methods of monitoring the soil behaviour range from the use of simple surveying techniques for measuring changes in level or distance to relatively sophisticated sensors for recording pressures and displacements. However, the introduction of any extraneous measuring device will inevitably change the *in situ* regime that it is intended to measure, and therefore it is essential that instrumentation equipment is designed so as to reduce this change to a minimum. Another important but often conflicting factor in the design of such equipment is that it must be capable of withstanding relatively rough treatment during and after installation, and of operating in a somewhat harsh environment, often submerged below groundwater level. An extensive review of field instrumentation equipment, its installation and uses is given by Hanna (1973).

The principal applications of field instrumentation are in the measurement of total pressure, porewater pressure, and horizontal and vertical displacement.

Measurement of total pressure Most *in situ* measurements of total pressure are made using earth pressure cells which operate on the deflecting diaphragm principle, the deflection being measured either by electrical resistance strain gauges mounted on the diaphragm or by monitoring the changes in frequency of a vibrating wire connected to the diaphragm. In order to have the minimum influence on the *in situ* stress regime, these cells are made as flat as possible with a stiff diaphragm having a maximum deflection only about 1/2000th of the diameter. Figure 9.7 shows a typical vibrating wire type cell developed by Thomas and Ward (1969).

Alternatively, earth pressure cells may operate on a hydraulic principle. The commonest of this type is the Glotzl cell which consists of a thin, flat, oil-filled sensing pad embedded in the soil. Any change in pressure on the pad results in an equal pressure change in the oil which can be measured by mechanical means.

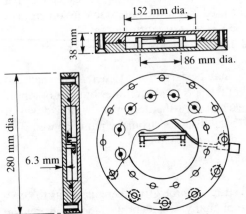

Figure 9.7 Total pressure cell. (From Thomas and Ward, 1969.)

Measurement of porewater pressure To determine the *in situ* effective stresses in a soil mass, we need to monitor not only values of total stress but also values of pore pressure. *In situ* measurements of porewater pressure are made using *piezometers*. The operating principles of the piezometer have been described earlier in this section in connection with the determination of groundwater conditions, where it is explained that for efficient and reliable performance a piezometer should require the minimum of flow in or out and should have the shortest possible response time.

Also described earlier are piezometers designed particularly for installation in boreholes: the simple *standpipe* piezometer, Fig. 9.8a, which supports a standing column of water the top level of which defines the porewater pressure at the piezometer tip, and the more widely used twin-tube *hydraulic* piezometer, Fig. 9.8b, which incorporates fine-bore tubing and a closed pressure system connected to a mercury manometer or Bourdon gauge. The twin tubes enable de-aired water to be circulated through the system to flush out any air, the presence of which has an adverse effect on the response time.

For installation in partly saturated fill materials, hydraulic piezometers require additional features to restrict the build-up of air in the system. The piezometer tip has a fine-grained ceramic element with a high air-entry value, and the twin tubes are of polythene-coated nylon to prevent the diffusion of air or water through the walls of the tubing, nylon being impermeable to air and polythene to water. A Bishop-type hydraulic piezometer suitable for use in embankment fill materials is shown in Fig. 9.8c. An additional feature of the twin-tube hydraulic piezometer is the facility to carry out direct measurements of *in situ* permeability—see, for example, Bishop and Al-Dhahir (1970).

Alternative types include the *electrical* piezometer in which the *in situ* porewater pressure is transmitted through a porous element and acts on a diaphragm, deflections of which are recorded using either vibrating wire gauges or electrical resistance strain gauges, and the *pneumatic* piezometer which has twin air lines connected to a valve located within the tip close to the porous element, opening of the valve occurring when a gradually increasing air supply pressure in one of the lines just balances the *in situ* porewater pressure transmitted through the porous element. In some types of pneumatic piezometer, nitrogen or oil is used instead of air as the pressurizing fluid. In the absence of twin hydraulic leads, neither electrical nor pneumatic piezometers permit circulation of de-aired water through the tip or the facility for *in situ* permeability measurements.

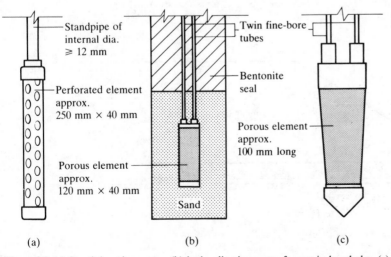

(a)　　　　　　　　(b)　　　　　　　　(c)

Figure 9.8 (a) Standpipe piezometer, (b) hydraulic piezometer for use in boreholes, (c) hydraulic piezometer for use in embankments.

Measurement of displacement The simplest method of establishing the extent of any displacement of a structure is through the use of precise levelling techniques and accurate electronic distance measurement to determine changes in level and position of clearly defined reference points on the structure. However, different techniques are required to monitor internal displacements within a soil structure or a foundation stratum.

Single point remote settlement gauges can be used to monitor vertical displacements of a number of discrete points in the soil. The most elementary of these gauges operates on a simple overflow principle, as shown diagrammatically in Fig. 9.9a. One end of a flexible tube is located within a measuring cell and positioned in the soil at the point where the settlement is to be monitored. Water fed into the other end of the tube overflows at the measuring cell. If the input end has a graduated vertical standpipe, this will then register a water level coincident with the elevation of the overflow end of the tube. More sophisticated versions of single and multiple point remote settlement gauges are described by Hanna (1973).

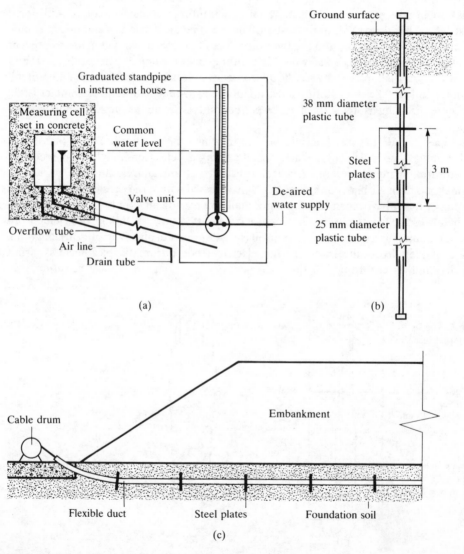

(a)

(b)

(c)

Figure 9.9 Schematic representation of (a) single point remote settlement gauge, (b) vertical tube settlement gauge, (c) full profile gauge.

Vertical tube settlement gauges allow the settlement to be monitored at various points on a vertical section through the soil mass. Each gauge consists of a series of telescopic plastic tubes to which a number of 300 mm square steel plates are attached, as shown in Fig. 9.9b. The steel plates are able to move with the soil and are free from any restraint by the tubing. The position of each plate is detected by an electronic probe lowered down the tube on the end of a graduated cable. Similar tube gauges can be installed to monitor movements in a horizontal direction in the soil.

Full profile gauges are used for measuring vertical and horizontal displacements, particularly under embankments, and operate on the principle of pulling a torpedo or probe through a flexible pipe duct buried in a trench across the line of the embankment, as shown in Fig. 9.9c. Steel plates are positioned over the pipe at regular intervals, as described for the tube settlement gauge. The vertical settlement profile of the duct is monitored using a torpedo which is fitted with either an overflow gauge operating as described above or a strain-gauged transducer, and is pulled through the duct on the end of a cable. Horizontal displacements are monitored in a similar manner by locating the positions of the steel plates using an electronic probe.

Inclinometer tubes offer an alternative method of monitoring horizontal displacements in foundation soils and embankments. In its simplest form this method measures the deformed profile of a flexible tube installed originally near-vertically in the ground. A torpedo fitted with wheels to run in guide slots on the inside of the tube is lowered down on a cable and registers the inclination of the tube from the vertical at pre-selected intervals of depth. Rotating the torpedo through 90° and lowering it down the tube again gives readings of slope in two mutually perpendicular directions, from which two components of horizontal deflection can be determined.

9.2 COMPACTION OF SOILS

Compaction is the term used to describe the process of densification of a material by mechanical means, the increase in density being achieved by decreasing the air voids content with the water content remaining approximately the same.

In practice, compaction is frequently carried out on materials which are being used as fill, as in the construction of embankments, but may also be carried out on natural soils *in situ*, as in the case of ground improvement projects.

The primary objective of compaction is to improve the engineering properties of the material in any or all of the following ways:

(a) by increasing the shear strength and thereby improving the stability of embankments and the bearing capacity of foundations and pavements,
(b) by decreasing the compressibility and thereby reducing settlements,
(c) by decreasing the void ratio and thereby reducing the permeability,
(d) by reducing the potential for swelling, shrinkage and frost heave.

The state of compaction of a soil or fill is measured quantitatively in terms of its dry density ρ_d. The dry density achieved by a process of compaction is found to depend upon the energy expended during the compaction process, referred to as the *compactive effort*, and also on the water content during compaction.

Typical relationships between dry density, water content and compactive effort are obtained from laboratory compaction tests.

Laboratory Compaction

Laboratory compaction essentially involves compacting a specimen of moist soil into a cylindrical mould of specified volume under a specified compactive effort. A number of different

Table 9.2 Laboratory compaction tests

Test	Standard reference	Rammer		Volume of mould	Layers	Blows per layer
		Mass	Height of fall			
2.5 kg rammer method	BS 1377: 1975 Test 12	2.5 kg	300 mm	1000 cm^3	3	27
4.5 kg rammer method	BS 1377: 1975 Test 13	4.5 kg	450 mm	1000 cm^3	5	27
(Standard) Proctor Standard AASHTO	ASTM D–698–78 AASHTO T–99	2.49 kg (5.5 lbs)	305 mm (12 in)	944 cm^3 ($\frac{1}{30}$ ft^3)	3	25
Modified Proctor Modified AASHTO	ASTM D–1557–78 AASHTO T–180	4.54 kg (10 lbs)	457 mm (18 in)	944 cm^3 ($\frac{1}{30}$ ft^3)	5	25
Vibrating hammer method	BS 1377: 1975 Test 14	This utilizes a CBR mould to compact a sample approximately 2360 cm^3 in volume using a vibrating hammer, the soil being compacted in 3 equal layers each vibrated for 60 seconds				

tests are in common use, three based on British standards and two on US standards. The characteristics of these tests and the reference sources are given in Table 9.2. The first four involve impact or dynamic compaction using a metal rammer of specified mass which is allowed to fall freely through a specified height, the soil being compacted in a specified number of equal layers, each layer receiving a specified number of blows. The fifth test, however, produces compaction by a combination of static pressure and vibratory action, the soil being compacted in three equal layers by pressing a vibrating hammer firmly down onto each layer for a period of 60 seconds.

Once the compacted specimen has been prepared, its bulk density and water content are readily determined and the corresponding dry density appropriate to that water content can be calculated using Eq. (1.23) in the form

$$\rho_d = \frac{\rho}{1 + w} \tag{9.3}$$

This procedure is carried out at least five times over a range of water contents and the compaction characteristics of the soil are presented in the form of a plot of dry density against water content.

Typical results obtained from standard compaction tests on a well-graded silty sand and a uniform sand are shown in Fig. 9.10. Both curves exhibit an essentially similar characteristic—the dry density initially increasing with increase in water content, then passing through a peak value and finally decreasing again at high water contents. The peak defines the *optimum water content* w_{opt} at which the soil obtains its *maximum dry density* $\rho_{d\,max}$. However, a comparison of curves (a) and (b) in Fig. 9.10 indicates that in the case of the uniform sand, variations in water content did not produce such a marked difference in dry density as that achieved in the well-graded silty sand. In fact, this trend is generally typical in that compaction is more effective in well-graded materials containing some fines than in uniformly graded materials devoid of fines.

The reason for this characteristic peak in the compaction curve, particularly pronounced in soils containing some fines, is not fully understood, but it is generally thought to be more than simply a matter of the addition of water contributing to lubrication at particle contact points and an improved workability. A possible explanation is that at low water contents the soil tends to be dry and lumpy. With little water to aid the breaking-up process, a significant proportion of the compactive effort is absorbed in simply crushing the lumps before any compaction of the particles

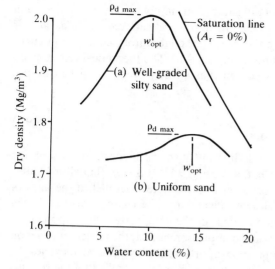

Figure 9.10 Typical laboratory compaction curves for well-graded and uniform soils.

can occur. At higher water contents, sufficient water becomes available to penetrate and help break up the lumps while allowing adsorbed water layers to develop more fully around the clay mineral particles in the fines. This reduces interparticle bonding, permitting a greater orientation of the clay particles and the development of a more dispersed microstructure. Thus, reductions in void space and higher densities are obtained. Beyond the optimum value, however, increases in water content are progressively less effective in reducing the now quite small air voids content. Much of the compactive effort is absorbed by the pore water as excess porewater pressures, the soil particles are displaced rather than compacted, and increases in void space and therefore lower densities result.

The effect of applying different compactive efforts is illustrated by the two compaction curves obtained for the same soil under different test conditions shown in Fig. 9.11. A higher compactive effort is seen to give a higher maximum dry density but at a lower optimum water content.

For any particular water content, the equivalent dry density of a soil will *theoretically* achieve its highest value at full saturation, i.e., when the air voids content is reduced to zero. In practice,

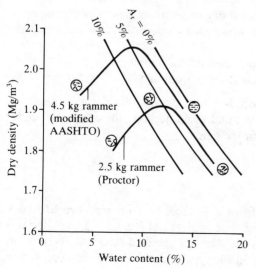

Figure 9.11 Influence of compactive effort on the compaction characteristics of soils.

however, it is not possible to achieve conditions of full saturation simply by compaction, a small quantity of air will always remain in the voids. Thus, if the theoretical *zero air voids line* or *saturation line* is superimposed on the plot of the test results, the laboratory compaction curve must lie entirely to the left of the zero air voids line, as in Fig. 9.10. The theoretical relationship between dry density, water content and air voids content has already been established by Eq. (1.24):

$$\rho_d = \frac{G_s(1 - A_r)}{(1 + G_s w)} \rho_w \qquad (9.4)$$

and can be used to plot not only the zero air voids line but also the theoretical lines of, for example, 5 per cent and 10 per cent air voids content, as in Fig. 9.11. It is seen that shortly after passing through the peak the compaction curve becomes approximately parallel to the lines of constant air voids, indicating an essentially constant *minimum air voids content*. Also it is seen that the minimum air voids content is largely independent of the compactive effort applied.

As might be anticipated in view of earlier discussion, compaction has a rather different effect on cohesionless soils than those containing a significant proportion of clay mineral particles. In compacted granular material, the engineering properties are primarily controlled by the relative density achieved by compaction and to a much lesser extent by the water content of the soil and the method of compaction employed; as a general rule the higher the density achieved, the higher the strength and the lower the compressibility.

However, the microstructure and engineering properties of compacted clays depend not only on the water content during compaction and the compactive effort applied, but also on the method of compaction and the particular type of soil. Research has shown that for a constant compactive effort the clay mineral particles tend to develop a progressively greater orientation as the water content during compaction is increased (Lambe, 1958): clays compacted at water contents on the dry side of optimum have a flocculated structure, but those compacted at water contents on the wet side of optimum have a much more dispersed structure, as in Fig. 9.11. At higher compactive efforts a greater degree of dispersion is observed, even at water contents on the dry side of optimum.

As a consequence of this the engineering behaviour of compacted clays is really rather complex (Lambe, 1958; Seed and Chan, 1959). However, some general trends can be noted:

(a) samples compacted dry of optimum have higher strengths than those compacted wet of optimum,
(b) at low consolidation pressures, samples compacted dry of optimum have lower compressibility than those compacted wet of optimum, while at high consolidation pressures the opposite trend is observed,
(c) the potential for swelling is greater in clays compacted dry of optimum,
(d) shrinkage is more pronounced in clays compacted wet of optimum.

Since the primary objective of field compaction is the improvement of the engineering properties of the soil, these factors must be borne in mind when deciding the conditions under which a particular material should be compacted in the field.

Field Compaction

Fill materials are usually either soils excavated from a suitable borrow area, crushed rock obtained from a quarry, or industrial waste products (e.g., pulverized fuel ash). The material is transported to the fill area and spread out in layers or *lifts* of a specified thickness. Typical lift thicknesses range from 150 to 500 mm, depending on the type of material and the compaction equipment to be used. If the material is not naturally at a water content within the specified range, it may require to be wetted or allowed to dry out prior to compaction.

The equipment used to produce compaction in the field includes vibrating plates, power rammers and many different types of roller, the commonest of which are described below. These achieve compaction through either or a combination of static pressure, kneading action, vibration or impact—the compactive effort to be applied being specified in terms of a certain number of *passes* or *coverages*. The choice of compaction equipment depends on the particular field application and the type of fill material. The performance of field compaction equipment has been extensively reviewed by D'Appolonia *et al.* (1969), Johnson and Sallberg (1960), Lewis (1960) and Selig and Yoo (1977).

Vibrating plates and *power rammers* are examples of hand-operated compaction equipment and are used particularly in small areas where access for larger plant such as rollers would be difficult or where their use would not be justified, e.g., compacting fill in narrow trenches, behind bridge abutments or retaining walls.

Smooth-wheeled rollers have hollow steel drums which can be filled with sand or water to add ballast, and may be self-propelled or towed. Unless fitted with vibrators, they compact under their static weight only with contact pressures up to about 400 kN/m². The principal application of smooth-wheeled rollers is for subgrade or base course compaction of well-graded sand/gravel mixtures and the compaction of asphalt pavements. However, they may also be used on fine-grained soil provided it is not too wet, but should not be employed in the compaction of the impermeable core section of water-retaining embankments where the smooth interface produced between successive lifts could constitute a possible source of seepage.

Sheepsfoot rollers have hollow steel drums attached to which are numerous round or rectangular tapered protrusions or 'feet', usually in the order of 150–250 mm in length and 25–80 cm² in end area. The feet generate very high contact pressures which may range from 1500 to 7500 kN/m², depending on the size of the feet and the drum, and whether or not it has added ballast. The rollers may be self-propelled or towed.

Initially, in the compaction of each lift the feet penetrate the soil to their full extent. With each pass of the roller the soil layer is compacted from the bottom upwards by a combination of static pressure and kneading action, until eventually the roller 'walks out' of the lift as the upper part is compacted. The sheepsfoot roller is effective in fine-grained soils and coarse-grained soils with more than about 20 per cent fines, and is particularly applicable in earth dam construction where bonding between successive lifts in the impermeable core is especially important.

Rubber-tyred rollers have between two and six closely spaced tyred wheels mounted on each of two axles, the rear axle usually having one more wheel than the front axle and the wheel tracks offset to ensure coverage of the entire soil surface. Typical tyre pressures may be up to 700 kN/m², producing compaction by a combination of static pressure and kneading action. The axles generally permit a certain amount of vertical movement of the wheels in order to prevent the bridging over of low spots on uneven ground. Rubber-tyred rollers are suitable for most fine and coarse grained soils except uniformly graded materials, and in common with the other types may be self-propelled or towed.

Vibratory rollers. Vibrators can be attached to any of the above types of roller to impart an additional vibratory action to the soil being compacted. The operating frequency is commonly within the range 20–80 Hz (Broms and Forssblad, 1969). Vibratory rollers are particularly effective in the compaction of granular soils in which there is a virtual absence of fines.

Specification and Control of Field Compaction

The extent to which field compaction is effective depends on many factors, including the type of soil, its water content, lift thickness, type of compaction equipment, speed of coverage and number of passes. Therefore once the compaction characteristics of the borrow materials have been defined by standard laboratory tests but before earthworks have begun, it is necessary to prepare specifications to ensure that adequate and effective field compaction is achieved. The compaction specifications either define the end result to be achieved or the method of compaction.

When specification is in terms of the *end result to be achieved*, common practice is to prescribe a required *relative compaction*, defined as the ratio of the field dry density to the maximum dry density obtained in a standard laboratory test. That is

$$\text{Relative compaction (RC)} = \frac{\rho_{d\,field}}{\rho_{d\,max}} \tag{9.5}$$

Relative compaction is usually expressed as a percentage, with the typical requirement being for values in the range 90–100 per cent.

However, specification of a relative compaction alone is not usually enough. By way of illustration, consider that the curve in Fig. 9.12 represents the maximum compactive effort available for a particular field application. In order to obtain the specified relative compaction, the placement water content should be within the range shown, otherwise it will probably be impossible to achieve the required dry density no matter how much the soil is compacted. Therefore the water content must also be a criterion for control. Furthermore the strength, compressibility, shrinkage and swelling characteristics of the soil will be influenced by whether it is compacted wet or dry of the optimum water content, and therefore the engineering properties required of the compacted soil are likely to dictate an even narrower range of water content over which compaction in the field may be carried out. This range of water content must then be prescribed in the compaction specification together with the required relative compaction.

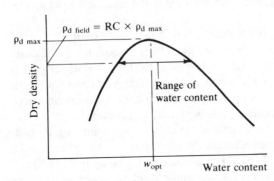

Figure 9.12 Range of placement water content for specified relative compaction.

An alternative way of specifying the end result to be achieved is in terms of a final air voids content with an associated maximum water content.

However, for granular soils containing little or no fines, the water content has a much less significant effect and the engineering properties are dependent essentially on the *relative density* achieved by compaction. For these materials, the water content is not necessarily a prescribed criterion and the compaction specification may simply be in terms of a required relative density or relative compaction. Lee and Singh (1971) conducted a review of published data on 47 different granular soils and, based on this, have suggested an approximate correlation between relative density and relative compaction within which relative density values from 0 to 100 per cent correspond with relative compaction values from 80 to 100 per cent.

When specification is in terms of the *method of compaction*, the type and weight of roller, the number of passes and the lift thicknesses are prescribed. This information is obtained at the design stage by constructing trial sections of earthworks using different compaction equipment and experimenting with various compactive efforts and lift thicknesses in order to determine the most effective and efficient combination. However, trial sections are expensive and therefore method specifications can be justified only on major earthwork projects such as earth dams.

Once the earthwork project is under way, *field control tests* must be carried out in order to ensure that the work meets the specifications for compaction. Control tests measure the density and water content of the compacted soil either by taking samples or by *in situ* methods.

In fine-grained cohesive soils, representative samples can generally be extracted using a cylindrical core-cutter which is pushed into the soil until full and then dug out. The ends of the sample are trimmed flush with the ends of the cylinder and the mass of soil occupying the known volume of cylinder is determined. A specimen of the sample is then taken for a water content determination (BS 1377: 1975, Test 15(D); ASTM D–2937–71).

In coarse-grained or granular soils a different technique is usually required. A hole is excavated at the desired level in the soil, the mass of material removed is recorded and a specimen of the excavated material is taken for water content determination. The volume of the hole is then measured using an appropriate technique such as the sand replacement method (BS 1377: 1975, Test 15(A)–(C); ASTM D–1556–64) or the rubber balloon method (ASTM D–2167–66).

Knowing the mass and volume of the sample removed, the bulk density of the compacted soil is then readily determined, and having calculated the water content of the soil the corresponding field dry density is obtained from Eq. (9.3). Comparing the field dry density with the maximum dry density from the specified laboratory test gives the relative compaction.

However, these field control techniques are not entirely satisfactory. In the first instance, determination of the water content by the traditional oven-drying method takes time, probably a full working day, and several lifts may have been placed and compacted over the test area before the results are available. To overcome this problem, attempts have been made to devise more rapid methods of determining the water content of samples. Pan drying over an open flame has been tried but without any great success, mainly because of difficulties in controlling the temperature. An alternative method that has proved rather more successful uses the *speedy moisture tester*. The sample of wet soil is weighed and then mixed with a quantity of calcium carbide in a sealed chamber. The water in the sample reacts with the carbide to form acetylene gas, the quantity of gas produced and hence the pressure generated in the sealed chamber being proportional to the amount of water in the sample. The gas pressure registers on a calibrated gauge attached to the chamber and from this reading the water content of the soil can be obtained.

Another problem inherent in these field density tests concerns the determination of the volume of the excavated hole. Neither the sand replacement nor the balloon method is particularly precise. The sand replacement method relies on the sand filling the hole at the calibrated density otherwise the volume recorded will be in error, and therefore the method is very sensitive to vibrations from nearby plant and equipment which may cause the sand in the hole to compact. The balloon method is known to be subject to error if the compacted soil contains large particles which cause the sides and base of the hole to be very uneven and pitted.

Because of these shortcomings in the traditional field density and water content tests, it has become increasingly common in recent years to employ *nuclear methods* for *in situ* determinations of bulk density and water content. The fundamental principles involved in these nuclear methods are fairly straightforward, but a detailed explanation of the physics is very complex and beyond the scope of this treatment.

Basically, two emission sources and two detectors are necessary to determine both density and water content. Gamma ray emission is used to determine the density of the soil. Gamma radiation emitted from the source is scattered on collision with the soil particles. The amount of scatter is detected by a Geiger counter and is proportional to the density of the soil (ASTM D–2922–78).

Fast neutron emission is used to determine the water content of the soil. Neutrons emitted from the source scatter and lose energy on collision with hydrogen atoms in the pore water. The slow neutrons so produced are detected by a counter, the number being proportional to the amount of water present in the voids.

There are two main types of equipment in general use. One is the *direct transmission* apparatus which has the emission source located in a probe which is inserted into a hole formed in the soil, and the detector located in a unit placed on the soil surface. In coarse-grained soils where insertion of the probe may prove difficult, it is probably preferable to use the alternative *backscatter* apparatus in which both the emission source and the detector are housed in a unit which rests on or just above the soil surface.

A major advantage of nuclear methods is that results are obtained within minutes and if necessary remedial action can be taken to improve the quality of a lift before too much additional material has been placed. Also each test gives average values of density and water content over a significant volume of soil, and since it is quick and easy to carry out a large number of tests the use of these techniques affords a better statistical control of the fill.

If the quality of field compaction is to be assessed by density measurements then field control tests must be carried out frequently. No absolute criterion has been established to govern the frequency of testing but, depending on the extent and nature of the earthworks and the control required, tests would typically be conducted for every 200–2000 m^3 of material placed. However, because of the inherent variability of soils, the assessment of quality must be based on the results of a number of tests and not just one, and therefore the results of control tests are well suited to evaluation by statistical methods. A detailed treatment of the statistical approach to quality assurance is presented by Lee *et al.* (1983).

Methods of Deep Compaction

The use of surface rollers for field compaction is particularly suitable for fill materials placed in lifts of controlled thickness. However, in an existing layer of soil the influence of this type of equipment is confined to only a few metres below the surface (D'Appolonia *et al.*, 1969). Therefore when it is necessary to densify existing deep deposits of loose granular soil or soft clay, even the heaviest surface rollers are ineffective and other techniques must be employed.

Vibroflotation This technique utilizes a large probe or *vibroflot* consisting of a cylindrical tube with water jets top and bottom and housing eccentrically rotating weights to produce vibratory motion in a horizontal plane. The probe is some 400 mm in diameter, 2 m in length and has a mass of about 2 tonnes.

Suspended vertically from a crane, the vibrating probe is jetted downwards into the soil until the required penetration depth is achieved. The jetting pressure is then reduced and the water directed to the upper jets to maintain a clear space around the probe into which sand or river gravel is fed from the surface. The probe is progressively raised in about 300-mm thick lifts, the fill in each lift being compacted in turn until ground surface is reached, as shown in Fig. 9.13. The extent of the compacted zone produced around the probe depends upon the type of vibroflot used, but generally has a radius of some 2–3 m (Brown, 1977).

Vibroflotation is particularly effective in loose sands or granular fills, but can operate successfully in soils containing up to 25 per cent silt or 5 per cent clay.

Vibroreplacement This technique utilizes a large vibrator or probe similar to the vibroflot but without the water jets top and bottom. The vibrator is suspended from a crane and penetrates the ground by displacing the soil radially under its own weight and by the horizontal vibratory motion. When the required depth is reached, the vibrator is withdrawn and a small quantity of

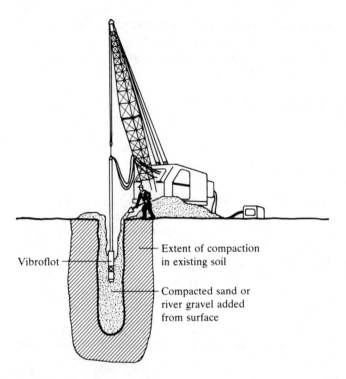

Figure 9.13 Principle of vibroflotation.

graded aggregate up to 75 mm in size is fed into the hole. The vibrator is re-introduced to compact the aggregate or displace it into the surrounding soil. This process is repeated until compacted aggregate forms a *stone column* up to ground level. When loaded, the column derives strength by mobilizing passive resistance in the surrounding soil.

This technique is particularly applicable in soft silts and clays and improves the capacity of the ground to support light foundation loads. However, the stone columns cannot be relied upon to carry heavy concentrated loads without the possibility of excessive settlement (Hughes and Withers, 1974). A number of papers reviewing the performance of stone columns formed by vibroreplacement and vibroflotation techniques are included in a publication by the Institution of Civil Engineers (1976).

Dynamic consolidation This technique involves dropping very heavy weights onto the surface of loose granular soils or soft cohesive soils in order to achieve densification. A crane or tripod frame is used to raise the weight, usually between 6 and 40 tonnes in mass, and then release it to fall freely through a height of up to 30 m or more. With a 40 tonne mass falling through 30 m it would be reasonable to expect significant improvements in density up to a depth in the order of 15–20 m (Leonards *et al.*, 1980).

The impact of the falling weight forms a crater on the ground surface and sends violent shock waves through the soil to a considerable depth. These shock waves produce surface cracking and fissuring in the soil mass, and induce liquefaction followed by densification in granular soils and very high pore pressures followed by consolidation in cohesive soils. The presence of the fissures contributes to rapid pore pressure dissipation and therefore rapid consolidation (Ménard and Broise, 1975).

A square grid is established across the site, the grid spacing typically being between 5 and 15 m, and the weight is repeatedly dropped usually between 3 and 10 times at each grid point. After all the grid points have been pounded, the craters are filled with sand and compacted. If one pass of the ground surface proves insufficient, the process can be repeated as many times as necessary, each time using a successively closer grid spacing. The optimum mass, height of drop, number of drops and grid spacing appropriate for any particular application are selected after preliminary field trials have been carried out.

Applications of this technique are described by Ménard and Broise (1975), Leonards *et al.* (1980) and Lukas (1980).

9.3 CHEMICAL STABILIZATION AND GROUTING

It is possible to improve the engineering properties of some soils and rocks by the addition of chemical stabilizers. The treatment of subsurface layers in this way is usually done by injecting the stabilizing agent under pressure into the pores or fissures of the soil or rock, a process referred to as *grouting*. However, surface layers of soil can be treated by mixing the appropriate chemical additive into the pulverized soil and then carrying out compaction. This process is generally referred to as *chemical stabilization*.

Chemical Stabilization

Chemical stabilization is usually carried out to achieve one or more of the following improvements:

(a) an increase in strength and durability of the soil,
(b) waterproofing of the soil to inhibit the ingress of water,
(c) a decrease in potential for volume changes in the soil due to shrinkage and swelling,
(d) an improvement in the workability of the soil.

The additives that may be used include cement, lime, bituminous materials and pulverized fuel ash (fly-ash). A detailed review of the use of these materials is given by Ingles and Metcalf (1972).

Cement is probably the additive most widely used for chemical stabilization when the main aim is for improved strength and durability, and can be added to almost all soils with the exception of highly organic materials. The technique involves breaking up the soil, mixing in the cement, and then watering and compacting in the conventional manner. However, with moist cohesive soils in which the clay mineral content is high, the mixing process proves very difficult and the technique therefore tends to be restricted to soils with less than 40 per cent fines and a liquid limit less than about 45.

Normal practice is to use ordinary Portland cement, and at some preliminary stage it is necessary to select a cement content that will give the required increase in strength and durability. This is usually based on the results obtained from tests on laboratory trial mixes. However, it is generally accepted that the full-scale field mixing process is less efficient than the laboratory technique and therefore it is common practice to increase the laboratory determined value by a factor of about 1.5 to give the cement content appropriate in the field. Typical values of cement content as a percentage by weight range from 2–4 for granular soils to 10–15 for clays (Ingles and Metcalf, 1972).

Lime stabilization is generally achieved with the use of hydrated lime (calcium hydroxide) and to a lesser extent with quicklime (calcium oxide).

It is particularly effective in the treatment of clay soils, producing a flocculation and cementing of the clay mineral particles into larger clusters, and thereby creating a more friable soil structure with improved workability and increased strength. The addition of lime also decreases the liquid limit and plasticity index of many clays and reduces the volume change potential. Lime is frequently used as an initial pretreatment of the soil in preparation for further additions of lime or cement, and as a convenient short-term means of producing sufficient improvement in a soil to allow support for construction traffic.

Addition of the lime may be effected either by mixing it with the soil *in situ* and then compacting at a suitable water content, or by mixing borrow material with lime and water at a mixing plant and then hauling it to the site for placement and compaction. Alternatively, lime slurry can in some cases be pressure injected into the soil to a depth of about 3 m.

In most cases the quantity of lime used for stabilization will typically be within the range 2–8 per cent of the dry weight of soil (Ingles and Metcalf, 1972).

Bitumen stabilization has applications mainly to granular soils where it can be used to create a cohesive texture in the soil and to effect waterproofing, but it has also been used with some success in clay soils, mainly to provide waterproofing and hence prevent a loss in strength due to increases in water content. It achieves these effects partly by the formation of thin films around the particles which bind them together and prevent them absorbing water, and partly by simply blocking the voids to inhibit the ingress of water.

Because of difficulties of mixing the materials in the field and the fact that bituminous materials are generally more expensive than cement or lime, bitumen stabilization is not widely used.

Pulverized fuel ash or *fly-ash* is a by-product of the combustion of pulverized coal and is obtained mainly from electricity generating power stations. It is a fine-grained dust composed principally of silica, alumina and various oxides and alkalis, and will react with hydrated lime to form cementitious compounds. Therefore, mixtures of fly-ash and lime can sometimes be used for stabilization purposes, and in some cases of cement stabilization fly-ash may be used to replace part of the required cement content.

Grouting

The process of grouting involves injecting suspensions of fine material or fluid chemicals into the pores or fissures of a soil or rock stratum in order to improve its engineering properties. The particular objectives usually are:

(a) to cement the soil or rock macrostructure and thereby increase the strength of the mass,
(b) to infill the pores or fissures and thereby reduce the compressibility and permeability of the mass.

In the latter case, grouting is used extensively as a means of controlling the flow of groundwater through soils and rocks.

The effectiveness of the technique depends on the ability of the grout to penetrate the pores or fissures in the soil or rock mass. It is most effective in soils with a coefficient of permeability not less than about 10^{-5} m/s and therefore is principally applicable in gravels and sands. In soils predominantly of silt size grouting is likely to prove difficult, and in clays it is effective only for the infilling of fissures and cracks. The choice of grout depends on the pore size of the soil, and therefore its particle size distribution, or on the fineness of the fissures in the rock. The materials commonly used include suspensions of cement or bentonite clay, bitumen emulsions or chemical fluid grouts.

Grouting is an expensive method of ground improvement, and it is therefore important to use the least expensive and most readily available grout consistent with achieving the required improvement in engineering properties. The extent to which a grout penetrates depends on its viscosity and on the pressure of injection. Thus, in cases where it is desirable to limit the spread of the grout through the ground, various additives may be used to control the viscosity and the gelling properties of the suspensions and fluid chemical grouts. In soils which have a wide range of pore size, an effective technique is initially to inject a relatively high viscosity grout which will fill the larger pores and then follow up with an injection of lower viscosity grout to seal the smaller pores.

The injection process is usually carried out by pumping the grout through holes in the base or sides of a pipe either driven directly into the soil or sealed into a pre-drilled hole. It is important to regulate the grouting pressure so that it is always less than the total overburden stress at the level of grouting, otherwise heave of the ground surface may occur and fissures may open up within the mass. Care must also be exercised when grouting near existing underground structures which may be susceptible to displacement or infilling by the grout.

Cement grouting is limited by pore size to gravels and coarse sands, and is effective both in strengthening the soil mass and in reducing its permeability. *Suspensions of bentonite* and *bitumen emulsions* are effective only in reducing the permeability and are applicable to most soils down to about medium sand size. For the treatment of fine sands, *chemical grouts* are the most suitable. One of the most commonly used chemicals is sodium silicate which in reaction with certain other compounds, such as calcium chloride, forms a stiff *silica gel*. The two chemicals may be injected separately to react within the pores of the soil, or they may be mixed together prior to injection. In the latter case a retarding agent is added at the mixing stage to delay formation of the gel until adequate penetration is achieved.

9.4 GEOTEXTILES AND GEOMEMBRANES

One of the major developments in ground engineering in the seventies and eighties has been the widespread increase in the use of polymer fabrics to improve the engineering performance of soil structures. From early applications as an expedient in the construction of temporary haul roads and access roads across soft ground, these materials are now being used extensively in the permanent construction of major highways, railways, canals, dams, marine structures, bridges, slopes for embankments and cuttings, retaining walls and in the foundations of buildings.

A vast range of fabrics produced world-wide by many manufacturers is now being marketed under numerous trade names in the form of geotextiles, geomembranes, open meshes or geogrids. Many of the common polymer plastics are used in the manufacture of these materials, but probably the most popular are polypropylene, polyester, polyethylene and polyamide. While there is no formally agreed terminology for the description of these fabrics, there is a tendency to refer to those that are permeable as *geotextiles* and those that are impermeable as *geomembranes*. Geomembranes may be produced, for example, by a process of extrusion in the form of continuous sheets and have particular use as impermeable linings in canals, reservoirs, etc. Geotextiles, on the other hand, come into the two broad categories of woven fabrics produced by a traditional weaving process and non-woven fabrics produced by modern techniques such as heat bonding and needle-punching, and have a much wider use.

When incorporated into a soil structure, these fabrics generally contribute one or more of four fundamental functions:

reinforcement—to improve the strength and reduce the deformation characteristics of the soil mass,

separation —to maintain a well-defined interface between adjacent materials during construction and throughout the working life of the structure,

filtration —to permit the free flow of water across the interface between two materials of different grading without fines being washed out of one and into the other,

drainage —to collect and channel away groundwater and surface water.

The following give simple illustrations of each of these as the primary function.

Reinforcement

A common problem in the construction of embankments over soft ground is instability in the short term owing to the low strength of the foundation soil. It may be possible to overcome this by placing a geotextile between the soft ground and the embankment fill material, as shown in Fig. 9.14a. In the short term the tensile strength of the fabric provides the additional resistance necessary to prevent shear along a potential slip surface through the foundation soil. However, as consolidation of the soil occurs, its shear strength increases and stability in the long term may not depend on the presence of the fabric.

Construction of reinforced earth retaining structures incorporating thin metal reinforcing strips is described in Sec. 6.7. Geotextiles can be used for a similar reinforcement purpose in the manner indicated in Fig. 9.14b. To contain the fill at the exposed face, the fabric is folded back and secured by the next layer of fill. The face may then be masked with suitable vegetation.

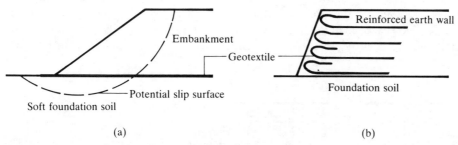

Figure 9.14 Use of geotextile fabric for reinforcement.

Separation

The sub-base of roadways constructed over weak ground may be susceptible to breakdown as a result of upward migration of sub-grade fines and downward displacement and loss of sub-base material, as shown in Fig. 9.15a. This leads to a reduction in the effective depth of sub-base, a deterioration in its performance and eventual failure. The inclusion of a geotextile fabric as shown in Fig. 9.15b has been found to maintain separation of the two layers and thus preserve the integrity of the sub-base.

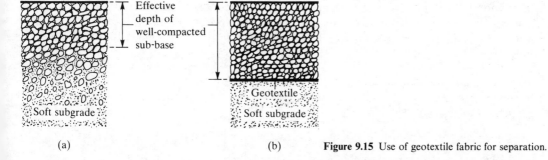

Figure 9.15 Use of geotextile fabric for separation.

In erosion control structures subject to direct wave action, Fig. 9.16, the principle of design is that on impact the wave energy is dissipated by compressing the air in the large void spaces between the stones and in the generation of turbulence. If fines from the natural soil are able to migrate into and fill up these spaces, the wave energy cannot be dissipated, damage to and movement of the stones result and eventually the structure collapses. Separation of the two layers can be maintained by the provision of a geotextile at the interface as shown in Fig. 9.16.

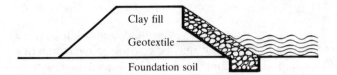

Figure 9.16 Use of geotextile fabric for separation.

Filtration

An example of the filtration function of geotextiles is their use in ground drains. The traditional drain shown in Fig. 9.17a contains a graded filter aggregate which is designed to prevent the fines from the surrounding soil being washed through and into the drain pipe. However, the provision of a geotextile within the drain, as shown in Fig. 9.17b, radically alters the operational principle of the drain. It is generally agreed that the geotextile does not itself filter the soil directly, but by supporting the face of soil exposed in the trench it allows the soil to build up its own internal filter adjacent to the fabric. This provides a relatively cheap, easy to install and efficient drainage system.

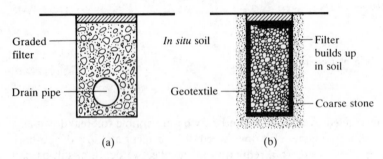

Figure 9.17 Use of geotextile fabric for filtration.

Drainage

Specially formulated, highly permeable geotextile drainage fabrics can be used as shown in Fig. 9.18 as an alternative to the more traditional aggregate or porous block drains provided behind basement walls and retaining walls to prevent the build-up of water against the structure.

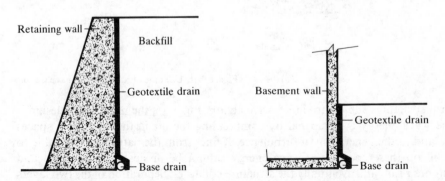

Figure 9.18 Use of geotextile fabric for drainage.

In selecting an appropriate fabric for any field application, the engineer must compare the properties of the material with the performance required of the fabric in that application. For example, within the vast range of available fabrics there is great variation in stress–strain characteristics. Thus, it will be necessary to consider not only the ultimate tensile strength that can be achieved in a particular fabric but also the elongation associated with the development of that ultimate strength. In certain situations where the principal function is that of reinforcement, the specification will be for a high tensile strength achieved with little extension of the fabric. On the other hand, there will be situations where significant deformations of the soil mass are unavoidable and the requirement is for the fabric to remain intact during and after construction in order to fulfill say a separation or filtration function. In such cases the specification will be for a fabric capable of continued extension without the risk of rupture while movements of the soil mass are taking place.

Now non-woven fabrics tend to exhibit essentially uniform strength and elongation characteristics in all directions in the plane of the fabric. In contrast, a feature of woven fabrics is anisotropy in respect of strength and elongation. This can be due simply to the structure of the weave in which the maximum strength and also the maximum elongation occurs at 45° to the warp and weft directions, or it may be the direct consequence of using different strength fibres in the warp from those in the weft. Thus, it is difficult to generalize on the stress–strain characteristics of the various materials, but by and large on a weight-for-weight basis non-woven fabrics achieve slightly lower ultimate strengths than woven fabrics but develop these at significantly higher values of strain.

Other factors will also have to be considered before a choice is made: e.g., impact and abrasion resistance will be important if the fabric is to have large stones or jagged lumps of rock dumped onto it, permeability and hole size distribution if it is to be used for filtration purposes, and resistance to chemical attack if it will be in contact with hazardous materials. Moreover, where fabrics will be required to perform effectively over the working life of a permanent structure, their ability to resist long-term *in situ* weathering and environmental degradation is a factor of major importance. Of course the climatic environment in which they are placed may be temperate, tropical, desert or permafrost, with the agents of weathering and degradation being different in each, and fabrics which weather well in one environment may deteriorate rapidly in another. However, as yet there has been little opportunity to gather field information on the life expectancy of these materials when installed in an actively hostile environment.

The use of polymer fabrics in the form of geotextiles, geomembranes and geogrids has become an established aspect of ground engineering. Although much experience has already been gained, research and field monitoring of the performance of these materials continues to be undertaken and it is to be expected that a fuller understanding of their behaviour will result and further innovative uses for these materials will emerge.

For further reading on this topic, reference may be made to the text by Rankilor (1981) and the *Proceedings of the Second International Conference on Geotextiles* (1982).

REFERENCES

Ahlvin, R. G. and H. H. Ulery (1962) 'Tabulated values for determining the complete pattern of stresses, strains, and deflections beneath a uniform circular load on a homogeneous half-space', *HRB Bulletin No. 342*, Highway Research Board, Washington DC, pages 1–13.

Akroyd, T. N. W. (1957) *Laboratory Testing in Soil Engineering*, Soil Mechanics, London.

American Society for Testing and Materials (1980) *Annual Book of ASTM Standards, Part 19: Natural Building Stones; Soil and Rock*, ASTM, Philadelphia, Pennsylvania.

Audova, H. J. (1978) 'Gabion and mattress works on main roads in New South Wales', *Proceedings of the Symposium on Soil Reinforcing and Stabilizing Techniques*, The New South Wales Institute of Technology and The University of New South Wales, Sydney, Australia, pages 307–328.

Barron, R. A. (1948) 'Consolidation of fine grained soils by drain wells', *Transactions of the ASCE*, **113**, 718–742.

Berry, P. L. (1983) 'Application of consolidation theory for peat to the design of a reclamation scheme by preloading', *Quarterly Journal of Engineering Geology, London*, **16**, 2, 103–112.

Bishop, A. W. (1948) 'A new sampling tool for use in cohesionless sands below ground water level', *Geotechnique*, **1**, 2, 125–131.

Bishop, A. W. (1955) 'The use of the slip circle in the stability analysis of slopes', *Geotechnique*, **5**, 1, 7–17.

Bishop, A. W. (1972) 'Shear strength parameters for undisturbed and remoulded soil specimens', *Stress–Strain Behavior of Soils—Proceedings of the Roscoe Memorial Symposium, Cambridge*, Foulis, Sparkford, pages 3–58.

Bishop, A. W. and Z. A. Al-Dhahir (1970) 'Some comparisons between laboratory tests, *in situ* tests and full scale performance, with special reference to permeability and coefficient of consolidation', *Proceedings of the Conference on In situ Investigations in Soils and Rocks*, ICE, London, pages 251–264.

Bishop, A. W. and L. Bjerrum (1960) 'The relevance of the triaxial test to the solution of stability problems', *Proceedings of the ASCE Research Conference on Shear Strength of Cohesive Soils, Boulder, Colorado*, pages 437–501.

Bishop, A. W. and D. J. Henkel (1962) *The Measurement of Soil Properties in the Triaxial Test*, 2nd edn, Arnold, London.

Bishop, A. W., G. E. Green, V. K. Garga, A. Andresen and J. D. Brown (1971) 'A new ring shear apparatus and its application to the measurement of residual strength', *Geotechnique*, **21**, 4, 273–328.

Bjerrum, L. (1954) 'Geotechnical properties of Norwegian marine clays', *Geotechnique*, **4**, 2, 49–69.

Bjerrum, L. and A. Eggestad (1963) 'Interpretation of loading tests on sands', *Proceedings of the European Conference on Soil Mechanics and Foundation Engineering, Wiesbaden*, Vol. 1, pages 199–204.

Bjerrum, L. and O. Eide (1956) 'Stability of strutted excavations in clay', *Geotechnique*, **6**, 1, 32–47.

Blum, H. (1931) *'Einspannungsverhältnisse bei Bohlwerken'*, *Diss. Tech. Hochschule Braunschweig*, Ernst und Sohn, Berlin.

Blyth, F. G. H. and M. H. De Freitas (1984) *A Geology for Engineers*, 7th edn, Arnold, London.

Broms, B. B. and L. Forssblad (1969) 'Vibratory compaction of cohesionless soils', *Proceedings of Speciality Session No. 2 on Soil Dynamics, 7th International Conference on Soil Mechanics and Foundation Engineering, Mexico City*, pages 101–118.

Brown, R. E. (1977) 'Vibroflotation compaction of cohesionless soils', *Journal of the Geotechnical Engineering Division, ASCE*, **103**, GT 12, 1437–1451.

BS 1377 (1975) Methods of test for soils for civil engineering purposes, British Standards Institution, London.

BS 5930 (*1981*) *Code of practice for site investigations*, British Standards Institution, London.

Carrillo, N. (1942) 'Simple two and three dimensional cases in the theory of consolidation of soils', *Journal of Mathematics and Physics*, **21**, 1, Pt. 1, 1–5.

Casagrande, A. (1937) 'Seepage through dams', *Journal of the New England Water Works Association*. Reprinted in *Contributions to Soil Mechanics, 1925–1940*, Boston Society of Civil Engineers, Boston, 1940.

Code of Practice No. 2 (1951) *Earth Retaining Structures*, Institution of Structural Engineers, London.

Collins, K. and A. McGown (1974) 'The form and function of microfabric features in a variety of natural soils', *Geotechnique*, **24**, 2, 223–254.

Cooling, L. F. and H. Q. Golder (1942) 'The analysis of the failure of an earth dam during construction', *Journal of the Institution of Civil Engineers*, **19**, 38–55.

Coulomb, C. A. (1776) 'Essai sur une application des règles des maximis et minimis à quelques problèmes de statique relatifs à l'architecture', *Memorandum Academie Royale, Prés. Divers Savants*, **7**, 343–382.

Danish Society of Engineers (1926) 'Preliminary regulations for the calculation and execution of marine structures in reinforced concrete', trans. in appendix to *Earth-Pressure On Flexible Walls*, R. N. Stroyer, *Minutes of Proceedings of the Institution of Civil Engineers*, London, **226**, 1927–28, Pt 2, 130–134.

D'Appolonia, D. J., E. D'Appolonia and R. F. Brisette (1968) 'Settlement of spread footings on sand', *Journal of the Soil Mechanics and Foundations Division, ASCE*, **94**, SM 3, 735–760.

D'Appolonia, D. J., R. V. Whitman and E. D'Appolonia (1969) 'Sand compaction with vibratory rollers', *Journal of the Soil Mechanics and Foundations Division, ASCE*, **95**, SM 1, 263–284.

De Beer, E. E. and A. Martens (1957) 'Method of computation of an upper limit for the influence of heterogenuity of sand layers on the settlement of bridges', *Proceedings of the 4th International Conference on Soil Mechanics and Foundation Engineering, London*, Vol. 1, pages 275–281.

De Ruiter, J. (1982) 'The static cone penetration test—a state-of-the-art report', *Proceedings of the European Symposium on Penetration Testing, Amsterdam*, Vol. 2, pages 389–405.

Derbyshire, E. (1975) 'The formation and distribution of glacial materials', *The Engineering Behaviour of Glacial Materials—Proceedings of the Symposium of Midland Soil Mechanics and Foundation Engineering Society, Birmingham*, pages 6–17.

Desai, C. S. (1977) 'Flow through porous media', Chapter 14 in *Numerical Methods in Geotechnical Engineering*, C. S. Desai and J. T. Christian (eds), McGraw-Hill, New York.

Fadum, R. E. (1948) 'Influence values for estimating stresses in elastic foundations', *Proceedings of the 2nd International Conference on Soil Mechanics and Foundation Engineering, Rotterdam*, Vol. 3, pages 77–84.

Flint, R. F. and B. J. Skinner (1977) *Physical Geology*, 2nd edn, Wiley, New York.

Fookes, P. G., D. L. Gordon and I. E. Higginbottom (1975) 'Glacial landforms, their deposits and engineering characteristics', *The Engineering Behaviour of Glacial Materials—Proceedings of the Symposium of the Midland Soil Mechanics and Foundation Engineering Society, Birmingham*, pages 18–51.

Foster, C. R. and R. G. Ahlvin (1954) 'Stresses and deflections induced by a uniform circular load', *Proceedings of Highway Research Board, Washington DC*, **33**, 467–470.

Grim, R. E. (1962) *Applied Clay Mineralogy*, McGraw-Hill, New York.

Grim, R. E. (1968) *Clay Mineralogy*, 2nd edn, McGraw-Hill, New York.

Hanna, T. H. (1973) *Foundation Instrumentation*, Trans. Tech. Publications, Cleveland, Ohio.

Hansen, J. B. (1953) *Earth Pressure Calculation*, Danish Technical Press, Copenhagen.

Harr, M. E. (1962) *Groundwater and Seepage*, McGraw-Hill, New York.

Harr, M. E. (1966) *Foundations of Theoretical Soil Mechanics*, McGraw-Hill, New York.

Horne, M. R. (1965) 'The behaviour of an assembly of rotund, rigid, cohesionless particles, I and II', *Proceedings of the Royal Society of London, Series A*, **286**, 62–97.

Horne, M. R. (1969) 'The behaviour of an assembly of rotund, rigid, cohesionless particles, III', *Proceedings of the Royal Society of London, Series A*, **310**, 21–34.

Hughes, J. M. O. and N. J. Withers (1974) 'Reinforcing of soft cohesive soils with stone columns', *Ground Engineering*, **7**, 3, 42–49.

Ingles, O. G. and J. B. Metcalf (1972) *Soil Stabilization—Principles and Practice*, Butterworths, Sydney, Australia.

Institution of Civil Engineers (1976) *Ground Treatment by Deep Compaction*, Thomas Telford, London. (First published as a Symposium in Print in *Geotechnique*, March 1975.)

Jaky, J. (1944) 'The coefficient of earth pressure at rest', *Journal of the Society of Hungarian Architects and Engineers*, 355–358.

Janbu, N. and K. Senneset (1973) 'Field compressometer—principles and applications', *Proceedings of the 8th International Conference on Soil Mechanics and Foundation Engineering, Moscow*, Vol. 1.1, pages 191–198.

Johnson, A. W. and J. R. Sallberg (1960) 'Factors that influence field compaction of soils', *HRB Bulletin No. 272*, Highway Research Board, Washington DC.

Johnson, S. J. (1970) 'Precompression for improving foundation soils', *Journal of the Soil Mechanics and Foundations Division, ASCE*, **96**, SM 1, Paper 7020, 111–144.

Jonas, E. (1964) 'Subsurface stabilization of organic silty clay by precompression', *Journal of the Soil Mechanics and Foundations Division, ASCE*, **90**, SM 5, Paper 4031, 363–376.

Joyce, M. D. (1982) *Site Investigation Practice*, Spon, London.

Kay, J. N. and R. H. G. Parry (1982) 'Screw plate tests in a stiff clay', *Ground Engineering*, **15**, 6, 22–30.

Kjellman, W., T. Kallstenius and O. Wager (1950) 'Soil sampler with metal foils. Device for taking undisturbed samples of very great length', *Proceedings of the Royal Swedish Geotechnical Institute*, No. 1.

Krey, H. (1936) *Erddruck, Erdwiderstand und Tragfähigkeit des Baugrundes*, 5th edn, Ernst, Berlin.

Lambe, T. W. (1958) 'The structure of compacted clay', *Journal of the Soil Mechanics and Foundations Division, ASCE*, **84**, SM 2, 1655-1–1655-35.

Lambe, T. W. and R. V. Whitman (1979) *Soil Mechanics, SI Version*, Wiley, New York.

Lea, N. D. and C. O. Brawner (1963) 'Highway design and construction over peat deposits in lower British Columbia', *Highway Research Record No. 7*, Highway Research Board, Washington DC.

Lee, K. L. and A. Singh (1971) 'Relative density and relative compaction', *Journal of the Soil Mechanics and Foundations Division, ASCE*, **97**, SM 7, 1049–1052.

Lee, K. L., B. D. Adams and J. M. J. Vagneron (1973) 'Reinforced earth retaining walls', *Journal of the Soil Mechanics and Foundations Division, ASCE*, **99**, SM 10, Paper 10068, 745–764.

Lee, K. L., W. White and O. G. Ingles (1983) *Geotechnical Engineering*, Pitman.

Legget, R. F. (ed.) (1976) *Glacial Till—An Inter-Disciplinary Study*, The Royal Society of Canada, Ottawa.

Leonards, G. A., C. A. Cutter and R. D. Holtz (1980) 'Dynamic compaction of granular soils', *Journal of the Geotechnical Engineering Division, ASCE*, **106**, GT 1, 35–44.

Lewis, W. A. (1960) 'Full scale compaction studies at the British Road Research Laboratory', *HRB Bulletin No. 254*, Highway Research Board, Washington DC, pages 1–11.

Lukas, R. G. (1980) 'Densification of loose deposits by pounding', *Journal of the Geotechnical Engineering Division, ASCE*, **106**, GT 4, 435–446.

McGown, A. and E. Derbyshire (1977) 'Genetic influences on the properties of tills', *Quarterly Journal of Engineering Geology*, **10**, 4, 389–410.

McKinlay, D. G. (1961) 'A laboratory study of rates of consolidation in clays with particular reference to conditions of radial porewater drainage', *Proceedings of the 5th International Conference on Soil Mechanics and Foundation Engineering, Paris*, Vol. 1, pages 225–228.

McKinlay, D. G. and W. F. Anderson (1975) 'Determination of the modulus of deformation of a till using a pressuremeter', *Ground Engineering*, **8**, 6, 51–54.

Ménard, L. (1965) 'Rules for the calculation of bearing capacity and foundation settlement based on pressuremeter tests', *Proceedings of the 6th International Conference on Soil Mechanics and Foundation Engineering, Montreal*, Vol. 2, pages 295–299.

Ménard, L. and Y. Broise (1975) 'Theoretical and practical aspects of dynamic consolidation', *Geotechnique*, **25**, 1, 3–18.

Meyerhof, G. G. (1965) 'Shallow foundations', *Journal of the Soil Mechanics and Foundations Division, ASCE*, **91**, SM 2, 21–31.

Meyerhof, G. G. (1976) 'Bearing capacity and settlement of pile foundations', *Journal of the Geotechnical Engineering Division, ASCE*, **102**, GT 3, Paper 11962, 197–228.

Milligan, V., L. G. Soderman and A. Rutka (1962) 'Experience with Canadian varved clays', *Journal of the Soil Mechanics and Foundations Division, ASCE*, **88**, SM 4, Paper 3224, 31–67.

Morgenstern, N. R. and V. E. Price (1965) 'The analysis of the stability of general slip surfaces', *Geotechnique*, **15**, 1, 79–93.

Newmark, N. M. (1942) 'Influence charts for computation of stresses in elastic foundations', *Engineering Experiment Station Bulletin No. 338*, University of Illinois, Urbana, Ill.

Peck, R. B., W. E. Hanson and T. H. Thornburn (1974) *Foundation Engineering*, 2nd edn, Wiley, New York.

Pennoyer, R. A. (1933) 'Design of sheet piling bulkheads', *Civil Engineering*, **November**, 615.

Poulos, H. G. and E. H. Davis (1974) *Elastic Solutions for Soil and Rock Mechanics*, Wiley, New York.

Prandtl, L. (1921) 'Hauptaufsätze über die Eindringungsfestigkeit (Härte) plastischer Baustoffe und die Festigkeit von Schneiden', *Zeitschrift für Angewandte Mathematik und Mechanik*, **1**, 1, 15–20.

Proceedings of the Second International Conference on Geotextiles, Las Vegas, August 1982.

Rankilor, P. R. (1981) *Membranes in Ground Engineering*, Wiley, Chichester.

Rankine, W. J. M. (1857) 'On the stability of loose earth', *Philosophical Transactions of the Royal Society, London, Part 1*, **147**, 9–27.

Rodin, S., B. O. Corbett, D. E. Sherwood and S. Thorburn (1974) 'Penetration testing in the United Kingdom', *Proceedings of the European Symposium on Penetration Testing, Stockholm*.

Rowe, P. W. (1951) 'Cantilever sheet piling in cohesionless soil', *Engineering*, **172**, 316–319.

Rowe, P. W. (1952) 'Anchored sheet-pile walls', *Proceedings of the Institution of Civil Engineers, London, Part 1*, **1**, January, 27–70.

Rowe, P. W. (1955a) 'A theoretical and experimental analysis of sheet-pile walls', *Proceedings of the Institution of Civil Engineers, London, Part 1*, **4**, January, 32–69.

Rowe, P. W. (1955b) 'Sheet-pile walls encastré at the anchorage', *Proceedings of the Institution of Civil Engineers, London, Part 1*, **4**, January, 70–87.

Rowe, P. W. (1956) 'Sheet-pile walls at failure', *Proceedings of the Institution of Civil Engineers, London, Part 1*, **5**, May, 276–315.

Rowe, P. W. (1957a) 'Sheet-pile walls in clay', *Proceedings of the Institution of Civil Engineers, London*, **7**, 629–654.

Rowe, P. W. (1957b) 'Sheet-pile walls subject to line resistance above the anchorage', *Proceedings of the Institution of Civil Engineers, London*, **7**, 879–896.

Rowe, P. W. (1962) 'The stress–dilatancy relation for static equilibrium of an assembly of particles in contact', *Proceedings of the Royal Society of London, Series A*, **269**, 500–527.

Rowe, P. W. (1968a) 'Failure of foundations and slopes on layered deposits in relation to site investigation practice', *Proceedings of the Institution of Civil Engineers, London*, Paper 7057 S. Supplementary volume.

Rowe, P. W. (1968b) 'The influence of geological features of clay deposits on the design and performance of sand drains', *Proceedings of the Institution of Civil Engineers, London*, Paper 7058 S. Supplementary volume.

Rowe, P. W. (1972a) 'Theoretical meaning and observed values of deformation parameters for soil', *Stress–Strain Behaviour of Soils—Proceedings of the Roscoe Memorial Symposium, Cambridge*, Foulis, Sparkford, pages 143–194.

Rowe, P. W. (1972b) 'The relevance of soil fabric to site investigation practice', *Geotechnique*, **22**, 2, 195–300.

Rowe, P. W. and L. Barden (1966) 'A new consolidation cell', *Geotechnique*, **16**, 2, 162–170.

Rowe, P. W. and K. Peaker (1965) 'Passive earth pressure measurements', *Geotechnique*, **15**, 1, 57–78.

Schmertmann, J. H. (1970) 'Static cone to compute static settlement over sand', *Journal of the Soil Mechanics and Foundations Division, ASCE*, **96**, SM 3, 1011–1043.

Schmertmann, J. H., J. P. Hartman and P. R. Brown (1978) 'Improved strain influence factor diagrams', *Journal of the Geotechnical Engineering Division, ASCE*, **104**, GT 8, 1131–1135.

Scott, R. F. (1963) *Principles of Soil Mechanics*, Addison-Wesley, Reading, Massachusetts.

Seed, H. B. and C. K. Chan (1959) 'Structure and strength characteristics of compacted clays', *Journal of the Soil Mechanics and Foundations Division, ASCE*, **85**, SM 5, 87–128.

Selig, E. T. and T-S. Yoo (1977) 'Fundamentals of vibratory roller behaviour', *Proceedings of the 9th International Conference on Soil Mechanics and Foundation Engineering, Tokyo*, Vol. 2, pages 375–380.

Serota, S. and R. A. Jennings (1958) 'Undisturbed sampling techniques for sands and very soft clays', *Proceedings of the 4th International Conference on Soil Mechanics and Foundation Engineering, London*, Vol. 1, pages 245–248.

Skempton, A. W. (1948) 'The $\phi = 0$ analysis of stability and its theoretical basis', *Proceedings of the 2nd International Conference on Soil Mechanics and Foundation Engineering, Rotterdam*, Vol. 1, pages 72–78.

Skempton, A. W. (1951) 'The bearing capacity of clays', *Proceedings of Building Research Congress*, **1**, 180–189.

Skempton, A. W. (1953) 'The colloidal "activity" of clays', *Proceedings of the 3rd International Conference on Soil Mechanics and Foundation Engineering, Zurich*, Vol. 1, pages 57–61.

Skempton, A. W. (1954) 'The pore–pressure coefficients A and B', *Geotechnique*, **4**, 4, 143–147.

Skempton, A. W. (1957) 'Discussion on "The planning and design of the new Hong Kong airport"', *Proceedings of the Institution of Civil Engineers, London*, **7**, 305–307.

Skempton, A. W. (1964) 'Long-term stability of slopes', *Geotechnique*, **14**, 2, 77–101.

Skempton, A. W. and L. Bjerrum (1957) 'A contribution to the settlement analysis of foundations on clay', *Geotechnique*, **7**, 4, 168–178.

Skempton, A. W. and H. Q. Golder (1948) 'Practical examples of the $\phi = 0$ analysis of stability of clays', *Proceedings of the 2nd International Conference on Soil Mechanics and Foundation Engineering, Rotterdam*, Vol. 2, pages 63–70.

Skempton, A. W. and D. J. Henkel (1953) 'The post-glacial clays of the Thames Estuary at Tilbury and Shellhaven', *Proceedings of the 3rd International Conference on Soil Mechanics and Foundation Engineering, Zurich*, Vol. 1, pages 302–308.

Skempton, A. W. and R. D. Northey (1952) 'The sensitivity of clays', *Geotechnique*, **3**, 1, 30–53.

Stroyer, J. P. R. N. (1935) 'Earth pressure on flexible walls', *Journal of the Institution of Civil Engineers, London*, **1**, November, 94.

Sutherland, H. B. (1963) 'The use of *in situ* tests to estimate the allowable bearing pressure of cohesionless soils', *Structural Engineer*, **41**, 3, 85–92.

Taylor, D. W. (1948) *Fundamentals of Soil Mechanics*, Wiley, New York.

Terzaghi, K. (1934) 'Large retaining wall tests, parts 1–5', *Engineering News Record*, **112**, 136–140, 259–262, 316–318, 403–406, 503–508.

Terzaghi, K. (1943) *Theoretical Soil Mechanics*, Wiley, New York.

Terzaghi, K. (1954) 'Anchored bulkheads', *Transactions of the ASCE*, **119**, 1243–1280.

Terzaghi, K. and R. B. Peck (1967) *Soil Mechanics in Engineering Practice*, 2nd edn, Wiley, New York.

Thomas, H. S. W. and W. H. Ward (1969) 'The design, construction and performance of a vibrating-wire earth pressure cell', *Geotechnique*, **19**, 1, 39–51.

Tschebotarioff, G. P. (1951) *Soil Mechanics, Foundations, and Earth Structures*, McGraw-Hill, New York.

Verruijt, A. (1970) *Theory of Groundwater Flow*, Macmillan, London.

Vidal, H. (1969) 'The principle of reinforced earth', *Highway Research Record No. 282*, Highway Research Board, Washington DC, pages 1–16.

Weltman, A. J. and J. M. Head (1983) *Site Investigation Manual, CIRIA Special Publication 25/PSA Civil Engineering Technical Guide 35*, Construction Industry Research and Information Association, London.

Windle, D. and C. P. Wroth (1977) 'The use of a self-boring pressuremeter to determine the undrained properties of clays', *Ground Engineering*, **10**, 6, 37–46.

Winterkorn, H. F. and H. Y. Fang (eds) (1975) *Foundation Engineering Handbook*, Van Nostrand Reinhold, New York.

Wroth, C. P. (1984) 'The interpretation of *in situ* soil tests', *Geotechnique*, **34**, 4, 449–489.

Wroth, C. P. and J. M. O. Hughes (1973) 'An instrument for the *in situ* measurement of the properties of soft clays', *Proceedings of the 8th International Conference on Soil Mechanics and Foundation Engineering, Moscow*, Vol. 1.2, pages 487–494.

Yong, R. N. and B. P. Warkentin (1975) *Soil Properties and Behaviour, Developments in Geotechnical Engineering 5*, Elsevier, Amsterdam.